PROGRESS IN BRAIN RESEARCH

PROGRESS IN BRAIN RESEARCH

VOLUME 13

MECHANISMS OF NEURAL REGENERATION

EDITED BY

M. SINGER

Department of Anatomy, School of Medicine and Developmental Biology Center,
Western Reserve University, Cleveland, Ohio (U.S.A.)

AND

J. P. SCHADÉ

Central Institute for Brain Research, Amsterdam

ELSEVIER PUBLISHING COMPANY

AMSTERDAM / LONDON / NEW YORK

1964

ELSEVIER PUBLISHING COMPANY
335 JAN VAN GALENSTRAAT, P.O. BOX 211, AMSTERDAM

AMERICAN ELSEVIER PUBLISHING COMPANY, INC.
52 VANDERBILT AVENUE, NEW YORK, N.Y. 10017

ELSEVIER PUBLISHING COMPANY LIMITED
RIPPLESIDE COMMERCIAL ESTATE
RIPPLE ROAD, BARKING, ESSEX

This volume contains a series of lectures delivered during a workshop on
MECHANISMS OF NEURAL REGENERATION
which was held as part of the first International Summer School of Brain Research,
at the Royal Academy of Sciences, Amsterdam (The Netherlands)
from 15–26 July, 1963
This meeting was organized by the Central Institute for Brain Research
and sponsored by the Netherlands Government and the NATO
Advanced Study Institute Program

LIBRARY OF CONGRESS CATALOG CARD NUMBER 64–18525

WITH 116 ILLUSTRATIONS AND 11 TABLES

List of Contributors

E. Gutmann, Institute of Physiology, Czechoslovak Academy of Sciences, Prague.

C. N. Liu, Departments of Physiology and Anatomy, School of Medicine, University of Pennsylvania, Philadelphia, Pa. (U.S.A.).

L. Lubińska, Nencki Institute of Experimental Biology, Department of Neurophysiology, Warsaw.

N. Miani, Department of Anatomy, University of Padua, Padua (Italy).

D. Scott, Jr., Departments of Physiology and Anatomy, School of Medicine, University of Pennsylvania, Philadelphia, Pa. (U.S.A.).

M. Singer, Department of Anatomy, School of Medicine and Developmental Biology Center, Western Reserve University, Cleveland, Ohio (U.S.A.).

H. A. L. Trampusch, Division of Experimental Morphology, Department of Anatomy and Embryology, University of Amsterdam, Amsterdam.

H. De F. Webster, Massachusetts General Hospital, Boston, Mass. (U.S.A.).

J. Zelená, Institute of Physiology, Czechoslovak Academy of Sciences, Prague.

Preface

The reviews of this volume are not meant to exhaust all topics within the subject of degeneration and regeneration but rather to probe deeply into a few selected aspects of the subject. The unique morphology of the neuron with its long cytoplasmic processes and its tremendous volume of distally situated cytoplasm transfers the problem of injury and regeneration to a different setting from the case in other tissues. Destruction of nervous tissue is significant of processes of a cell and less that of the entire cell, the problem of recovery and regeneration being mainly that of the processes of the individual neuron. Unlike other tissues when damaged, there is no neuronal multiplication, accumulation of cells and differentiation of cells. Therefore, our study of degeneration and regeneration of the nervous system is primarily a study of the neuron itself, in its reaction to injury, its physiology, its structure and the nature and growth of its cytoplasmic processes. This does not mean that there are no other consequences of nerve injury. Indeed, there are profound changes but they reflect the primary injury of the cytoplasmic processes: for example, changes both in the sheaths that surround the axonal threads and in some of the organs upon which the neuron ends. All these changes will be touched upon in the volume, but it is primarily the living threads of cytoplasm that we will deal with: their morphology, function and chemistry.

The Editors

Contents

Axoplasmic Streaming in Regenerating and in Normal Nerve Fibres

Nencki Institute of Experimental Biology, Department of Neurophysiology, Warsaw

CONTENTS

INTRODUCTION

'I put forward the hypothesis that in the body of the nerve cell a substance is formed from the nucleus and Nissl bodies which gradually passes into the nerve fibres; and also that stimulation of other cells by a nerve fibre is brought about by the passage of some of this substance into the cells on which the fibre acts . . . The nerve cells secrete a substance the passage of which from the nerve endings is necessary to stimulation'. 'The recovery of effect after transient fatigue I attribute to the passage of a portion of this substance down the nerve fibre to the nerve ending. The absence of recovery after prolonged stimulation I attribute to the whole of the substance in the nerve fibres being used up, and to their being incapable of making more when severed from their nerve cells'.

These sentences were written by F. H. Scott in 1906. Audacious as they appear on the basis of the scant experimental evidence available at that early date, they formulate, in general terms, hypotheses of the chemical mediation of synaptic transmission, of perikaryal synthesis of some substances and of their transport along the axons, as well as interpretation of the disappearance of synaptic function after nerve section by the exhaustion of relevant materials and the impossibility of renewed supply.

All these hypotheses are still valid although their further elaboration and replacement of general by concrete terms has been unequal. Whereas immense developments have taken place during the intervening 60 years concerning the mechanism of synaptic transmission and of protein synthesis in the perikarya, our ideas concerning the mode of transport along axons remain uncertain.

This is due partly to inherent difficulties of detection and partly to the fact that relatively few investigations were undertaken with the explicit purpose of studying the movements of axonal contents. The data concerning these movements were obtained mostly in experiments in which other problems such as the site of synthesis or the physiological role of various materials were investigated together with the question of transport. The proposed interpretations dealt with all these interconnected problems and, so far as the axonal flow is concerned, often led to conflicting inferences. Thus, whereas the existence of some kind of transport of materials along axons is assumed, on various grounds, by most workers, opinions differ as to the mode of migration and the parameters of the postulated flow.

The purpose of this paper is to review and analyze some of the experimental results either suggesting or directly demonstrating the existence of axoplasmic movements (for embryological data see Levi-Montalcini and Angeletti, 1962), and to try to resolve, where possible, the apparent contradictions. A comment may be useful to clarify the relations between the content of the Tables and the text in chapters concerning indirect indications of the existence of axoplasmic flow. Some of the tabulated data were obtained with other purposes in mind and the problem of axoplasmic flow was touched upon by the authors only parenthetically or not at all. The interpretation of the authors where available is noted in the Tables. The interpretation proposed in the text is mine and is sometimes in conflict with the original proposals. In some instances unpublished details of experiments or of interpretation were kindly supplied by the authors and have been acknowledged in the footnotes.

I. MOVEMENTS OF AXOPLASM IN REGENERATING NERVE FIBRES

The most conspicuous shifts of axoplasm occur during the elongation of regenerating nerve fibres. The study of this phase of regeneration provided many quantitative data which greatly influenced the present concepts concerning the flow of axoplasm. It seems useful therefore to review briefly the behaviour and main features of elongating nerve fibres, although the various stages of regeneration, the formation of growth cones, the elongation of regenerating sprouts, their subsequent maturation and establishment of peripheral connections, the relationship between morphological and physiological features of these processes, as well as the functional recovery of innervated organs have been subjects of extensive reviews (Cajal, 1928; Young, 1942; Seddon, 1954; Guth, 1956; Gutmann, 1958).

(a) Fibres in nerve trunks

Out of the end of the central part of a cut or crushed fibre, after a latent period of the order of days, one or several thin sprouts emerge. If the local conditions at the lesion are such that the growing sprouts may enter the nerve tubes of the peripheral stump, they grow there.

The presence of Schwann cells influences the rate of elongation (Williams, 1930) but regeneration is possible also without Schwann cells, as in cornea (Rexed and Rexed, 1951; Zander and Weddell, 1951).

From the very beginning the regenerating tip of the fibre is able to generate impulses on mechanical stimulation. In contrast to their poor electrical excitability the tips of regenerating fibres have a very low threshold to mechanical stimulation. It increases progressively with the ageing of regenerated parts (Konorski and Lubińska, 1946). Electrophysiological characteristics also change with progressive maturation of fibres (Berry et al., 1944; Hursh, 1939; Erlanger and Schoepfle, 1946). Both Tinel's (1915) sign and Young and Medawar's (1940) 'pinch' method are based on mechanical excitability of regenerating sprouts. They permit the measurement of the length of regenerated fibres in the early stages, before functional completion, and the estimation of the rate of elongation of fibres uncomplicated by delays introduced by reinnervation of end organs.

The rate of regeneration is a few mm a day and varies little in peripheral nerves of various mammals (Table I). The only exception described so far is the trigeminal branch to the antlers of deer (Wislocki and Singer, 1946) which regenerates during their regrowth at a rate about ten times faster than that of other sensory fibres. The rate of regeneration of motor fibres, determined indirectly (Gutmann et al., 1942) seems to be somewhat slower. An indication of slower regeneration of motor fibres is also suggested by Diamond's (1959) experiments, in which impulses in ventral and dorsal roots generated by pinching the regenerating nerve were recorded.

Regeneration may be induced repeatedly in the same group of axons without apparent impairment. Thus Duncan and Jarvis (1943) crushed 9 times a branch of the facial nerve in cat, obtaining after each lesion a complete recovery at similar periods of time.

The rate of regeneration is very temperature-dependent (Tables II and III). No elongation occurs below a certain critical value: 8° for the sciatic of frogs (Lubińska, 1952a) 26° for tissue cultures of chick embryos (Mossa, 1927) and an environmental temperature of below 2° for the caudal nerve of rats (Gamble, 1957). Above these values the rate of regeneration increases with temperature within the physiological range (Mossa, 1927; Lubińska and Olekiewicz, 1950). Subsequent maturation of regenerating fibres is also accelerated by temperature (Gamble, 1958; Jha et al., 1959).

TABLE I

RATES OF ELONGATION OF REGENERATING MAMMALIAN NERVE FIBRES*

Animal	Nerve	Lesion	Rate in mm/24 h	Remarks	References
Mouse	Sciatic	Crush	2–3		Wyrwicka, 1950
Rat	Tibial	Crush	3.3		Konorski and Lubińska, 1945
	Peroneal	Crush	2.4		
Rabbit	Dorsal auricular	Crush	2.5		Weddell, 1942
	Peroneal	Cut and suture	3.5		Gutmann et al., 1942
		Crush	4.4		
	Peroneal	Cut and suture, at hip	2.6	In cross-unions tibial–peroneal and peroneal–tibial the growth rate is that of the central stump	Haftek, 1963
		Cut and suture, at knee	1.9		
	Tibial	Cut and suture, at hip	3.3		
		Cut and suture, at knee	2.6		
	Tibial	Crush	3.4		Konorski and Lubińska, 1945
		Cut and suture	3.3		
	Median	Crush	4.5		
	Ulnar	Crush	3.2		
	Radial	Crush	2.3		
Cat	Sciatic	Cut and suture	3–4		Berry et al., 1944
	Peroneal	Crush	4.8		Konorski and Lubińska, 1945
	Median	Crush	4.7		
	Ulnar	Crush	4.5		
	Radial	Crush	4.9		
Dog	Phrenic	Crush	4.8	Action potentials	Erlanger and Schoepfle, 1946
	Tibial	Crush	3.7		Konorski and Lubińska, 1945
	Peroneal	Crush	3.4		
Monkey	Tibial	Crush	3.5		Konorski and Lubińska, 1945
Baboon	Tibial	Crush	3.9		Konorski and Lubińska, 1945
	Peroneal	Crush	2.5		

Subject	Nerve	Lesion	Rate	Sensory fibres during growth of new antlers	Reference
Deer	Trigeminal	Shedding of antlers	15–20		Wislocki and Singer, 1946
Man	Radial	Cut and suture	1.6	Motor recovery	Seddon et al., 1943
			1.7	Tinel's sign	
	Median, Ulnar		3 Forearm	Tinel's sign	Sunderland, 1947
			0.5 Wrist	Tinel's sign	
	Sciatic		2 Leg	Tinel's sign	
			0.5 Ankle	Tinel's sign	
	Radial	Axonotmesis	1.9 Elbow	Motor recovery	Sunderland and Bradley, 1952
	Radial	Axonotmesis	0.8 Mid-forearm	Motor recovery	
	Radial	Suture	1.2 Elbow	Motor recovery	
	Median	Suture	$5.8 \to 1.4$	Tinel's sign	
	Ulnar	Suture	$2.8 \to 0.1$	Tinel's sign	
	Musculo-cutaneous	Suture	$2.7 \to 0.8$	Tinel's sign	
In developing animals:					
Cats, dogs and rabbits several weeks old	Sciatic		2–3	Regeneration. Histological methods	Cajal, 1928
Rat 1–3 days old	Caudal cutaneous nerves		2	Growth	Lubińska (unpublished)
4–26 days old	Caudal cutaneous nerves		2.8	Growth	
Embryo of guinea-pig	Pyramidal tract		6–7	Growth. Histological methods	Kimel and Kavaler, cited by Flexner, 1950
Chick embryo 3 days	Not stated		0.24	Growth. Histological methods	Cajal, 1928

Rate fast initially then slowing down

Initial rate depends on the level of the lesion

* The data collected in this Table were obtained directly on the regenerating fibres. Transsynaptic tests were used only for human motor fibres. For other rates of regeneration, estimated from times of functional recovery, see Gutmann et al. (1942). The character of regenerating fibres is undetermined in the data obtained by histological methods or by testing the action potentials. All other data concern sensory fibres.

TABLE II

RATES OF ELONGATION OF REGENERATING AMPHIBIAN NERVE FIBRES

Animal	Nerve	Lesion	Temperature °C	Rate in mm/24 h	Remarks	References
Toad, *Bufo bufo*	Sciatic	Crush	9.1 12.1 15.7 21.8 25.8	0.6 0.6 0.6 1.0 1.4		Lubińska and Olekiewicz, 1950
Frog, *Rana esculenta*	Sciatic	Crush	8.9 12.5 17.1 21.9 25.9	0.6 0.6 0.8 1.2 2.2		Lubińska and Olekiewicz, 1950
Salamander	Cutaneous branches in the tail	Cut	—	0.48	Observed for 1 h. Average over longer periods is lower	Speidel, 1935b
Hyla crucifer, tadpole	Cutaneous branches in the fin	— Cut	— —	0.4–1.4 0.2–2.0	Outgrowth of new fibres Regeneration	Speidel, 1933, 1950 Speidel, 1935a
Rana sylvatica, tadpole	Cutaneous branches	Cut	20	0.3 In Schwann sheaths 0.12 Without sheaths	Figures corrected for latent period Figures corrected for latent period	Williams, 1930
Hyla crucifer, tadpole	Lateral line nerve	Cut	20	0.4 In Schwann sheaths 0.12 Without sheaths	Figures corrected for latent period Figures corrected for latent period	Williams, 1930

It is not clear, as yet, whether the rate of regeneration changes with the distance of fibre tips from cell bodies. Whereas both in the rabbit (Gutmann *et al.*, 1942) and in frogs and toads (Lubińska and Olekiewicz, 1950), the rate of advance of regenerating fibres appears to be constant throughout the length of the nerve, in man a declining rate of regeneration along the limbs and a marked fall (to about 1/6) in the wrist and the foot were observed (Seddon *et al.*, 1943; Sunderland, 1947; Sunderland and Bradley, 1952). Since the rate of regeneration is greatly influenced by temperature, the strong decrease of the rate in the distal parts of human nerves is probably at least partly due to temperature gradients along the limbs.

However even when precautions were taken to maintain a constant temperature along the regenerating nerve (Haftek, 1963) a difference of rates appeared (in the rabbit) according to the distance of the lesion from cell bodies, faster growth being observed with more proximal lesions. The initial rate was in each case maintained throughout later regeneration. These experiments seem to indicate that only the level of lesion and not the distance travelled by axon tips influences the rate of regeneration.

(b) Individual fibres in vivo and in culture

Whereas the study of regenerating nerve trunks at daily intervals indicates a steady advance of regenerating fibres, direct microscopical observations of individual fibres reveal a more complex behaviour. The main source of information concerning the behaviour of individual growing and regenerating fibres *in vivo* is Speidel's (1932, 1933, 1935a, b, 1950) remarkable series of experiments in which cutaneous nerves in the dorsal fin of tadpoles were observed over long periods in intact animals. He describes the emission of new nerve sprouts, the proliferation of primitive Schwann cells, their migration between and along fibres, their orderly application to successive stretches of axons, and formation of myelinated internodes in normal development and during regeneration. Speidel also studied the influence of various factors on the behaviour and appearance of axons and myelin and the sequence of changes in fibres undergoing Wallerian degeneration.

The growing axons present terminal enlargements, growth cones, with many branching pseudopods. The growth cones advance through the tissues by typical amoeboid motion, pseudopods being incessantly extended and retracted. The encountered obstacles may block the progress, causing enlargement of the growth cone and further branching at or near the tip. The branching may be temporary or permanent. Rarely the terminal portion of the axon is pinched off and degenerates. Sometimes the fibre recedes. A growth cone about to retract draws in its filamentous processes and becomes smoothly rounded. After a time the advance is resumed. Thus the elongation of fibres is intermittent, periods of advance alternating with those of arrest or retraction.

The back and forth movements of axoplasm are not confined to the growth cones. Slow protoplasmic streaming of both granular materials and clear neuroplasm may be discerned along the axons. It occurs in both directions but the flow towards

References p. 56–66

L. LUBIŃSKA

TABLE III

RATES OF ELONGATION OF GROWING AND REGENERATING FIBRES IN TISSUE CULTURES*

Animal	Tissue	Temperature in °C	Rate in mm/24 h	References
Rana palustris, embryo	Walls of the neural tube, primordia of cranial ganglia		0.37–1.34	Harrison, 1910
Chick embryo	Various parts of the nervous system	38	0.56	Levi, 1934
Chick embryo, 7 days incubation	Mesencephalon	26	0.06	Mossa, 1927
	Mesencephalon	37	0.20	
	Mesencephalon	38	0.43	
	Mesencephalon	39	0.79	
	Mesencephalon	41	0.34	
Chick embryo, 8–12 days incubation	Spinal ganglia	37	0.41	Nakai, 1956
	Dissociated neurons from spinal ganglia	37	0.16	
Chick embryo, 7–12 days incubation	Lumbar ganglion	—	1.2	Hughes, 1953
	Midbrain	—	0.62–1.01	

* Most of these observations were made on regenerating fibres or on mixtures of growing and regenerating fibres. The initial outgrowth from neuroblasts is seen only in Harrison's experiments, where parts of the neural tube were explanted before differentiation. All observers stress the discontinuous character of elongation, intervening periods of rest and variable velocities at various moments.

growth cones predominates. Speidel stresses the close resemblance of behaviour of nerve fibres in living tadpoles and in tissue cultures.

In cultures *in vitro* the amoeboid activity of the ends of growing nerve fibres, involving incessant changes of shape and formation and disappearance of branches was

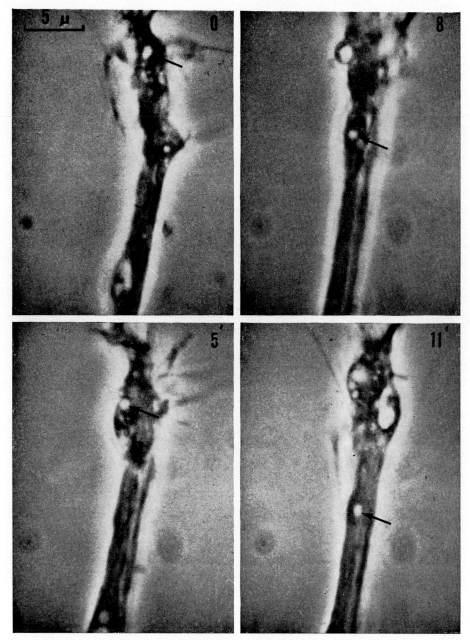

Fig. 1. Terminal part of an axon in tissue culture (from the dorsal root ganglion of an 8-day-old chick embryo). Vacuole taken in at the tip migrates in the axon in cellulipetal direction. Time intervals indicated in min. (From a film of C. M. Pomerat kindly supplied by the author.)

first described by Harrison (1910) and was seen by all later workers. The advance of growing tips in culture is also variable and intermittent. Average rates are shown in Table III.

Bidirectional migration of mitochondria and other granules along the axons and ascent of droplets (Fig. 1) pinocytozed at the endings was seen in cultures from various parts of the nervous system of various animals (Matsumoto, 1920; Hild, 1954; Hughes, 1953;Hayden *et al.*, 1954; Nakai, 1956; Geiger, 1958; Rhines, 1959, and many others). This incessant movement of particles up and down the axons in tissue cultures is conspicuous in the beautiful films of Pomerat (1960) and Nakai (1956), unfortunately irreproducible here.

The bidirectional pattern of streaming is not a particular characteristic of growing axons. It was seen in many types of elongated cells or cell processes in plants, protozoa and cultures *in vitro* of metazoan tissues. For example, Jahn and Rinaldi (1959) describe cytoplasmic streaming in reticulopods of a Foraminiferan, *Allogromia*. The configuration and dimensions of these thin processes, a few microns in diameter and up to 15 mm in length, resemble those of axons. In every pseudopod the streaming occurs always simultaneously in both directions. In radial reticulopods one stream goes toward the body and the other away from the body. In reticulopods that form cross-connections of the reticulum, each stream goes in the direction opposite from the other. In thin pseudopods all of the visible granules are streaming. The granules can be traced individually as they move to the tip of the filament and then turn 180° around the tip and start back toward the base of the filament. In larger pseudopodia many narrow pathways of the stream lying side by side are observed. The rate of streaming under conditions of observation was about 8–15 μ/sec.

A very wide range of rates of streaming was observed in various materials. In plant cells the velocities are of several microns per second in root hair and pollen tubes, 40–80 μ/sec in the internodes of *Characeae* and over a millimetre per second in plasmodia (Kamiya, 1959). In animal cells the streaming is usually considerably slower.

The streaming is influenced by a great variety of external and metabolic factors. It may be arrested for a while by mechanical, electrical or optical stimulation and resumed shortly afterwards. In *Characeae* the cessation is correlated with the occurrence of action potentials. The vast experimental material obtained on plant cells is analyzed in Kamiya's (1959) monograph.

In regenerating nerve fibres in culture two types of axoplasmic motion may be detected: a bulk advance of axoplasm in the proximo-distal direction and a bidirectional streaming in the axons as visualized by movements of axoplasmic inclusions. What is the relation between these phenomena? The answer to this question is suggested by the study of velocities of both processes. In a few cases the rate of axoplasmic streaming and that of elongation of fibres, both very variable, were measured under the same experimental conditions. The velocity of streaming was found to be 8–40 times higher than that of elongation. These results are shown in Table IV which also includes data calculated from other types of experiments showing similar ratios of velocities of both processes.

TABLE IV

COMPARISON OF RATES OF REGENERATION AND OF AXOPLASMIC STREAMING

Material	Rate of axoplasmic streaming		Rate of regeneration μ/h	Ratio of rates	References
	Basis of calculation	μ/h			
Chick spinal ganglia in culture	Ascent of pinocytozed vacuoles	420–2000	51	8–40	Hughes, 1953
Dissociated neurons from chick spinal ganglia in culture	Ascent of pinocytozed vacuoles	60–300	6.7	9·45	Nakai, 1956
Rabbit, hypoglossal	Migration of radioactive tracers	1700	82	21	Miani, 1962
Dog, peroneal Dog, tibial	Accumulation of AChE at cut ends of fibres	1430 2700	141 154	10 18	Lubińska et al., unpublished
Frog, kept at 25°, sciatic	Accumulation of AChE at cut ends of fibres	650	80	8	Niemierko and Zawadzka, unpublished*
Frog, kept at 8°, sciatic		430	0	—	

* I am greatly indebted to Dr. S. Niemierko for permission to use unpublished results.

There seems to be a connection between the rate of growth and the rate of streaming. In plants the growth promoting substances accelerate also the rate of streaming (Kelso and Turner, 1955), the optimal concentration for stimulation being similar for both processes. In cultures of dissociated neurons from chick spinal ganglia both growth and axoplasmic streaming are much slower than in the usual type of culture of these ganglia (*cf.* Table IV). The relation is not a simple one, however. Thus, in frogs kept at 8° the rate of axoplasmic streaming is only slightly reduced as compared with that of frogs kept at 25° (Niemierko and Zawadzka, personal communication) whereas the regeneration of fibres is completely arrested at 8°.

The elongation of a fibre seems to reflect the difference between the amount of materials transported from the cell body to the axon tip and that flown back along the axon to the cell body and is not directly dependent on the absolute rate of streaming. Similar relations were observed between the rate of streaming (Allen, 1961) and that of advance of pseudopods in *Amoebae* (Mast and Prosser, 1932).

Summary

Attention is focussed in this chapter on two sets of facts involving movements of the axoplasm in regenerating nerve fibres.

(1) When regeneration is studied in nerve trunks by usual methods, that is when the advance of growing tips of a huge axonal population is followed at daily or longer time intervals, a steady elongation of fibres by several millimetres a day is observed, indicating bulk shifts of axoplasm in the proximo-distal direction.

(2) When experiments are made under conditions of a better temporal and spatial resolution, by continual observations under the microscope of individual growing or regenerating fibres, a more complex pattern of axoplasmic movements emerges.

The tips of fibres exhibit intense amoeboid activity, pseudopods are incessantly emitted and withdrawn, the advance of growth cones is irregular, its velocity changes from moment to moment, periods of rest or retraction alternate with those of advance. Besides the amoeboid activity at axon tips a bidirectional streaming of materials is seen in the fibres. Granules and vacuoles migrate in both directions, up and down the axons. A similar pattern of cytoplasmic streaming was observed in many other types of cells.

The rate of intraaxonal migrations is many times greater than that of advance of growth cones.

The rapid bidirectional streaming of axoplasm on the one hand, and the relatively slow growth of fibres in the proximo-distal direction on the other, suggest that the latter reflects the difference between the amount of axoplasm transported to the axon tip and that flown back towards the cell body in the investigated time interval.

II. MOVEMENTS OF AXOPLASM IN NERVE FIBRES SEPARATED FROM THEIR CELL BODIES

Few characteristics of nerve fibres are altered immediately after nerve section. Various physiological and morphological changes develop progressively at different rates.

The huge literature concerning Wallerian degeneration is full of conflicting data concerning the time course and the spatial sequence of the observed changes. This is due partly to the extreme variability of the observed phenomena and partly to different criteria used to estimate the loss of function.

(a) Observations on individual cut nerve fibres and anucleated cell fragments of other cells

The fate of peripheral parts of nerve fibres separated from their cells of origin was followed under the microscope *in vivo* by Speidel (1935a) and in tissue culture by many workers. Before it finally degenerates, a cut nerve fibre continues for many hours the activity it manifested before the transection. The growth cone advances, filopods are put forward and withdrawn, back and forth movements of granules are visible along the axon. Pinocytosis continues and the droplets taken in at the tip ascend the axon and may accumulate at the opposite end of the fibre (Hughes, 1953). Often a bulbous enlargement appears at the proximal end of the cut segment and a new set of filopodia and ruffling membranes is emitted there (Levi, 1925, 1934; Hughes, 1953).

The maintenance of cytoplasmic streaming in surviving anucleated fragments of cells was often observed in other materials. Jahn and Rinaldi (1959), sectioning at both ends a filopod of *Allogromia*, observed the two-way streaming immediately after the cuts were made. Soon such fragments rounded up and extended several fine pseudopodia which also exhibited the two-way streaming exactly similar to that of the intact organism. Allen *et al.* (1960) describe organized streaming in portions of Amoeba cytoplasm aspired into a capillary tube. In such portions, deprived of cell membrane, the streaming either continues uninterrupted or is resumed after a short arrest. The pattern of streaming is initially similar to that of the intact pseudopod and later breaks into several U-shaped elements in which the flow along each arm goes in opposite direction*. Thus, neither the integrity of the cell nor the presence of the ectoplasmic tube are necessary to maintain the streaming. The disorganization of streaming sets in only when the cytoplasm becomes moribund. The pattern of streaming is very stable under a variety of experimental conditions (see Kamiya, 1959). It is not easily disturbed even by multiple surgical divisions of the cell. Thus, when successive portions of an internode of Nitella were tied off, after each operation streaming at the former rate of 65 μ/sec was soon resumed in the remaining fragment of the internode (Kuroda, 1958, quoted by Kamiya, 1959).

The persistence of streaming in fragments of the internode indicates, as Kamiya has pointed out, that the factors generating the flow are not confined to particular loci in the cell but are present everywhere in the cytoplasm, probably arising in the

---

* *Note added in proof*: Bidirectional flow appears also under appropriate conditions in the cytoplasm of Amoebae separated by centrifugation from nuclei and heavy particles and gently homogenized. When the cytoplasm is kept at 4° only Brownian movement of granules is visible. Addition of ATP induces organization of movements. Streams of granules arranged in parallel lines are seen moving in opposite directions through the bulk of cytoplasm at rates of up to 80 μ/sec (Thompson and Wolpert, 1963).

material itself. Similar views were expressed by other workers (Jahn and Rinaldi, 1959; Stewart and Stewart, 1961).

(b) Experiments on nerve trunks and tracts of white matter

The observations on individual fibres separated from their cell bodies suggest that in the study of cut nerve trunks two phases should be distinguished. An early stage of incipient degenerative changes in which the physiological properties of nerve fibres are practically unaltered, and a stage of fully developed Wallerian degeneration characterized by disintegration of axons and by intense proliferation of Schwann cells. The persistence of axoplasmic streaming can be expected only in the stage preceding the breakdown of axons into ovoids.

(1) Proximal end of the peripheral stump

The fate of the peripheral stump in the initial period following the sectioning of the nerve was less extensively investigated than that in the later stages of degeneration. In a few experiments however a close similarity of behaviour of cut fibres in nerve trunks and in culture was detected. Thus, Ranson (1912) in dogs and Cajal (1928) in young cats give the following description of early changes occurring near the site of section of the sciatic nerve.

One day after transection at the upper end of the peripheral stump the fibres have emitted many thin lateral branches and both the branches and the blind ends of parent fibres produced bulbous terminal enlargements. Many of the bulbs have grown up to the edge of the stump. The picture was initially similar to that observed at the end of the proximal stump but the subsequent evolution was different. In the distal stump the growth of lateral branches and the formation of end bulbs did not progress after the first day. It remained stationary during 3–4 days and later the branches and bulbs disappeared. These phenomena, called 'abortive regeneration' by Ranson and 'ephemeral regenerative reactions' by Cajal, show that in the cut fibres in the nerve trunk the streaming of axoplasm continues for about a day after operation. The new growth cones exhibiting amoeboid activity are formed at the proximal end of fibres of cut nerve trunks *in vivo*. They resemble closely those described by Hughes (1953) and Levi (1934) in cut fibres in tissue cultures.

It will be seen later that this survival of streaming provides important clues for interpretation of many phenomena observed after nerve section.

(2) Nerve terminals and synaptic transmission

After division of the nerve the earliest signs of degeneration appear at nerve endings. Ranvier (1878) was the first to observe the early destruction of the nerve endings and the fragmentation of intramuscular nerve twigs after section at a time when scarcely any change is seen in fibres in the nerve trunk. He studied this stage of degeneration in various laboratory mammals, young and adult, in birds, lizards and frogs and found that the failure of neuromuscular transmission coincides with degeneration of the endings. Ranvier's observations have been confirmed since by many workers on various animals (Huber, 1900; Titeca, 1935; Gutmann et al., 1955, Lissák et al., 1939).

Similar relations were observed at interneuronal synapses. In the superior sympathetic ganglion of the cat the transmission is affected much earlier than the conduction of impulses along the sectioned preganglionic trunk (Davidovich and Luco, 1956). A sharp drop in the acetylcholine content (MacIntosh, 1938, Feldberg, 1943) in the ganglion accompanies the arrest of synaptic transmission. After section of dorsal roots the conduction of impulses remains normal for 80 h whereas the first disturbances of transmission to motoneurons in the monosynaptic arc appear in about 30 h and transmission is completely abolished in 72 h (Vera and Luco, 1958, Kostyuk and Savoskina, 1963, Kostyuk, 1963). With the electron microscope De Robertis (1959) found swelling of endings, agglutination and lysis of synaptic vesicles and disintegration of mitochondria at the time when synaptic transmission fails in the acoustic ganglion after destruction of the cochlea.

The early appearance of degenerative changes is not limited to the synaptic region. The intramuscular twigs and the terminal portions of fibres in cutaneous nerve plexuses (Weddell and Glees, 1942; Weddell and Zander, 1951) also degenerate much earlier than the fibres in the nerve trunks. No modern explanation of this difference seems to have been offered. Ranvier, who thought that degeneration is due to activities of Schwann cells, attributed the early breakdown of the intramuscular twigs to the fact that the internodes are shorter there than in nerve trunks and, consequently, there are more Schwann cells for the same length of fibres, thus accelerating the process of degeneration. This idea of Ranvier does not seem to have been taken up. It is to some extent confirmed by his own findings that in very young animals (where internodes are short), the cut nerve fibres degenerate more rapidly than in adults. It should not be difficult to test his hypothesis directly by comparing the rate of degeneration of regenerated nerve fibres with that of unaffected parent fibres in the same nerve trunk.

The duration of survival of synaptic transmission in severed nerve fibres seems to depend on the functional load. Abrams and Gerard (1953) in the frog sciatic and Cook and Gerard (1931) in the sciatic of dog found that intense electrical stimulation reduces slightly the time of maintained synaptic transmission as compared with that of the resting nerve. Gerard (1932) attributed these results to a more rapid exhaustion during activity of the respiratory enzymes initially present in the fibres.

The time course of development of several changes at the synapse was seen to depend on the length of the peripheral stump left in continuity with the end organ. With longer peripheral stumps the nerve endings degenerate later (Gutmann et al., 1955) and the disturbances of the synaptic transmission at the neuromuscular junction (Eyzaguirre et al., 1952) and in the superior cervical ganglion (Davidovich and Luco, 1956) develop more slowly. Many transsynaptic changes, such as the onset of fibrillation and hypersensitivity to acetylcholine (Luco and Eyzaguirre, 1955) as well as disturbances of metabolism of the denervated muscle (Gutmann, 1962) are also delayed.

This delay in the onset of changes when the peripheral stump is long seems to indicate that the maintenance of synaptic integrity may depend on the amount of certain relevant substances stored in the peripheral stump. It also suggests that some

TABLE V

TIME OF APPEARANCE OF CHANGES AFTER NERVE SECTION

Animal	Nerve	Changes	Time at which changes appear	Remarks	References
I. Nerve endings					
Man	Median	Disappearance of neuro-muscular transmission	94–121 h	Decrease of maximal contraction after 48 h	Landau, 1953
	Facial	Disappearance of neuro-muscular transmission	66–91 h		
	Ulnar	Disappearance of neuro-muscular transmission	71–128 h		
Monkey	Ulnar	Disappearance of neuro-muscular transmission	72 to 89 h		Landau, 1953
	Median	Disappearance of neuro-muscular transmission	54 to 72 h		
Dog	Sciatic	Disappearance of neuro-muscular transmission	96 h		Ranvier, 1878
Dog	Sciatic	Disappearance of neuro-muscular transmission	67 h	Maximal motor effect persists 30–40 h	Cook and Gerard, 1931
Cat	Sciatic	Disappearance of neuro-muscular transmission	30 h	Nerve conduction unaffected	Titeca, 1935
Rabbit	Sciatic	Disappearance of neuro-muscular transmission	48 h	Earlier in young animals	Ranvier, 1878
Rabbit	Sciatic	Disintegration of endings and disappearance of neuro-muscular transmission	32 h*	Axonal excitability mostly intact in the trunk	Gutmann et al., 1955
	Sciatic	Disintegration of intramuscular twigs	70 h		
Guinea-pig	Sciatic	Disappearance of neuro-muscular transmission	48 h		Ranvier, 1878
Rat	Sciatic	Disappearance of neuro-muscular transmission	48 h		Ranvier, 1878
Pigeon	Sciatic	Disappearance of neuro-muscular transmission	72 h		Ranvier, 1878
Frog	Sciatic	Disappearance of neuro-muscular transmission	10–30 days		Ranvier, 1878
Frog	Sciatic	Disappearance of neuro-muscular transmission	10 days at 20°	Accelerated by increasing temperature. Nerve conduction unaffected	Titeca, 1935
Frog	Sciatic	Disappearance of neuro-muscular transmission	16–20 days* at 18°		Parker, 1933

Animal	Structure	Observation	Time	Notes	Reference
Fishes	—	Disappearance of neuro-muscular transmission	up to 6 weeks		Ranvier, 1878
Cat	Preganglionic cervical sympathetic	Decrease of synaptic transmission tested by contraction of the nictitating membrane	20–40 h	Completely abolished at 45–72 h when conduction in the trunk is unaffected	Coppée and Bacq, 1938
Cat	Cervical sympathetic ganglion	Sharp decrease in ACh content of the ganglion and disappearance of synaptic transmission	48–72 h	ACh falls by 74 % when synaptic transmission fails completely	MacIntosh, 1938
Cat	Preganglionic cervical sympathetic	Disturbances of synaptic transmission		Nerve cut close to the ganglion on one side and far on the other. Changes appear earlier with short preganglionic stump.	Davidovich and Luco, 1956
Cat	Dorsal roots	Decrease of monosynaptic reflex at motoneurons	50 h	Records from ventral roots. Fatiguability, intensified and prolonged posttetanic potentiation	Vera and Luco, 1958
Cat		Disappearance of monosynaptic reflexes	80–90 h	Conduction in the dorsal roots unaffected at that time	
Cat	Dorsal roots	Decrease of monosynaptic reflexes at motoneurons	24 h	Intracellular recording from motoneurons	Kostyuk, 1963
		Disappearance of monosynaptic reflexes	72 h		
Guinea-pig	Acoustic ganglion	Agglutination and lysis of synaptic vesicles, disappearance of synaptic transmission	22 h		De Robertis, 1959
Rabbit	Cutaneous plexus in the ear	Degeneration of terminals	12 h		Weddell and Glees, 1942
Frog tadpole	Cutaneous nerves in the fin	Breaking into ovoids	6 h		Speidel, 1935a

II. Transsynaptic effects

Animal	Structure	Observation	Time	Notes	Reference
Cat	Nerve to tenuissimus	Fibrillation and hypersensitivity to ACh	90–120 h*	Proximo-distal spread of disturbance at 48 mm/day initially, slowing down at later stages	Luco and Eyzaguirre, 1955

Continued overleaf

TABLE V (continued)

Animal	Nerve	Changes	Time at which changes appear	Remarks	References
Rat	Sciatic	Glycogen content of muscle	24 h*	Greater with longer stumps	Gutmann et al., 1955
Rat	Sciatic	Metabolic overshoot reactions	24 h*	More pronounced with longer stumps	Gutmann, 1962
Rat	Phrenic	Transitory hypertrophy of muscle	7–14 days	Increased content of contractile and plasma proteins	Stewart and Martin, 1956
Chicken	Nerve to m. anterior latissimus dorsi	Hypertrophy of the muscle. Increase in dry weight of 50 to 110%	2 weeks	Increased size of muscle fibres and increased content of non-connective tissue proteins	Feng et al. 1963
III. Fibres in nerve trunks					
Dog	Phrenic	Disappearance of nerve impulses	4 days	Failure at random loci	Erlanger and Schoepfle, 1946
Cat	Sciatic	Disappearance of nerve impulses	4 days	Simultaneous in the whole trunk	Titeca, 1935
Rabbit	Sural	Breakdown of fibres and disappearance of nerve impulses	63–80 h	Simultaneous in the whole trunk	Gutmann and Holubar, 1950
	Peroneal, in vivo	Breakdown of fibres and disappearance of nerve impulses	72–80 h	Simultaneous in the whole trunk	
	In Ringer in vitro	Breakdown of fibres and disappearance of nerve impulses	36 h		
	In dead animal	Disappearance of nerve impulses. No breakdown of fibres	2–4 h		
Rabbit	Phrenic	Demyelination at the nodes	less than 48 h*	Spreads in the proximo-distal direction	Causey and Palmer, 1953
Frog	Sciatic	Disappearance of nerve impulses	22 days at 20°		Titeca, 1935

Frog	Sciatic	Fatiguability, delayed recovery, increased staining with methylene blue	2 days* at 20°	Disturbances detectable only at a transient stage. Spread along the nerve in the proximo-distal direction at a rate of 20 mm a day	Titeca, 1935
Catfish	N. to lateral line	Alteration of myelin and neurofibrils	11–13 days*	Proximo-distal spread along the nerve at a rate of 20–30 mm a day. Calculated from observations of symmetrical nerves cut at various times	Parker and Paine, 1934
IV. Fibres in central tracts					
Man	Pyramidal tract	Breakdown of fibres	3 days	Simultaneous in the whole tract	Glees, 1948
Monkey	Pyramidal tract	Breakdown of fibres	7–15 days		Lassek, 1946
Cat	Pyramidal tract	Breakdown of fibres	Starts after 3 days complete in 6 months		Verhaart and Van Crevel, 1961
Cat	Efferent mammillary tract	Breakdown of fibres	Starts at 10 days		Guillery, 1961
Lizard	Optic nerve	Breakdown of fibres	12–34 days at 30°	No degeneration in 17 days at room temperature	Armstrong, 1950
Lizard	Ventral longitudinal bundle	Breakdown of fibres	Starts after 8–15 days*	Possibly spreads in the proximo-distal direction	Goldby and Robinson, 1961

* The results in which the length of the peripheral stump influenced the time of appearance of changes or where a spread of the disturbance along the nerve was detected are marked by an asterisk.

kind of transport continues for a time in the peripheral stump so that materials may be brought to the end-plate region from the remote proximal parts of the stump. It should be stressed that these phenomena are transient in character and detectable only at very determined stages after nerve section. They always precede gross manifestations of degeneration in the trunks.

(3) Fibres in nerve trunks

Fine cytological changes in cut nerves were observed with electron microscope as early as 24 h after section by Vial (1958), Ohmi (1961), and Honjin *et al.* (1959) at a period when electrophysiological properties of fibres are practically unaltered. It is well known from other sources that deep morphological alterations of fibres under various experimental conditions may develop without impairment of action potentials (Sato and Schneider, 1954; Denny-Brown and Brenner, 1944). The most dramatic illustration of this point is provided by experiments on giant fibres of the squid which continue to propagate impulses after removal of about 95 % of their axoplasm (Baker *et al.*,1961). It is true that in these emptied fibres a layer of axoplasm of several microns is preserved at the fibre surface. This is more than many normal vertebrate fibres have at their disposal.

The time at which severed fibres break up into ovoids varies from species to species. It is very variable also in different fibres from the same animal. Numerous attempts to correlate the resistance to degeneration with the physiological character of fibres or with their dimensions were not very successful. The sensory fibres are believed to degenerate earlier than the motor ones and small diameter fibres earlier than large fibres. It may often be seen, however, that of two neighbouring fibres of the same caliber one is completely broken into ovoids whereas the other preserves an almost normal appearance.

Practically all peripheral nerve fibres of laboratory mammals are completely disintegrated in 4–8 days. Central fibres usually survive longer and degenerate at very scattered rates (*cf.* Table V). A remarkably long survival, of up to 6 months was described in the axons of the pyramidal tract in cat (Van Crevel, 1958; Verhaart and Van Crevel, 1961).

In amphibians and fishes the integrity of cut nerve fibres is preserved much longer than in mammals. This is probably due to differences in temperature since lowering of temperature considerably delays both the degeneration of nerve fibres and the time of disappearance of synaptic transmission.

The question whether the degeneration begins simultaneously in the whole length of degenerating fibres or spreads progres sively from the site of lesion towards the periphery is not definitely settled. Earlier results pointed to a progressive spread of degeneration but the criteria used to detect it were not always adequate. The increase of both muscular contraction (Parker, 1933) and of the compound action potential (Rosenbluth and Del Pozo, 1943) observed when a cut nerve is stimulated in the more distal parts may be due to other factors than the proximo-distal spread of degeneration along the nerve fibres. More recent experiments seem to indicate that, apart from terminal branches, in the peripheral nerves both morphological disintegration and failure of conduction seem to occur simultaneously throughout the length of fibres (Erlanger and Schoepfle, 1946; Gutmann and Holubar, 1950). A few subtler changes however were seen to spread along cut fibres in the proximo-distal direction. Thus, one of the early alterations appearing after nerve section, the retraction of myelin from the nodal region, begins near the site of lesion and involves progressively more distal parts of the nerve (Causey and Palmer, 1953). In the lateral line of catfish (Parker, 1932) a structural change of myelin progresses along cut fibres at a rate of 20–30 mm a day.

After nerve section the fibres become more fatiguable (Titeca, 1935). The fatiguable stretch is also more easily stained by methylene blue than the unaltered parts of fibres. In the sciatic of frog both fatiguability and increased stainability begin near the site of section and advance along the nerve in the peripheral direction at a rate of about 20 mm a day (at 20°).

There are indications that in the tracts of white matter even the fragmentation of fibres may spread in the proximo-distal direction and the time of survival of fibres may be influenced by the length of the peripheral stump. For discussion see Goldby and Robinson (1961).

Is there a biochemical cause of breakdown into ovoids of axons separated from their perikarya? Whereas the idea of depletion of some essential substances in cut nerve fibres was corroborated by experimental findings concerning the disappearance of synaptic transmission, no determined chemical change was, so far, correlated with disintegration of nerve fibres. The main difficulty here is due to the intimate anatomical association of axons with Schwann cells so that chemical determinations are nearly always made on a mixture of both cellular components. The exceptions are the analyses of the extruded axoplasm (Maxfield, 1953; Thornburg and De Robertis, 1956) and the beautiful separation of axoplasm from Schwann cell in the neurons from Deiters nucleus made by Edström (1960) and Edström et al. (1962) who succeeded in determining the composition of nucleotides in each of these cellular components of the fibre. In degenerating nerves however no such separation was as yet attempted.

Since in the Wallerian degeneration the destruction of axons overlaps in time with proliferation of Schwann cells, it would be anticipated that substances of axonal origin will decrease in amount whereas those of Schwann cell will increase. With the exception of nuclear components however, such an assumption may not be correct, because proliferating Schwann cells may acquire new metabolic features after disappearance of axons (cf. Lubińska, 1961). Some recent work on the ACh system after denervation (Birks et al., 1960; Mitchell and Silver, 1963) seems to confirm such possibility.

In spite of lack of conspicuous success in determining the nature of substances responsible for the maintenance of integrity of nerve fibres, the prevailing tendency at present is to ascribe the fragmentation of fibres to a chemical depletion in terms not very different from those used by Scott in 1906.

It is assumed that some proteins necessary for axonal metabolism or their precursors cannot be manufactured in the axons since these lack ribosomal RNA necessary for protein synthesis and that the fibre perishes after separation from the cell body when the proteins stored in the cut segment are used up and cannot be replenished by a new supply from the perikaryon. Certain facts suggesting the possibility of axonal synthesis of an enzyme, acetylcholinesterase (Koenig and Koelle, 1961; Clouet and Waelsch, 1961) seem to undermine somewhat the generality of this theory. The problem was discussed recently by Waelsch and Lajtha (1961).

The current tendency to look for a biochemical origin of degeneration of fibres has led to a certain neglect of purely physical factors which may be responsible both for

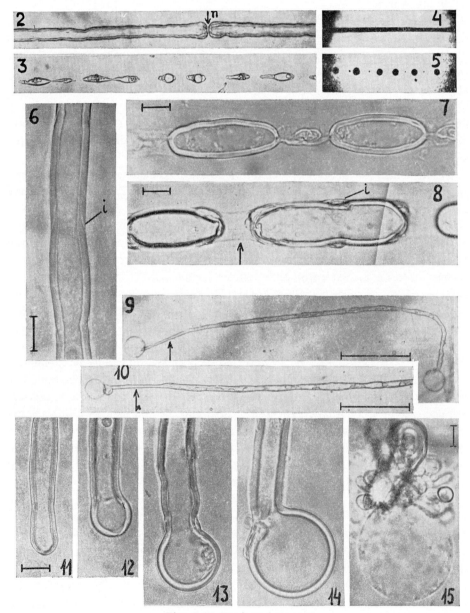

Figs. 2–15. For legend see p. 23.

the maintenance of continuity of normal fibres and for their fragmentation after nerve section. An elongated liquid or semiliquid thread is essentially unstable since every liquid surface tends to contract to the smallest possible area under influence of surface tension. A cylinder will tend to assume an unduloid outline and then break up into a series of droplets. The time during which a liquid cylinder may maintain its shape depends on a series of parameters such as diameter, surface tension and viscosity of the liquid, external pressure and a series of other factors (*cf.* Kuhn, 1953).

The ovoids in degenerating nerve fibres resemble closely the string of droplets resulting from breakdown of a liquid column (Figs. 2, 3, 6, 7, 8). Long threads of protoplasm of other types of cells also tend to disperse into droplets (Chambers and Kao, 1952; D'Arcy Thompson, 1942). Young (1944a, 1945) assumed that in normal fibres the force counteracting the disruptive effect of surface tension is the turgor pressure in axons originating in the perikaryon. Another possibility is that the very existence of axonal flow maintains the continuity of fibres and that fibres break up when the axoplasmic streaming is brought to a standstill. Taylor (1935) has shown that a liquid column is stable in a field of flow and breaks up into a string of droplets when the flow is arrested (Figs. 4, 5).

Several facts are consistent with physico-chemical interpretation of nerve degeneration. An increased external pressure delays degeneration of nerve fibres (Weiss and Burt, 1944). No ovoids are formed in nerves left *in situ* in dead animals in which the axoplasm ceases to exhibit properties of a liquid. Similarly when gelation of axoplasm is induced by mechanical stimulation (Flaig, 1947; Lubińska, 1956a) and gelated fibres are left to degenerate *in vitro*, they preserve their cylindrical shape whereas unstimulated fibres with liquid axoplasm disintegrate intoov oids (Lubińska, 1956a).

It seems that the physico-chemical changes of axoplasm should be taken into account in a full theory of Wallerian degeneration.

Summary

In the initial period following nerve section the axoplasmic motion continues for some

---

Figs. 2 and 3. Normal and degenerating nerve fibres from the sciatic of rabbit.
All photographs of Figs. 2–15 except those of Figs. 4 and 5 are of fresh unfixed fibres; n = node of Ranvier; i = incisures.
Figs. 4 and 5. A drop of oil in sirup pulled out into a cylindrical thread in a field of flow, breaking up into a string of droplets when the flow was stopped (Taylor, 1935, Fig. 7).
Figs. 6, 7 and 8. Normal and degenerating nerve fibres at higher magnification to show details. Myelin encloses completely the ovoids. Arrow = reduced lumen of the neurilemma between ovoids. Scale 10 μ.
Figs. 9 and 10. General view of excised frog nerve fibres with outflowing droplets of content at the ends, 27 h after cutting. Kept in Ringer. Arrows = reduced diameter of the depleted terminal parts of fibres. Scale 100 μ.
Fig. 11. Cut border of myelin has coalesced over the meniscus of axoplasm 1 h after the transection. Scale 10 μ.
Figs. 12, 13 and 14. Progressively increasing droplets of outflowing axoplasm covered by myelin.
Fig. 15. Burst shell of myelin thrown into irregular folds at the orifice of the fibre, leaving a naked spherical drop of axoplasm, 36 h after transection (Lubińska, 1956b).

References p. 56–66

time. Movements of granules and ascent of pinocytozed droplets may be observed directly in nerve fibres freshly separated from their cell bodies in tissue culture. Both in cultures and in cut nerve trunks *in vivo*, new growth cones, exhibiting amoeboid activity may appear at the proximal end of cut fibres.

A few morphological and physiological disturbances were seen to spread in the proximo-distal direction along degenerating fibres at a rate of about 20–30 mm/24 h. In some cases the longitudinal spread was not detected, or not looked for, but the length of the peripheral stump was seen to influence the intensity or duration of synaptic activity suggesting that some materials continue to be transported toward the region of synapse even after nerve section. The data on this subject are scarce, however, and sometimes contradictory. These phenomena may be discovered only during the relatively short period after nerve section between the moment when the disturbance becomes detectable and the disintegration of fibres or endings. The success of detection will depend therefore on sensitivity of the methods and on the correct timing of experiments. This is probably the reason why the most convincing evidence of spread (Parker and Paine, 1934; Titeca, 1935) was obtained on cold-blooded animals where all processes of degeneration are much slower than in mammals.

Thus, in nerve fibres separated from cell bodies the axoplasmic motion is manifested for some time. It may be detected directly by cinematography of cut nerve fibres in tissue cultures and inferred from the proximo-distal spread of some morphological and physiological disturbances in cut nerve trunks *in vivo*.

III. DATA SUGGESTING THE EXISTENCE OF AXOPLASMIC STREAMING IN NORMAL MATURE NERVE FIBRES

Suppositions have been formulated sometimes (Weiss, 1963) that the bidirectional pattern of axoplasmic streaming observed in tissue cultures is particular to these experimental conditions and does not exist in mature fibres *in situ*. Since with modern techniques of tissue culture many parts of the nervous system of various animals were cultured under long term conditions permitting myelination of nerve fibres and the appearance of morphological, enzymological and electrophysiological correlates of maturation (*cf.* Murray, 1959; Murray *et al.*, 1962; Peterson and Murray, 1960; Yonezawa *et al.*, 1962a, b; Crain and Peterson, 1963; and others) it seems unlikely that the pattern of axoplasmic streaming would be fundamentally different in culture and *in situ* conditions. The more so that the streaming is an intracellular phenomenon and is probably to some extent independent of the establishment of intercellular connections or of other influences exerted by the rest of the organism.

The direct detection of axoplasmic streaming in mature nerve fibres *in situ* has, however, proved to be elusive. Since such fibres are usually inaccessible to microscopical observation under sufficiently high power, only indirect information about the streaming of their axoplasm is available at present.

The existence of movements of axoplasm in mature nerve fibres has been inferred indirectly from various biochemical and histological features. Most of them taken separately might also be interpreted differently and it is only when the whole of the available evidence, gathered by various methods, is analyzed that the existence of axonal flow seems to be demonstrated. Even so opinions diverge as to the pattern of streaming. The most widely accepted is Weiss' concept of the proximo-distal flow at a rate of a 1–2 mm a day. Some recent experimental data point, however, to the existence of a much more rapid and bidirectional streaming similar to that observed directly in tissue cultures. A review of results suggesting either type of axoplasmic motion is given here.

(a) Uninterrupted fibres

(1) Biochemical gradients

When the biochemical composition of a peripheral nerve is studied at various distances from cell bodies, it is seen that some compounds exhibit a proximo-distal gradient of concentration or activity whereas others are distributed uniformly. The longitudinal distribution of relatively few components was studied systematically. Those in which a gradient was detected and measured are listed in Table VI.

Sometimes divergent results are obtained with various materials. Thus, whereas the intensity of respiration decreases along the sciatic of rat (Majno and Karnovsky, 1958), it was found to be constant along the sciatic of frog (Gerard, 1930) and exhibit a maximum in the middle in the optic nerve of *Limulus* (Guttman, 1935; Shapiro, 1937).

Several other substances, besides those listed in Table VI, were observed to be more concentrated in the proximal than in the distal parts of nerves. Thus, proteolipids are more abundant in anterior and posterior roots than in sciatic and brachial nerves (Heald, 1961). Abood and Gerard (1954) found 2.5 times more phosphorylated intermediates in spinal than in sciatic nerves of frog. Concentration of choline acetylase is higher in the upper part of the sciatic than at the more distal levels of this nerve (Hebb, 1963). In all these cases, as Hebb pointed out for choline acetylase, the observed difference may be due to branches given off by the nerve trunk. In a branching nerve the fibre composition varies along the main trunk and it is always possible that the fibres richest in the investigated constituent might have left the trunk at one of the more proximal branchings.

On the other hand a real decrease of concentration of these substances along individual axons cannot be ruled out. To settle this point it would be necessary to use nerves having the same axonal population at all investigated levels. Since most of mammalian nerves either start from plexuses or branch profusely, or both, the length of nerves available for the study of axonal gradients is that of their shortest branch.

In some instances biochemical analyses were made on various parts of nerves in which the number of fibres and their diameters were invariable throughout the analyzed length (for discussion of morphological characteristics see Lubińska *et al.*, 1963a). Such experiments may provide information about the longitudinal distribution of axonal constituents if the presence of materials from Schwann cells in the analyzed nerve homogenates does not complicate the picture. As already referred to, the contribution of Schwann cells constituents is difficult to assess. So far as gradients

References p. 56–66

TABLE VI

BIOCHEMICAL GRADIENTS ALONG NERVES*

Animal	Nerve	Substance or activity	Number of nerves	Number of levels in each nerve	Decrease over 10 mm in % of the value in the uppermost part	Remarks	References
Squid	Giant axon	Homarine	8	4	11.5	Gradient found in 8 out of 13 nerves. No relation to axons volume or surface	Gasteiger et al., 1960
Rat	Sciatic	Respiration	12	2	6.5	Sciatic divided into 2 parts. Tibial was also examined, showing further decrease	Majno and Karnovsky, 1958****
		Lipid contents	12	2	5.0		
		Acetate incorporation	12	2	2.0		
Spider monkey	Sciatic	Lysine in proteins	6	2	4.0	Between hip and knee	Lajtha, 1961a***
Frog	Sciatic	Lysine in proteins	6	4	12**	2 out of 6 frog nerves did not show gradient	
Frog	Lumbar-Sciatic	Acid-insoluble P	4	3	21**		Gerard and Tupikova, 1939
		Acid-soluble P	6	3	16**		
Bullfrog	Lumbar-Sciatic	Acid-insoluble P	4	3	39**		
		Acid-soluble P	4	3	20**		
Dog	N. to gastrocnemius	Acetylcholinesterase activity	5	3	5.7	Substrate acetylthiocholine, pseudo-ChE inhibited with DFP. Decrease of activity is linear along the nerve	Lubińska et al., 1963a
	Hypoglossal		10	4	4.6		
	Suprascapular		6	3	4.0		
	N. to lev. scap.		6	3	3.6		
	Sural		8	3	3.5		
	Tibial		9	4	3.0		
	Phrenic		12	5	1.8		
	Peroneal		20	4	0.9		
	Saphenus		4	2	0.4		
Rabbit	Sciatic	Lipolytic esterase activity	4	3	1.8	Substrate methylbutyrate	Lumsden, 1952

* The average decrease along 10 mm of nerve was calculated from the difference in concentration or activity between the uppermost and the lowermost analyzed segments divided by the distance between the midpoints of these segments.

** Decrease over the whole nerve. Length not stated.

*** I am greatly indebted to Dr. A. Lajtha and Dr. G. Majno for communication of unpublished details of experiments. Dr. Lajtha thinks that gradients may be due to some factor other than different composition of axoplasmic proteins along the nerve.

along nerves are concerned, unless the investigated compound is known to be localized exclusively in the axons, a tacit assumption has to be made that the composition of Schwann cells is uniform throughout the whole length of the nerve. Such assumption may not be necessarily correct.

It will be seen in Table VI that certain biochemical features of nerve fibres exhibit a systematic change with the increasing distance from cell bodies along regions of axons which are dimensionally and structurally uniform. As would be expected from structural uniformity, the concentration of bulk components usually remains constant throughout the length of the nerve. The observed changes are those of enzymes or other substances forming an insignificant part of the volume of axoplasm. An illustration of this point is provided by the phrenic nerve of dog. In this long un-branched nerve trunk the fibres do not taper peripherally (Rexed, 1944) and the concentration of proteins, total N, total P and nucleic acid phosphorus remains constant throughout, whereas acetylcholinesterase activity decreases progressively, falling by about 40 % between the beginning and the end of the nerve. The gradient of AChE activity varies with the kind of nerve, being usually, but not always, steeper in short nerves.

Probably other components, besides those listed in Table VI, also exhibit proximo-distal gradients. The decrease being slight along short stretches of nerves, the phenom-enon would not be detected unless looked for. The existence of biochemical gradients is however strongly suggested by the well known fact of unequal resistance of various parts of fibres to damage of neurons. In many peripheral neuropathies the distal parts of nerves degenerate or demyelinate at a stage when no histological alterations are seen in the more proximal parts. The same sequence of appearance of lesions is observed after poisoning with organo-phosphorus compounds (Cavanagh, 1954; Majno and Karnovsky, 1961).

To what extent the existence of biochemical gradients along nerve fibres may be taken as indication of migration of axoplasmic components? If the components or their precursors are synthesized only in the perikaryon, their presence in the other parts of the neuron shows that some kind of transport must have taken place. It is possible that these migrations occurred during ontogenesis (Hughes and Tschumi, 1957; Bonichon 1958; Zelená and Szentágothai, 1957) and the gradients were built up at that time and have remained unchanged in the adult life. A more dynamic interpretation, implying continual axonal transport seems more plausible. It is suggested, besides other indications, by the great lability of longitudinal distribution of axonal components. Thus, for example, the normal gradient of AChE in the phrenic disappears several days after section of the contralateral nerve. The peak of activity is found then somewhere in the middle of the nerve (Lubińska et al., 1961). It is not certain whether this is due to the increased functional load on the innervated hemi-diaphragm or to contralateral repercussions on the ability of motoneurons to synthesize the enzyme, or both. The phenomenon suggests nevertheless that in the steady state the gradient is the resultant of the rates of synthesis, transport and utilization of neuronal materials and breaks down when the relationships between these factors are altered.

TABLE VII

RADIOACTIVE TRACERS IN UNINTERRUPTED NERVE FIBRES

Animal	Nerve, levels and length of segments	Tracer and site of injection	Method of detection	Time after injection	Rate mm/24 h	Length of active segment after 24 h in mm	Remarks	References
Frog	Lumbar plexus-sciatic, divided into 4 parts	^{14}C-lysine intraperitoneal injection	Activity of protein bound lysine	8, 17, 28 and 38 days	—	—	A strong proximo-distal gradient was observed after 8 days, the lowermost level exhibiting only 25% of activity of the uppermost. Later activity in the proximal part decreased progressively, while that in distal part rose slightly	Waelsch, 1958; Lajtha, 1961a
Rat	Superior cervical ganglion	^{35}S-methionine intraperitoneal injection	Autoradiography	30 min, 24 and 72 h	—	—	30 min activity in perikarya and Schwann cells; 24 h in post-ganglionic fibres activity as strong as in perikarya; activity has increased 6 to 8 times during this time interval. In the preganglionic fibres activity is 2–4 times weaker	Verne and Droz, 1960
Rat	Supraoptic nucleus-infundibulum	^{35}S-cysteine and ^{35}S-methionine	Autoradiography	15 sec to 96 h	—	—	Radioactivity appears first in the nucleus later in infundibulum. Considered as proof of perikaryal synthesis	Sloper et al., 1960
Guinea-pig	Sciatic, pelvis and knee levels	^{32}P repeated injections into blood stream	Activity in various chemical fractions. Ratio of the upper to lower level changed only for phospho-proteins P (or inositol P)	First measurements 10 days after the last injection	2–3	—	Anticipated tide of high specific activity along the nerve was not observed	Samuels et al., 1951
Cat	Ventral roots, throughout the length, every 3 mm	^{32}P injection into grey matter of the spinal cord	Counts in the whole root. Half activity points of slopes at various times used to estimate the rate	1 to 20 days	4.5	30	Authors think that the figure observed at 24 h may be fortuitous*. An inactive distal part is visible only after 1 day, later activity is seen throughout the length of the root	Ochs et al., 1962

Rabbit	Vagus, 9 segments between nodose ganglion and subclavian vessels	^{32}P-orthophosphate placed for 2.5 h on the floor of 4th ventricle	Activity in phospholipid fraction	24, 38, 61 h; 3, 5, 10 and 17 days	41	77	No activity in the nerve when the axons were cut previously at medulla, indicating that the incorporation occurs in cell bodies only. In crushed nerves the rate of advance of radioactivity is similar to that of elongation of regenerating fibres, about 2 mm a day	Miani, 1962
	Hypoglossal, 4 segments of 8 mm	^{32}P-orthophosphate placed for 2.5 h on the floor of 4th ventricle	Activity in phospholipid fraction	24, 38, 61 h; 3, 5, 10, 17 days	41	45		
Cat	Ulnar, consecutive segments of 10 mm	^{35}S-methionine and ^{14}C-glycine subarachnoid injection	Activity in proteins	4 h to 30 days	4–5	—	Peaks of activity, separated by less active segments. With increasing time intervals peaks were present farther distal. Peaks suggest migration at different rates. A few days after injection activity is 2 to 7 times higher in the proximal than in the distal segments	Koenig, 1958
	Sciatic, consecutive segments of 10 mm	^{35}S-methionine and ^{14}C-glycine subarachnoid injection	Activity in proteins	4 h to 30 days	7–11	—		
Rat	Sciatic at 8 and 26 mm from the vertebrae	^{3}H-leucine 9 injections in 24 h	Counts per 10 μ^2 of axonal area in transverse histological sections. Only proteins remain after processing	30 min, 27 h 4 and 16 days	1.5	—	After 27 h activity insignificant in axons. After 4 days strong activity at the proximal level, weak (or none) at the distal. This relation is reversed after 16 days	Droz and Leblond, 1962
Axolotl	Lateral line nerve, throughout its length	^{14}C-amino acids intraperitoneal injections	Densitometry along the nerve	164 and 214 days	1	—	Activity falls to background level at 160 mm from cell bodies after 160 days. The result is considered by the author to be 'suggestive rather than conclusive because of tapering of the nerve'	Weiss, 1961

* Personal communication by Dr. Ochs.

The existence of gradients thus lends some support to the concept of axonal flow, at least in the direction from cell body towards axon terminals. It should be stressed, however, that an absence of gradient of a substance along the axon does not indicate an absence of migration. If the metabolism of a compound is slow, as compared with the rate of transport, a uniform concentration throughout the length of the fibre may be established.

(2) Migration of radioactive tracers

When radioactive tracers are injected subarachnoidally or directly into the central nervous system, radioactivity most often appears first in the perikarya and later in the axons. In the axons it is initially stronger in the proximal than in the peripheral parts. At later stages the difference in activity disappears or is reversed. This type of results is usually interpreted in terms of uptake and incorporation of tracers in the perikarya, followed by a discharge of tagged synthesized materials into the axons along which they subsequently migrate in the proximo-distal direction (Table VII). Some authors calculated the velocity of migration of tagged materials from the progressively varying ratios of activity in the proximal to that in the distal part of the nerve and obtained rates of 1–4 mm a day.

The difficulties of interpretation of experiments with tracers, concerning various steps of incorporation into various tissue compartments, variable half life time of labelled compounds and their further metabolism, were discussed by Waelsch and Lajtha (1961), Davison and Dobbing (1961), Dobbing (1961), Waelsch (1962) and by Lajtha (1961). The last author also stressed the necessity of taking into account the possibility of preexistent gradients of the investigated compounds along nerves.

If attention is confined to the much simpler problem of detection and measurement of axoplasmic flow with help of radioactive tracers, following factors which may obscure the actual rate of migration should be considered.

Various compounds or various portions of the same compound incorporated into different subcellular structures may not leave the perikaryon simultaneously but in successive steps. In the pool of parent cells of fibres of the investigated nerve various perikarya may start to discharge the labelled substances into axons at various times. Additionally the rates of migration may be different in various fibres. Thus, for example, the appearance of several peaks of radioactivity along the nerve (Koenig, 1958) might be due to any of these asynchronous events as well as to an advance by spurts. If the axoplasmic flow in mature nerve fibres proves eventually to occur simultaneously in both directions, as it does in regenerating fibres, a certain time after injection both descending and ascending layers of axoplasm would carry radioactive components. The radioactivity at any one level of the nerve would be the resultant of all these complex factors of unknown time course. The estimation of rates of migration will therefore depend largely on the time elapsed between the injection and the testing and will be uncertain.

The following experimental data cast doubt on the correctness of the estimated rate of migration of a few millimetres a day:

(1) The whole length of the sciatic of frog was found to be already labelled eight

days after the injection (Waelsch and Lajtha, 1961). Similarly, against expectation that an advancing front of radioactivity may be detected somewhere along the nerve, Samuels *et al.* (1951) found the whole length of the sciatic of guinea-pig invaded by labelled compounds 10 days after the injection. These findings suggest a higher rate of advance of radioactive tracers since the distance between the cell bodies and the distal parts of the sciatic is too long to be covered in eight or ten days by substances migrating at a rate of 2–3 mm a day.

(2) In the published figures of experiments made early after the injection (Ochs *et al.*, 1962; Miani, 1962) it is seen that in the first 24 h the nerve is tagged over some 30–70 mm. Since the authors have shown that no spread of activity in the interstices between fibres has taken place under their experimental conditions, it seems that these figures reflect approximately the actual rate of migration of labelled compounds in the axons. This, incidentally, would be of the same order of magnitude than the rate of movement of granules in nerve fibres observed directly under the microscope (*cf.* Table IV). Miani's (1962) experiments are particularly interesting in this respect since he studied the spread of radioactivity both in normal uninterrupted nerves and in regenerating nerves. In the latter the advance of radioactivity was of about 2 mm a day showing that the tagging advanced only as far as the tips of regenerating axons.

The discrepancy between the rates apparent from the distance travelled during the first day after the injection and those calculated from relations observed at longer time intervals seems to be attributable to the temporal overlap of many complex processes mentioned earlier. As long as the time course of these processes is not elucidated the data obtained after the shortest time intervals seem to provide the best estimation of the actual rate of migration of tagged materials.

Summary

The experiments made on normal uninterrupted nerve fibres show the migration of radioactive tracers along axons in the proximo-distal direction. The rate of migration is estimated by most authors as 1–4 mm a day. It is shown that such rate fails to account for the presence of labelling over some 30–70 mm of nerve length in the 24 h after the injection and these last figures are proposed as a better approximation to the actual rate of migration of tracers.

The proximo-distal gradients of concentration or activity exhibited by some of the axonal components corroborate, if certain additional assumptions are made, the existence of migration of substances along the axons from the cell bodies to the nerve endings.

(b) Effects of occlusion of axonal pathways

Partial or total occlusion of axonal pathways has proved to be one of the most fruitful methods of indirect detection of axoplasmic flow in mature nerve fibres. Morphological and biochemical changes developing progressively near the site of lesion provided strong suggestions for the existence of flow. It has been the great merit of Weiss to draw attention to the dynamic character of these changes.

References p. 56–66

(1) Deformation of fibres

When a nerve is compressed over a short stretch, its fibres are deformed in the compressed zone and on both sides in the neighbouring regions. A detailed description of the immediate effects of compression was made by Calugareanu (1901a, b) who studied the disarrangement of axoplasm and myelin, the alterations of diameters of various parts of fibres and the reversibility of these disturbances after compressions of varying strengths and durations. He also investigated the ability of deformed fibres to conduct impulses. This work as well as less extensive later studies (Causey and Palmer, 1952; Lubińska, 1952b) have shown that myelin and variable amounts of axoplasm are removed from the compressed part of the fibres into adjacent uncompressed parts, which become dilated and filled with a mixture of myelin and axoplasm over some hundred microns. Further away from the site of compression the organization of the fibre seems undisturbed. In the compressed region the diameter of the fibres is reduced. The degree of reduction depends on the strength of compression. The disorganization of regions adjacent to the site of compression subsides partly in several hours.

When the fibres are cut, their contents flows out from the cross section (Young, 1937, 1944b; Lubińska, 1956a). The outflowing droplets appear at both ends of an excised segment (Fig. 9) and increase with time (Figs. 11–15). The outflow is accompanied by a reduction of diameter of the terminal parts of the fibre. The lumen of the neurilemma always decreases in parts of fibres from which the content was partially or completely removed. The reduction of diameter of the neurilemma is seen in the compressed region in the intervals between the ovoids of degenerating fibres (Fig. 8) as well as near the outflow at the cut. The tendency to reduction of diameter under all these circumstances indicates that the neurilemma in an intact fibre is both distended and elastic. By local application of graded external pressures to nerve fibres a progressive reduction of diameters of the compressed region, partly emptied of its contents was obtained. The neurilemmal tube in radial direction was found to obey Hooke's law. The calculated Young modulus, 4×10^9 dynes/cm^2, was of the same order as that of collagenous fibres (unpublished). It is probably the elastic tension of the neurilemma that squeezes out the content of the fibre at the cross section since the volume of the outpouring droplet increases proportionally to the square root of time Lubińska, 1956b). This relationship is characteristic for the outflow from elastic capillary tubes (*cf.* Hermans, 1952).

Although these data provide no information concerning the flow of axoplasm in intact fibres, they may be useful when the interpretation of the mechanism of axoplasmic motion is attempted.

When nerves are constricted for prolonged periods the acute effects subside and deformations of a different type develop progressively. They were first described by Cajal (1928). A detailed analysis of such deformations was made by Weiss and Hiscoe (1948). These authors used an arterial sleeve with a lumen slightly narrower than the nerve to produce a mild compression. The sleeve, about 1 cm long was slipped over the nerve and kept there from 4 to 35 weeks. The compression led to characteristic distortions of fibres beneath the sleeve as well as on its proximal and distal side.

In the compressed region the diameters of fibres were reduced. They were reduced also distally to the compressed part never widening appreciably over the size they had under the sleeve. Proximally to the site of constriction the fibres were deformed. They exhibited a series of rhythmic dilatations of variable shape: balloons separated by necks, beads or coils, all declining in size in the proximal direction. Such deformations were seen both in normal and in regenerating nerves.

The removal of the sleeve led to downward movement of axonal material, causing the draining of balloons and a partial redistention of fibres in the previously constricted and in the distal parts. The progress of the tidal wave could be followed for the first few days after removal of the constricting sleeve and was found to correspond to 1–2 mm a day. Several types of control experiments were performed which should be looked up in the original paper. It should be noted, however, that in chronic compression of shorter duration (8 days) Cajal (1928) observed multiple bulbous dilatations immediately below the compressed region and normal diameter of fibres in the more distal parts. The deformations observed by Cajal on the proximal side of the compression are similar to those described by Weiss and Hiscoe (1948). Weiss and Cavanaugh (1959) confirmed previous results and extended the period of recovery after release to 12–14 weeks during which a marked increase in diameters of the peripheral parts of fibres was observed. On the basis of these phenomena Weiss and Hiscoe, 1948, p. 338) developed the following concept of axonal flow.

'The nerve fibre is subject to a force which presses the column of axonal substance constantly and steadily forwards in the direction of periphery. When the width of the channel is reduced, a local bottleneck is created which retards the rate of passage. The portion immediately proximal to the bottleneck will receive more substance per unit of time than can be disposed of, and a surplus will begin to pile up'.

Weiss assumes that the axon receives all protoplasmic supply from the perikaryon and that the width of the fibre is normally so adjusted that it permits unobstructed passage of axoplasm at a rate corresponding to the metabolic activity of the fibre. In calculating the rate of protein breakdown in the nerve from the then available biochemical data, Weiss finds a remarkably close agreement (which he himself considers as coincidental) between the rate of advance of 1–2 mm a day of the axonal column and the amount of metabolized proteins.

When the lumen of the axon is narrowed locally, the supply of axoplasm to the distal part of the fibre is reduced, whereas, as Weiss assumes, the consumption of axonal materials is kept at normal level. This would explain the permanent reduction of fibre diameters distally to the constricting sleeve. Weiss generalizes this observation to state that the diameter of the narrowest point of the axon cannot be exceeded in any part of the fibre situated more distally. This statement however is contradicted by anatomical data. It is well known that when an axon dichotomizes the area of cross section of branches exceeds that of the parent fibre. But even in unbranched parts of axons narrower and wider regions alternate. In a motoneuron, for example, the axon emerging from the axon hillock is thin and increases abruptly in diameter at the first myelinated segment (Strong, 1906). Another stretch of reduced diameter appears when the fibre leaves the spinal cord and traverses the pial ring (Ranvier, 1882;

Tarlov, 1937). These are relatively long stretches of narrowed axon. But at each node of Ranvier the lumen of the fibre is reduced to less than a half of the diameter it has over the internode (Young, 1949; Gasser, 1952; Lubińska, 1954) to be resumed again after crossing the node. The same is true for the thin intercalated internodes appearing after a local destruction of myelin (Gombault, 1880–1881; Rénaut, 1881; Lubińska, 1958a, b, 1961).

At all these loci, as well as in the parts of fibres distal to compression in the experiments of Weiss and Hiscoe, the myelin is either thinned down or absent. Since there are many indications that myelin influences the diameter of the underlying axon which widens during myelination and becomes reduced when myelin disappears (Nageotte, 1921; Speidel, 1932; Hild, 1959; Quilliam, 1954; Bunge *et al.*, 1960) it seems that the permanent size deficit observed by Weiss and Hiscoe in the parts of fibres distal to the constricting sleeve cannot be attributed simply to the narrowing of the axonal pathway at the site of constriction.

Another difficulty raised by Weiss' theory concerns the fate of axonal material in the steadily proximo-distal advance of the fibre contents. In his analysis Weiss dealt only with proteins. However water contributes about 80% of the axonal volume. Since the fibre preserves a uniform diameter throughout most of its length, a rather elaborate set of hypotheses would be required to explain the absence of an ever increasing pool of water at the end of fibres.

In spite of these difficulties Weiss' theory offering an interpretation of many features of neuronal biology became widely accepted, at least in its broad terms.

(2) Biochemical and structural changes

When the continuity of axons is broken by a crush or section of the nerve various biochemical and morphological changes soon develop in the axons in the vicinity of the lesion. Several groups of enzymes and some other substances were found to accumulate near the ends of axons. A similar accumulation of neurosecretory materials was observed in the interrupted tracts of neurosecretory neurons. The electron micrographs of the region show a dense packing of mitochondria, vesicles and membranous profiles.

The results of observations fall into two categories: (1) Those in which the increase was observed proximally to the lesion; (2) Those in which the increase was seen on both sides of the lesion. The first type of results was obtained either in experiments in which the nerve on the distal side of the lesion was not analyzed at all or in experiments in which both sides were analyzed and no accumulation was found on the distal side.

In view of the importance of these local changes for the analysis of the character of axonal flow, a detailed summary of relevant experiments is given in Tables VIII, IX and X.

Enzymes, neurosecretory materials and some other substances. When examined by histochemical methods, the sites of increased activity of various enzymes at the section look remarkably similar (Figs. 19, 20, 21). The strongest staining for acetylcholinesterase, esterases, acid phosphatase, various dehydrogenases, DPN and TPN dia-

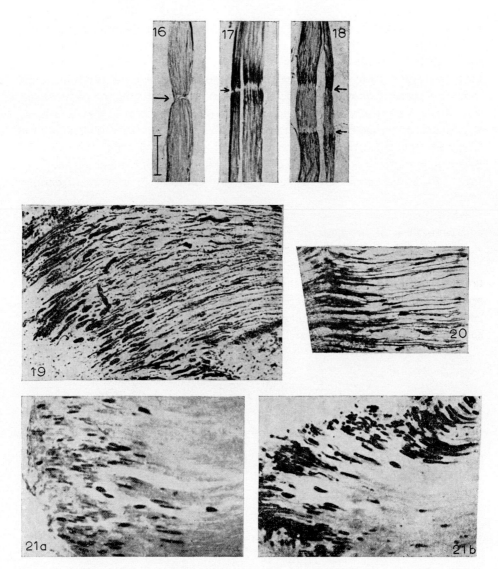

Fig. 16. Longitudinal section of a crushed sciatic nerve of the rabbit, removed immediately after crushing, stained for AChE activity by Koelle and Friedenwald method. Arrow = site of the crush. Fig. 17. A similarly treated section of a nerve removed 26 h after crushing. Increased activity of AChE is seen on both sides of the lesion. Arrow = site of the crush.

Fig. 18. A similarly treated section of the sciatic crushed in two places. Distance between crushes 3.4 mm. Increase of AChE activity above the proximal and below the distal lesion. No increase of AChE activity is visible in the short segment between the crushes (cf. Fig. 23 for long segments). Scale 3 mm. (Zelená and Lubińska, 1962).

Figs. 19–21. Sites of increased activity of enzymes on the distal side of the lesion in crushed or cut nerves. Fig. 19. DPN = diaphorase, 6 h after section. Rat, sciatic (Kreutzberg, 1963). Fig. 20. AChE, 18 h after crushing. Dog, peroneal (Zelená and Lubińska, 1962). Fig. 21a. Esterase, 24 h after section. Rat, sciatic (Gould and Holt, 1961). Fig. 21b. Acid phosphatase, 24 h after section. Rat, sciatic (Gould and Holt, 1961).

phorases is observed in the terminal club-like enlargements of axons, fading progressively away from the lesion to reach the colour of normal fibres some 100–300 μ from the end-bulbs. Actually there may be an increase of activity beyond this length but the limited sensitivity of histochemical methods used fails to detect it. When increased staining is observed on the distal side of the lesion, it resembles that on the proximal side, although small differences in shape of the terminal enlargement may sometimes be detected and the distance of stained endings from the site of the crush is somewhat longer. Accumulation of neurosecretory materials presents a similar picture. The general appearance of accumulation of AChE on both sides of the lesion is shown in Fig. 17 for a single crush and in Fig. 18 for two lesions made a few mm from one another.

When quantitative bioassays or biochemical determinations of nerve segments adjacent to the lesion are made, the narrow localization of maximum activity in a very short stretch of nerve is to be taken into account in the interpretation of results. Usually the segments of nerve taken for analysis are of about 10 mm, thus including both the most active region and the region of normal (or decreased) activity. The results obtained will show therefore an average value for the investigated segment and will fail to detect the strong increase of activity at the very ends. To enable the correct estimation of activity near the section and at various distances from it the

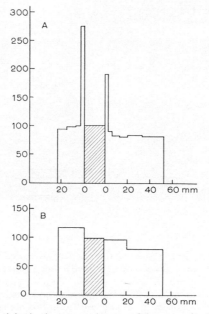

Fig. 22. Changes in AChE activity in the peroneal nerve of dog near the site of transection 4 h after cutting, in per cent of normal activity. (A) The solid line shows the length of segments used for analysis and the activity in each segment. Distances from transection are shown on abscissae. Normal activity in the segment removed immediately after operation hatched. (B) The same experiment. The data obtained on four short segments on the proximal side of the lesion and on four segments on the distal side have been pooled to show that when long stretches of nerve are used the increase of activity on the distal side may be masked. (The area under the solid line showing the total amount of the enzyme in the analyzed part of the nerve is the same in both graphs (Lubińska *et al.*, 1964).

nerve segments used for analysis should be as short as possible particularly in regions where abrupt changes are exhibited. This point is illustrated in Fig. 22 A showing AChE activity in a cut nerve in the vicinity of transection 4 h after operation. The same results calculated for longer stretches are shown in Fig. 22B. The details of distribution are here considerably smoothed down and the local increase on the distal side of the section is masked. Because of this effect information concerning the length of analyzed segments is included where available in Table VIII to enable the comparison of data obtained by various authors.

It will be seen in Tables VIII and IX that the experiments in which accumulation of materials was found also on the distal side of the lesion are more recent and less numerous. This is partly due to the fact that a local increase near the lesion is more likely to be missed in the peripheral than in the central stump of the nerve. Many of the investigated compounds decrease or disappear during Wallerian degeneration. Since the nerve segment taken for analysis is usually longer than that exhibiting the peak of concentration, the masking effect of dilution, described previously, will be stronger in the peripheral stump. Moreover, the local increase on the distal side of the lesion, reaches its maximum in about 24 h and declines in a few days so that it will not be found if longer periods after infliction of the lesion are examined.

In spite of these difficulties clearcut increases of concentration or activity on the distal side of the interruption of the axons were detected for acid phosphatase, nonspecific esterase (Gould and Holt, 1961), DPN-diaphorase, lactic, malic and succinic dehydrogenase (Kreutzberg, 1963), acetylcholinesterase (Zelená and Lubińska, 1962; Lubińska et al., 1963b) and neurosecretory material (Hild, 1951; Christ, 1962; Diepen, 1962). All these results were obtained in experiments made early after the division of the nerve or tract of white matter. The local increases at the ends of stumps were already visible within a few hours after infliction of the lesion.

The increase on the proximal side was interpreted usually in terms of Weiss' concept of the proximo-distal flow of axoplasm, as a piling up of materials dammed at the site of interruption of the axonal pathway. The increase of activity on the distal side did not fit in with this concept, neither could the usually assumed rate of flow of 1–2 mm a day account for the early appearance of accumulation on either side. Most authors tended therefore to deny any role to axonal flow in the phenomena they have observed and to interpret them either as degenerative changes or as the result of a local, injury-induced synthesis of the investigated compound in the axoplasm.

The hypothesis of a local production in the axoplasm near the ends of interrupted fibres has, however, proved to be incorrect for acetylcholinesterase, the only substance so far for which the course of accumulation was studied both histochemically and quantitatively.

In order to elucidate the origin of AChE accumulating near the cross sections of the nerve the following experiment was devised (Lubińska et al., 1964). The nerve was cut in two places some 50–100 mm apart and at each cut a small piece of nerve was removed to determine the normal level of the enzyme activity. From the obtained values and the length of the segment left between the cuts the total amount of the enzyme in the segment was calculated. Since the nerve was separated both from the

TABLE VIII

ENZYMES, ACETYLCHOLINE, 5-HYDROXYTRYPTAMINE, NORADRENALINE AND SUBSTANCE P NEAR THE ENDS OF INTERRUPTED NERVE FIBRES

Animal	Nerve	Constituent	Method of detection	Time after interruption of fibres	Changes near the site of interruption		References
					Proximal side	Distal side	
Sheep and cat	Cervical sympathetic	Choline acetylase	Bioassay	2–25 days	Increases reaching 150% in 5 days, then decreases to control values in 2–3 weeks	Falls to 5% after 1 week and to 0–1.5% after 4 weeks	Hebb and Waites, 1956
Goat	Sciatic	Choline acetylase	Bioassay	7 days	Increases in the terminal 2–2.5 cm to over 200%. No change in more proximal parts	Falls to 6%	Hebb and Silver, 1961
Cat	Cervical sympathetic	Acetylcholin-esterase	Biochemical	2–24 days	—	Falls to about 20% of the normal during the first week	Sawyer and Hollinshead, 1945
Guinea-pig	Sciatic	Acetylcholin-esterase	Biochemical	2–38 days	Increases in the terminal neuroma taken with a short stretch of nerve to 300% of the normal in 5 days	Falls to 40% after 10 days No further loss up to 38 days	Sawyer, 1946
Dog	Phrenic	Acetylcholin-esterase	Biochemical	4 and 6 days	Increase up to 300% of the normal in terminal 20 mm. Slight decrease in the more proximal parts of the nerve	—	Lubińska et al., unpublished
	Peroneal			2 to 96 h	Increases up to 275% in the terminal 2–3 mm after 4 h	Increases up to 190% in the terminal 2–3 mm after 4 h	
	Tibial			2 to 96 h	Increases up to 350% in the terminal 2–3 mm after 4 h	Increases up to 230% in the terminal 2–3 mm after 4 h	
Frog, 25°	Sciatic	Acetylcholin-esterase	Biochemical	6 to 24 h	Increases up to 280% in 6 h in the terminal 2 mm	Increases up to 170% in 6 h in the terminal 2 mm	Niemierko and Zawadzka, unpublished*
Frog, 8°	Sciatic	Acetylcholin-esterase	Biochemical	6 to 24 h	Increases up to 220% in 6 h in the terminal 2.2 mm	Increases up to 160% in 6 h in the terminal 2.3 mm	

Guinea-pig	Sciatic	Cholin-esterases	Histochemical	1 day–6 weeks	Increase at the cut end and in the regenerating sprouts. More proximally normal appearance	Fall with progressing degeneration	Snell, 1957
Xenopus larvae	Nerves to hind-limb	Acetylcholin-esterase	Histochemical	Several hours to several days	Increases strongly at tips within a few hours, later the increase extends backwards towards the spinal cord at a rate of about 0.5 mm a day	—	Hughes and Lewis, 1961
Rat	Cingulum, dorsal fornix and fimbria	Acetylcholin-esterase	Histochemical	4–20 days	Increases in the terminal 2 mm, normal more proximally. With time the length of the stained segment increases but intensity lessens	No increase or a diffuse blur. Sometimes a completely inactive segment is seen immediately distal to the cut	Shute and Lewis, 1961a and b
Rat, rabbit, dog	Sciatic	Acetylcholin-esterase	Histochemical	4–48 h	Increases strongly in the terminal 0.7–1.2 mm. Most intense staining in the club-like endings of axons	Increases over somewhat shorter distance (0.6–0.8 mm) than on the proximal side. In nerves crushed in two places separated by a few mm, staining appears in two places above the proximal and below the distal lesion. If the distance between crushes is large, four sites of staining, on both sides of each lesion, appear	Zelená and Lubińska, 1962
Dog	Sciatic	Oxidative enzymes	Histochemical	30 h	Increase in terminal enlargements of axons	—	Marinesco, 1924
				7–30 days	Increase in terminal enlargements, in neuromas and in regenerating sprouts		
	Spinal cord	Oxidative enzymes	Histochemical	7–30 days	Increase in terminal enlargements of axons	Almost complete absence	

Continued overleaf

TABLE VIII (continued)

Animal	Nerve	Constituent	Method of detection	Time after interruption of fibres	Changes near the site of interruption		References
					Proximal side	Distal side	
Frog (winter)	Sciatic	Oxidative enzymes	Histochemical	30 days	Increase in sprouting tips of regenerating fibres, more intense at 22° than at 9°	Less active than the central stump	Friede, 1959
Pigeon	Sciatic	Oxidative enzymes		2 days	Increase in terminal parts of axons	—	
Cat	Descending tracts in the spinal cord	Succinic dehydrogenase and TPN diaphorase	Histochemical	4–36 days	Increase in the tracts and in tips of axons where the enzymes persist after their disappearance from the tracts at about 12th day	No changes	
Rat	Sciatic	Succinic dehydrogenase and TPN diaphorase		12 h–50 days	Increase in the terminal enlargements of fibres visible after 12 h. In the more proximal parts apparent after 1–3 days. Disappear after about 8 days. When the nerve was ligated 2–3 mm proximal to the section, increase was seen only above the ligature	No activity in axons throughout the investigated period	
Rat	Sciatic	DPN-diaphorase, lactic, malic and succinic dehydrogenases	Histochemical	3–48 h	Increase in terminal enlargements of axons	Increase progressively for 24–48 h in the terminal enlargements of axons. After 3 days persist in a few axons only	Kreutzberg, 1963 and personal communication
	Brain and spinal cord			6–24 h	Increase in terminal enlargements of axons, persists up to 3 weeks		Kreutzberg, 1962; Kreutzberg and Peters, 1962

Animal	Nerve	Substance	Method	Time			Reference
Rabbit	Sciatic	Ali-esterase	Biochemical	2–30 days	Increases up to 300% in the terminal part	Falls slowly to 40% throughout the length of the stump after 20 days	Lumsden, 1952
Rabbit	Sciatic	Acid phosphatase	Histochemical and biochemical	8–13 days	Increases progressively up to 400% of normal in the terminal part. More proximally up to 175%	Increases progressively up to 320%. Cellular localization uncertain	Samorajski, 1957
Rat	Sciatic	Acid phosphatase and non-specific esterase	Histochemical	1–2 days	Increase. Staining pattern appears identical for both enzymes. Extends to the nearest node of Ranvier. Sometimes to the next proximal node	Increase. Staining extends up to 0.5 mm, in the rest of the distal stump little or no activity	Gould and Holt, 1961 and personal communication by Gould*
				3 days		Increase. Staining persists in tips which already begun to break up	
				6 days	Increase of both enzymes spreads along the rest of the proximal stump. Persists for 20–30 days after nerve injury	Axons tips broken into droplets, still positively stained. Staining disappears after about 15–17 days	
Rabbit	Auricular	Substance P	Bioassay	4–56 days	Increases up to 600% in 4–5 days	Falls to 36% in 7 days and stays at this level up to 56 days	Holton, 1959
Rat	Sciatic	Noradrenaline	Histochemical	12–48 h	Increases progressively from 12 to 48 h in the terminal 3–5 mm with strong fluorescence intensity within distorted axons, especially in the distal enlargements of the axons	Increases progressively over much shorter distance (0.4–0.8 mm) with weak or medium fluorescence intensity within distorted axons	Dahlström and Fuxe,* (unpublished)

Continued overleaf

References p. 56–66

TABLE VIII *(continued)*

Animal	Nerve	Constituent	Method of detection	Time after interruption of fibres	Changes near the site of interruption		References
					Proximal side	Distal side	
Rat	Spinal cord	Noradrenaline and 5-hydroxy-tryptamine	Histochemical	7–48 h	Increases progressively for 7–24 h in the terminal 1–2 mm with strong fluorescence intensity within distorted axons and persists rather unchanged during the following 24 h	Increases progressively for 7–24 h over a short distance (0.1–0.2 mm) with medium or intense fluorescence intensity within deformed axons and persists rather unchanged during the following 24 h	Dahlström and Fuxe,* (unpublished)
Rabbit	Descending tracts in the spinal cord	5-Hydroxy-tryptamine	Biochemical	7 days	Increases up to 123%	Decreases to 19%	Carlsson et al., 1963
Rabbit	Sciatic	Acetylcholine	Bioassay	3–25 days	After 5 days increases up to 625% in the terminal 5 mm. No increase beyond 15 mm proximally to the lesion	After 5 days increases up to 540% in the terminal 5 mm	Saunders* (unpublished)
Cat	Ventral roots	Acetylcholine	Bioassay	5–13 days	Scattered results. After 3–5 days in the terminal 5 mm increase up to 580% in some nerves and decrease to 28% in others. In the more distal parts falls to 28% of the control		

* I am greatly indebted to Dr. K. Fuxe, Dr. R. P. Gould, Dr. S. Niemierko and Dr. N. Saunders for their kind communication of unpublished results.

cell bodies and from the endings, the possibility of new supply from the perikarya as well as of a loss towards the periphery was eliminated. Such isolated segment was left *in situ* for periods from 2 to 96 h then removed and cut into 6 to 12 short pieces which were analyzed separately for AChE activity. These experiments provided information about the distribution of the enzyme in the isolated nerve segment and, important for elucidation of the origin of local increases at the ends, about the total AChE content of the segment at the investigated time intervals. An experiment of this kind is shown in Fig. 23.

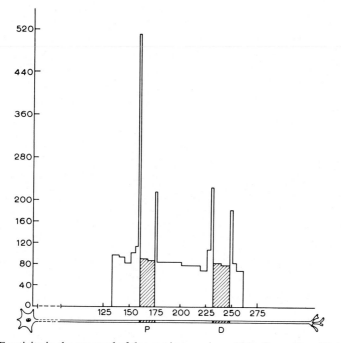

Fig. 23. AChE activity in the peroneal of dog cut in two places 18 h after cutting. Distance between cuts about 60 mm. P = proximal transection. D = distal transection. Solid line shows the length of pieces of nerve used for analyses and their activity in mμmoles of AThCh split by 1 mm of nerve in 2 h. Abscissae = distance from cell bodies in mm. An increase of AChE activity is seen on both sides of each lesion (Lubińska *et al.*, 1964).

An increase in acetylcholinesterase activity in the terminal parts of the isolated segment is detectable from 2 h onwards, rising progressively with time. The degree of increase depends also on the length of the isolated segment, being larger in longer stretches. The local accumulations at the ends are accompanied by a depletion in the middle parts of the segment so that, whatever the degree of the local increase, the total amount of the enzyme in the isolated segment remains unchanged. This was shown in 17 experiments in which the length of the segments varied from 20 to 110 mm and the time interval from 2 to 22 h. AChE activity in the terminal parts exhibited various degrees of increase (up to 400%). The average content of acetylcholinesterase in these segments amounted to 98.9 ± 2.9% of the normal.

The unchanged amount of AChE in the whole segment shows that the increase in activity near the transection of fibres is not due to a local production but results from the translocation of the preexisting enzyme along the nerve segment.

It is by no means certain that all substances accumulating at the cut ends of fibres have been transported there from other parts of the axons. Special experiments would have to be made for each compound to determine its origin. However, the remarkable similarity in the time of appearance, mode of localization and the length of the active stretches in histochemical pictures of various enzymes and neurosecretory materials makes it likely that, besides the AChE, many substances accumulating in the terminal regions of axons may have been carried there in a similar way.

The process of accumulation is arrested much sooner in the parts of fibres separated from cell bodies than in those remaining in continuity with their perikarya. It will be seen in Fig. 24 that on the distal side of a transection AChE increases for about

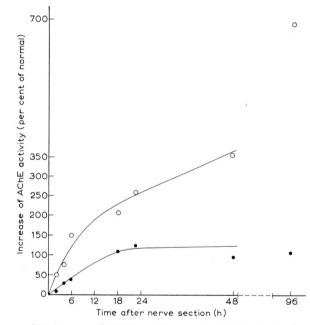

Fig. 24. Time course of the increase of AChE activity over the initial value in the terminal 6 mm of the nerve on each side of transection. In per cent of normal activity. Circles = proximal side. Dots = distal side. (Lubińska *et al.*, 1963).

20 h and is kept at this level for about 4 days. It will decrease progressively with the developing Wallerian degeneration. On the proximal side the increase continues at a slower rate than initially for many days.

These results were interpreted in the following way. The subcellular particles containing acetylcholinesterase are carried with the stream of axoplasm. They tend to settle down at the cut ends of axons. The accumulation of the enzyme on both sides of the transection indicates that the axoplasm is streaming both in the ascending and in the descending directions. The time course of accumulation of AChE provides a rough estimation of the rate of streaming at about 30–60 mm a day (*cf.* Table IV).

The progressive accumulation of the enzyme on the distal side of transection goes on (in the dog) for about 20 h indicating that during this period the flow of axoplasm is maintained in fibres separated from their cell bodies. More details about the mode of settling of particles in the terminal parts of interrupted axons will be given in the next chapter.

Most of the discrepancies seen in Table VIII concerning the rate and degree of accumulation and its location on the proximal side of the lesion only or on both sides of the lesion may be explained if the details of experimental procedure, in particular the length of the terminal segment and the time elapsed between the interruption of fibres and analyses is taken into account. A few divergences subsist, however. Thus Friede did not find any increase in oxidative enzymes on the distal side even as soon as 12 h after section whereas Kreutzberg could detect them clearly between 6 and 48 h.

As to the neurosecretory material (Table IX) the question is more complex. Although neurosecretory granules are produced in the perikarya (Bargmann and Scharrer, 1951; Palay, 1943, 1960) and carried down the axons, they may undergo an increase in size (Gerschenfeld et al., 1960; De Robertis, 1962) on their way. It is not known whether this change reflects an additional formation of neurosecretion in the axon or physico-chemical changes of other kind altering the size or stainability of particles. As Scharrer (1962) remarked recently the question may require more than one answer. For detailed discussion of various cases see the recent monograph on neurosecretion (Heller, 1962). The mode of accumulation of neurosecretory materials at the site of section of neurosecretory tracts resembles in many respects that of the enzymes. As with enzymes the increase was seen on the proximal side of the lesion only if the experiments were made several days or weeks after interruption and appeared on both sides of the lesion when tested within the first day after operation. Similarly also the presence of accumulation on the distal side and the early appearance of changes were considered to be incompatible with the concept of damming up of flow and were attributed to a local production in the axon or to degenerative changes (Hild, 1951; Christ, 1962; Diepen, 1962). Further quantitative data must be obtained, however, to decide whether the local accumulation of neurosecretory materials may be interpreted in the way outlined above for AChE as a result of translocation from other parts of the axon. The fact that up and down movements of neurosecretory granules were seen directly in axons of neurosecretory neurons in tissue culture (Hild, 1954) seems to corroborate such interpretation.

Noradrenaline (Dahlström and Fuxe, personal communication) and acetylcholine (Saunders, personal communication) also accumulate at he interrupted ends of axons. The fact that the concentration of ACh increases there in spite of the increased amount of AChE is another indication of its being enclosed in structural particles.

Structural particles at the ends of fibres. Although the accumulation of enzymes at the cut or crushed ends of fibres seems to be brought about by axoplasmic streaming, it is puzzling why the migrating enzyme-containing particles do stop there. No explanation can be offered at present. It should be noted, however, that crowding of particles is not a feature particular to the artificially cut ends of fibres.

References p. 56–66

TABLE IX

NEUROSECRETORY MATERIALS NEAR THE SITE OF INJURY OF NERVE FIBRES

Animal	Nerve	Lesion	Time after interruption of fibres	Changes near the site of interruption of fibres		Comment	References
				Proximal side	Distal side		
Dog	Supraoptic-hypophysial tract	Cut, after 14 days' thirst	4–8 days	Increase	Absence		Hild and Zetler, 1953
Frog, toad	Praeoptico-hypophysial tract	Cut	1–44 days	Increase	Increase initially	The increase on the distal side is considered as manifestation of the initial degeneration. After 5–11 days neuro-secretory material disappears on the distal side	Hild, 1951
Dog	Pituitary stalk	Cut	—	Increase	—	Interpreted as piling up above the site of interruption of axons. After several weeks material ceases to accumulate	Scharrer and Wittenstein, 1952
Calliphora	Cardiac-recurrent	Ligated	7 days	Increase	Absence	Interpreted as blocking of flow. Ends of fibres swollen	Thomsen, 1954
Rabbit	Hypothalamico-hypophysial tract	Coagulated by implanted electrodes	3, 6 and 24 h	Increase	Increase	Ends of fibres swollen at both ends. Neuro-secretory material located close to the surface of the axons. Findings suggest local production of materials by all viable parts of neurons. Flow is assumed to be too slow to account for the early appearance of changes	Christ, 1962
			2 months	Increase in regenerated axons	Absence		

Whereas mitochondria, membranes of endoplasmic reticulum, vesicles and other structural particles are scattered sparsely throughout the axoplasm along the axons, they are densely packed in all nerve endings. The abundance of ultrastructural elements characterizes axon terminals at all central synapses (Palay, 1956; De Robertis, 1959), at efferent endings of neuro-muscular junctions both in striated (Robertson, 1956; Katz, 1962) and in smooth muscles (Caesar and Edwards, 1957), in the electric organ of fishes (Luft, 1956), in the adrenal medulla (De Robertis and Vaz Ferreira, 1957b), in the hypophysis (Palay, 1960; Holmes and Knowles, 1960), in the spleen (Von Euler, 1958) and in the peripheral endings of sensory fibres (Pease and Quilliam, 1957; Fitzgerald, 1961; Cauna, 1961; De Robertis and Bleichmar, 1962). Even an unusual ending evaginating from the node of Ranvier of a myelinated fibre to a neighbouring dendrite in monkeys spinal cord (Bodian and Taylor, 1963) was filled with mitochondria and vesicles.

Tips of growing and regenerating fibres are also filled with particulate elements (Hay, 1960; De Robertis and Sotelo, 1952; Estable et al., 1957; Inuce, 1960; Wechsler and Hager, 1962). Whereas the advancing tip of the fibre carries the particles, the freshly formed stretch of axoplasm behind it has a normal appearance and scarcity of granules. In trying to find a dynamic interpretation of these morphological features it is tempting to assume that at axon terminals some local conditions prevail which favour settling of particulate elements.

Accumulation of structural particles in the axoplasm above the site of compression or section of nerve fibres was described by several authors (Table X). It was interpreted either as a damming up of particles coming from the perikaryon or as a local formation due to stimulation by injury. Although the distal side of the lesion was not examined, it was taken for granted by most authors that the crowding of particles occurs only on the proximal side. Thus, when a connective of an insect was examined, a bundle in which nerve fibres run in both directions, and crowding of structural elements near the lesion was observed in some of the axons, it was concluded that those are the fibres descending from perikarya (Melamed and Trujillo-Cenóz, 1963).

This conclusion is not correct, however, since as shown in Fig. 26, a similar crowding of particles occurs on the distal side of the lesion (Lubińska et al., 1963b). These results were obtained with light microscope on osmium tetroxide fixed fibres teased over the region of the crush and several mm on both sides of it. At such resolution the nature and details of accumulated particles are of course undistinguishable but the length and localization of the granulated region of axoplasm are easy to determine.

When the nerve is removed immediately after crushing, the fibres are thinned out in the crushed region and disorganized over some 200 μ or so on both sides of it, where the lumen is filled with a mixture of axoplasm and myelin. Farther away from the crush the normal appearance of fibres is resumed (Fig. 25). It is in this normally looking zone that from about 5 h after infliction of the lesion the axoplasm becomes filled with particles and vacuoles. The accumulating material is visible in fresh fibres in phase contrast and is strongly osmiophilic. Usually a short stretch of optically empty axoplasm separates the granulated material from the disorganized region (Fig. 26A and B). The stretch of granulated axoplasm corresponds probably to what was seen

TABLE X

ACCUMULATION OF STRUCTURAL PARTICLES NEAR THE SITE OF INTERRUPTION OF AXONS

Animal	Nerve	Lesion	Method of observation	Time after lesion	Increased amount of particles near the lesion		Comment	References
					Proximal side	Distal side		
Guinea-pig	Sciatic	Cut, regenerating	Electron microscope	1–12 days	Synaptic vesicles, mitochondria, multivesicular bodies	—	Image at the tip independent of the duration of regeneration	Estable et al., 1957
Amblystoma	Cutaneous fibres in epidermis	Amputation of limb	Electron microscope	—	Vesicles, mitochondria, granular material	—	In contact with epithelial cells axons form boutons	Hay, 1960
Newt	Regenerating fibres	Amputation of limb	Electron microscope	2, 4, 6 and 12 days	Granules, mitochondria, dense RNA (?) particles	—	Considered as organization of degenerating materials, perhaps with participation of Schwann cells	Inuce, 1960
Chick embryo in culture	Nervous system	Explantation	Electron microscope	—	Tightly packed synaptic vesicles in terminal enlargements	—		De Robertis and Sotelo, 1952
Rat	Spinal cord	Section	Electron microscope	12 h, 4 days	Vesicles and membranes of endoplasmic reticulum, mitochondria	—	Thought to be formed locally from small amounts of endoplasmic reticulum present initially as manifestation of primary retrograde axonal reaction	Schlote and Hager, 1960
Rat	Sciatic	Constriction	Electron microscope	—	Densely packed mitochondria and vesicles	—	Considered as manifestation of dammed flow	Weiss et al., 1962
Frog	Sciatic	Ligation	Electron microscope	3–30 days	Mitochondria, vesicles and membranes	—	Believed to originate in the perikaryon	Van Breemen et al., 1958

Animal	Nerve	Treatment	Method	Time	Observations		Remarks	Reference
Rat	Sciatic	Cut, regenerating	Electron microscope	24–47 h	Mitochondria, vesicles and tubules at tips. No neurofilaments. Less dense accumulation more proximally	—	Same appearance at the tips of regenerating sprouts. The early appearance points to local formation by stimulated axoplasm since the flow, considered to occur at a rate of 1 mm a day, would produce effects much later	Wechsler and Hager, 1962
			Electron microscope	3–5 days	Terminal zone as above. more proximally number of mitochondria has increased	—	5 mm proximal to the lesion axons appear normal. After 27 days axoplasm of freshly myelinated and unmyelinated fibres has again normal appearance	
Mouse	Dorso-spinal	Cut or crushed	Electron microscope and phase contrast	30, 60, 80, 100 min and 1–20 days	Mitochondria, vesicles and multivesicular bodies fill the lumen of the terminal part of axons	—	Appearance of granules interpreted as local neuroplasmic reaction. Sharp transition is seen between granulated and normal axoplasm	Wettstein and Sotelo, 1963
Insect, Lap-latactris dispar	Connective between 4th and 5th abdominal ganglia	Cut	Electron microscope	30 min–88 h	Mitochondria and vesicles fill the lumen of some fibres near the lesion	?	Assumed on the proximal side only. Fibres running in both directions, those in which no changes are observed are believed to be on the distal side of the lesion	Melamed and Trujillo-Cenóz, 1963
Rat, Rabbit, Frog	Sciatic	Crush or cut	Light microscope	5 h–3 days	Dense packing of osmiophilic granules and vacuoles somewhat above the lesion	Dense packing of osmiophilic granules and vacuoles somewhat below the lesion	Almost completely fill the lumen of the axon over about 100 μ. Sharply delimited from normally looking axoplasm nearer the lesion, gradual transition to normal axoplasm away from the lesion	Lubińska et al., 1963b

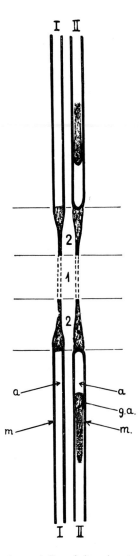

Fig. 25. Diagram showing configuration and sites of altered parts of a crushed nerve fibre. 1 = crushed part; 2 = disorganized region filled with mixed axoplasm and myelin on both sides of the crushed part; m = myelin; a = axoplasm; g.a. = granulated axoplasm. I = fibre removed immediately after crushing. II = fibre removed several hours after crushing showing accumulation of granulated osmiophilic materials in the preterminal region of axoplasm (g.a.) and closing of myelin separating the disorganized part of the fibre from the normally looking axoplasm.

with electron microscope as a region filled with mitochondria, vesicles and profiles of endoplasmic reticulum. As seen in Fig. 26 the accumulation of structural particles appears on both sides of the lesion. The comparison of these pictures obtained on isolated nerve fibres with sections of crushed nerves stained for acetylcholinesterase activity shows that localization of accumulation of this enzyme and of particulate materials coincide. The published pictures of other enzymes (Gould and Holt, 1961;

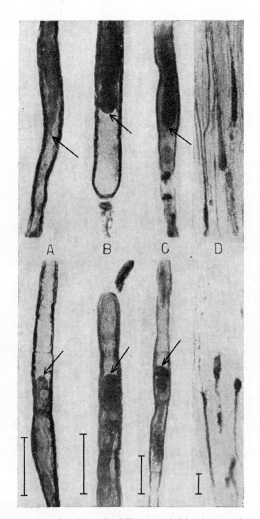

Fig. 26. Appearance of the granulated osmiophilic material in the axoplasm on the proximal and distal side of the crushed region in fibres from the sciatic of rat. Fibres were teased after fixation of the crushed nerve in osmium tetroxide. Proximo-distal orientation of fibres from top to bottom. Upper part = proximal side. Lower part = distal side. Arrows show the tips of the osmiophilic zones. Crushed zone is not shown. A = 5 h; B and C = 24 h after crushing; D = longitudinal section of the nerve stained for AChE activity by Koelle and Friedenwald (1949) method 24 h after crushing (Lubińska *et al.*, 1963b).

Kreutzberg, 1963) accumulating near the site of interruption of axons present similar localization.

It may be inferred from these data that sectioning or crushing of nerve fibres which produce blind ends at the place of a previously continuous axonal pathway leads to a progressive accumulation of structural elements, among them of enzyme containing particles, in the terminal cul-de-sac of axoplasm. Thus, so far as heaping up of structural elements is concerned, the artificial ends of fibres produced by interruption of axons exhibit similar properties to those of natural nerve endings. To some

References p. 56–66

extent, as Hebb (1957) remarked elsewhere, a cut end of fibre may be considered as a model of nerve terminal. It should be stressed that the proximal and, before its degeneration, the distal end of cut fibres behave similarly in this respect. The filling of all blind ends of axons, whether functional or not, suggests that it is the configuration of these sites that favours the deposition of structural particles carried by the axoplasmic stream.

Summary

A partial constriction or complete interruption of axons produces a series of changes which may be interpreted as results of interference with the normal flow of axoplasm.

Weiss' classical experiments and his concept of the proximo-distal flow of the whole axoplasmic column at a rate of 1–2 mm a day are analyzed and certain inherent difficulties of this theory are discussed.

It is shown that biochemical and structural changes observed near the site of interruption of axons during the period of survival of parts separated from cell bodies point to the existence of bidirectional streaming of axoplasm at a rate of about 30–60 mm a day.

Similarity between the accumulation of structural particles in the axoplasm near the cut ends of fibres both proximal and distal on the one hand, and crowding of mitochondria, granules and vesicles in all natural nerve endings on the other, is stressed.

IV. THE PATTERN OF CYTOPLASMIC STREAMING IN THE NEURON

Although cytoplasmic streaming was first described in the XVIII century and was being studied continually ever since, there is, as yet, no generally valid theory of the mechanism of streaming. At various periods one or another physico-chemical agent was thought to generate the motive force. Surface tension, contractility of the exoplasmic gel and reversible solation and gelation of various loci of the cell, changes of configuration and physical and chemical properties of protein molecules were invoked as a determining factor, only to be dropped when investigation of new materials or more extensive information concerning the materials studied hitherto became available. These theories were reviewed not long ago by Noland (1957) under the eloquent title 'A perennial puzzle'.

The pattern of cytoplasmic streaming in the neuron outlined here in purely descriptive terms is based mainly on the following experimental results discussed in the foregoing chapters:

(1) Rapid bidirectional streaming of axoplasm seen directly on accelerated cinematographic records of axons in tissue culture and the widespread occurrence of such type of streaming in elongated processes of other cells.

(2) Maintenance of streaming in axons freshly separated from their cell bodies.

(3) The crowding of structural elements at all natural nerve endings and at artificial ends both proximal and distal created by crushing or cutting the nerve fibres.

It will be seen that in spite of the extraordinary length of the axon the character of streaming in the neuron is fundamentally similar to that of many other types of cells.

In cells of usual dimensions continual back and forth streaming of materials between the perinuclear region and the periphery of the cell was often described (Goldstein, 1960; Rose, 1960; and others). In some cells the endoplasmic reticulum is visible *in vivo* with light microscope, the depth of focus including enough of the curvature of its profiles. Several instances have been described in which incessant rapid sinuous movements of the endoplasmic reticulum were observed directly (Rose, 1960; Thiery, 1960; Rose and Pomerat, 1960).

In the cell body of a neuron the cytoplasm also appears to be in a state of continual streaming involving the membranes and other structural elements. This was suggested even by inspection of electron micrographs of perikarya where 'the variability of orientation of endoplasmic reticulum indicates that the configuration of these elements is probably unstable, changing continually under the influence of streaming movements in the cytoplasm and metabolic transformations in the cell' (Palay and Palade, 1955).

In the living perikarya dissociated from dorsal root ganglia of rat, pig and hamster Adamstone and Taylor (1953) observed for several hours a slow sinuous undulating and shifting motion of an intricate net of membranes up and down the cell, sometimes rhythmic sometimes erratic. This motion stopped when the cells died.

Although it is unlikely that these movements do not spread all the way along the axon, no direct observations of the whole neuron are available, probably because of the great length of the axonal process. The movements observed in the perikaryon in conjunction with bidirectional streaming of axoplasm in the axons observed in other experiments suggest that the neuronal cytoplasm circulates from the cell body along axon to its endings and back again to the cell body.

The rate of streaming, either determined by direct measurements of translocation of granules in the axoplasm or calculated from various types of indirect evidence, such as the longitudinal propagation of some morphological and functional disturbances observed after nerve section, the course of accumulation of AChE near the cut ends and the initial spread of radioactivity in the axons after injection of radioactive tracers, appears to be some 30–70 mm a day.

There are indications that the Schwann cells may play a contributory role, both metabolic and mechanical, in the maintenance of streaming along axons.

Although certain structural elements, the nucleus and the RNA granules of the endoplasmic reticulum, are confined to the perikaryon, other — mitochondria and smaller particles and vesicles and loops of membranes — migrate with the stream in the axons.

The uneven distribution of structural particles in the axons seen in fixed preparations, their paucity in the cylindrical parts and extreme crowding at all blind ends, whether natural or artificial suggests a dynamic origin. It is tempting to speculate that particulate components carried with the axoplasmic stream tend to settle down at places where the rate and direction of streaming are changing. Although in the present state of axonal rheology no explanation of this tendency can be offered, this hypothesis is to some extent corroborated by a few other findings. Thus, at the nodes of Ranvier where the diameter of the axon is reduced to about a half and in the adjacent paranodal bulbs where it is dilated, the concentration of mitochondria and other particles is increased as compared with that in other parts of the internode (Robertson, 1960; Williams and Landon, 1963). The rate of flow through the nodal region was never measured, it may be surmised on general grounds that it is slowed in the bulbar dilatations and accelerated in the narrowed lumen of the node. Probably the increased density of neurofilaments in the node (Cajal, 1928) reflects the increased rate of flow at this point. On similar lines one may speculate that the absence of neurofilaments in the nerve endings (Wechsler and Hager, 1962; and others) may be an indication of the absence of flow there, since flowing elongated macromolecules tend to be oriented with their long axis parallel to the direction of flow and this orientation is lost on stopping.

In assuming that the mode of streaming in the normal neuron resembles a kind of cyclosis, the events occurring when the continuity of axonal process is interfered with may be described in the following way.

When a nerve fibre is cut, the amputated part will eventually degenerate. Between the moment of division and the onset of degeneration there is, however, a period of survival during which the axoplasmic streaming continues. In this respect the amputated parts of nerve fibres resemble the anucleated fragments of other cells, in which the surgical intervention does not abolish the motion of cytoplasm.

In transected nerve fibres new blind ends are created near which presumably the stream of axoplasm turns back. At these loci where the direction and rate of streaming change various particles carried by the streaming axoplasm tend to be deposited. In a fragment of fibre cut at both ends the settling of particles occurs at each transection. In cut mammalian fibres the streaming of axoplasm and the deposition of particles continue for about one day after section. The material accumulated at the newly created ends may be detected, however, for a longer period and remains sometimes trapped in the terminal region even after formation of ovoids.

The increased amount of mitochondria in the paranodal region observed by De Webster (1962) 24–36 hours after nerve section may be due to an incipient disorganization of streaming which would be apparent first not in the cylindrical part of the internode but at places where changes of rate of streaming are bound to occur.

On the proximal side of the section the ends of fibres remaining in continuity with the cell bodies behave initially similarly to those on the distal side. The time course of accumulation of materials at the ends is at the beginning similar to that of divided fibres, indicating that any events occurring at that time in the perikaryon are not yet felt at the axonal ends. The influence of the perikaryon becomes manifest at somewhat later stages leading to an orderly regeneration of the amputated part.

During the period of regrowth of the axon the general character of axoplasmic flow remains unaltered. The streaming of axoplasm in the regenerating part is bidirectional and particles are accumulating at the growing tip. Since the rate of streaming is considerably higher than that of the advance of the growing tip, the latter seems to be determined by the difference between the amount of axoplasm arriving from the perikaryon to the growing tip and that carried back to the cell body by ascending layers of axoplasm. The process of regeneration may be arrested under conditions which do not much affect the axoplasmic streaming. Thus, the lowering of temperature below a critical value stops the elongation of nerve fibres presumably by inhibition of some synthetic processes in the perikarya, whereas the axoplasmic streaming, at a slightly reduced rate may continue under these conditions.

The proposed description of axoplasmic motion in normal and regenerating fibres seems to offer a more unified interpretation of various aspects of physiology of the neuron than the concept of the proximo-distal advance of the whole axoplasmic column.

SUMMARY

Various types of experimental evidence either disclosing directly the movements of cytoplasm in the neuron or best interpreted by assumption of the existence of these movements, are analyzed. The description of the pattern of axoplasmic streaming proposed here is based on the following experimental results:

(1) In the isolated perikarya of neurons incessant movements of cytoplasm involving shifts of membranes and granules were observed.

(2) Direct observation of individual nerve fibres in tissue culture and *in vivo* shows bidirectional movements of granules in the axons and cellulipetal migration of droplets taken up by pinocytosis at the axon tips.

(3) The rate of displacements of granules, greatly exceeding that of elongation of regenerating fibres, indicates that the elongation is determined by the difference between the amount of axoplasm arriving from the perikaryon to the axon tip and that flown back to the perikaryon.

(4) The migration of radioactive tracers and the longitudinal spread of some physiological and morphological disturbances along the axons at rates of 20 to 70 mm a day.

(5) Temporary persistence of axoplasmic streaming in axons freshly separated from their cell bodies observed directly in individual fibres under the microscope and revealed in cut nerve trunks by the appearance of new growth cones and branching of fibres at the proximal end of the peripheral stump.

(6) Accumulation of granulated materials and various enzymes on the distal as well as on the proximal side of the lesion in cut or crushed nerves. This shows that during the period of survival of fibres separated from their cell bodies the blind ends of their axons created by transection exhibit properties similar to those of blind ends of fibres remaining in continuity with their cell bodies. A similar crowding of particles occurs at all natural nerve endings. A hypothesis is put forward that the membranes and granules carried by the stream of axoplasm tend to settle down at all terminal cul-de-sacs of axons whether natural or artificial.

These facts suggest the existence of a continual migration of the neuronal cytoplasm from the perikaryon to the nerve endings and from these back to the perikaryon ensuring the metabolic unity of the nerve cell. They suggest that the pattern of streaming in the axons is bidirectional, some axoplasmic layers moving in the cellulifugal and other cellulipetal direction. In warm-blooded animals the rate of streaming is about 30–70 mm a day. The similar character of streaming in the axons and in elongated processes of other types of cells is stressed.

References p. 56–66

REFERENCES

ABOOD, L. G., AND GERARD, R. W., (1954); Enzyme distribution in isolated particulates of rat peripheral nerve. *J. cell. comp. Physiol.*, **43**, 379–393.

ABRAMS, J., AND GERARD, R. W., (1933); The influence of activity on the survival of isolated nerve. *Amer. J. Physiol.*, **104**, 590–593.

ACS, G., NEIDLE, A., AND WAELSCH, H., (1961); Brain ribosomes and amino acid incorporation. *Biochim. biophys. Acta (Amst.)*, **50**, 403–404.

ADAMSTONE, F. B., AND TAYLOR, A. B., (1953); Structure and physical nature of the cytoplasm of living spinal ganglion cells of the adult rat. *J. Morphol.*, **92**, 513–530.

AITKEN, J. T., SHARMAN, M., AND YOUNG, J. Z., (1947); Maturation of regenerating nerve fibres with various peripheral connections. *J. Anat. (Lond.)*, **81**, 1–22.

ALDRIDGE, W. N., AND JOHNSON, M. L., (1959); Cholinesterase, succinic dehydrogenase, nucleic acids, esterase and glutathione reductase in sub-cellular fractions from rat brain. *Biochem. J.*, **73**, 270–276.

ALLEN, R. D., (1961); Ameboid movement. *The Cell.* J. Brachet and A. E. Mirsky, Editors. New York and London, Academic Press (Vol. II, pp. 135–216).

ALLEN, R. D., COOLEDGE, J. W., AND HALL, P. J., (1960); Streaming in cytoplasm dissociated from the giant amoeba *Chaos chaos. Nature (Lond.)*, **187**, 896–899.

ANDREWS, E. A., (1955); Some minute movements in protoplasm. *Biol. Bull. Marine biol. Lab.*, **108**, 121–124.

ARMSTRONG, J. A., (1950); An experimental study of the visual pathways in a reptile (*Lacerta vivipara*). *J. Anat. (Lond.)*, **84**, 146–167.

BAKER, P. F., HODGKIN, A. L., AND SHAW, T. I., (1961); Replacement of the protoplasm of a giant nerve fibre with artificial solutions. *Nature (Lond.)*, **190**, 885–887.

BARGMANN, W., AND SCHARRER, E., (1951); The site of origin of the hormones of the posterior pituitary. *Amer. Scientist*, **39**, 255–259.

BARRNETT, R. J., (1962); The fine structural localization of acetylcholinesterase at the myoneural junction. *J. Cell Biol.*, **12**, 247–263.

BARTOSZYŃSKI, R., LUBIŃSKA, L., and NIEMIERKO, S., (1962); A stochastic model of AChE transportation in the peripheral nerve trunks. *Biometrika*, **49**, 447–454.

BERRY, C. M., GRUNDFEST, H., AND HINSEY, J. C., (1944); The electrical activity of regenerating nerves in the cat. *J. Neurophysiol.*, **7**, 103–115.

BIRKS, R., KATZ, B., AND MILEDI, R., (1960); Physiological and structural changes at the amphibian myoneural junction, in the course of nerve degeneration. *J. Physiol. (Lond.)*, **150**, 145–168.

BODIAN, D., AND TAYLOR, N., (1963); Synapse arising at central node of Ranvier, and note on fixation of the central nervous system. *Science*, **139**, 330–332.

BONICHON, A., (1958); Acetylcholinesterase in neurons and nerve fibres during development. I. Early biochemical differentiation of the neuroblasts. *Ann. Histochim.*, **3**, 85–93.

BRATTGÄRD, S. O., EDSTRÖM, J. E., AND HYDÉN, H., (1958); The productive capacity of the neuron in retrograde reaction. *Exp. Cell Res. Suppl.*, **5**, 185–200.

BUNGE, R. P., BUNGE, M. B., AND RIS, H., (1960); Electron microscopic study of demyelination in an experimentally induced lesion in adult cats spinal cord. *J. biophys. biochem. Cytol.*, **7**, 685–696.

CAESAR, R., AND EDWARDS, G. A., (1957); Architecture and nerve supply of mammalian smooth muscle tissue. *J. biophys. biochem. Cytol.*, **3**, 867–887.

CAJAL, S. R. Y, (1928); *Degeneration and Regeneration of the Nervous System.* London, Oxford University Press.

CALUGAREANU, D., (1901a); Contribution à l'étude de la compression des nerfs. *J. Physiol. Pathol. gén.*, **3**, 393–404.

CALUGAREANU, D., (1901b); Recherches sur les modifications histologiques dans les nerfs comprimés. *J. Physiol. Pathol. gén.*, **3**, 413–423.

CARLSSON, A., MAGNUSSON, T., AND ROSENGREN, E., (1963); 5-Hydroxytryptamine of the spinal cord normally and after transection. *Experientia (Basel)*, **19**, 359.

CAUNA, N., (1961); The submicroscopical relationship between the nervous and non-nervous elements of the cutaneous receptor organs and its significance. *Cytology of Nervous Tissue.* Proceedings of the Anatomical Society of Great Britain and Ireland. London, Taylor and Francis (pp. 17–19).

CAUSEY, G., AND PALMER, E., (1952a); The mixing of the myelin and axoplasm and their subsequent separation following the crushing of mammalian nerves. *J. Physiol. (Lond.)*, **117**, 20P.

CAUSEY, G., AND PALMER, E., (1952b); Early changes in degenerating mammalian nerves. *Proc. roy. Soc. B.*, **155**, 597–609.

CAUSEY, G., AND PALMER, E., (1953); The centrifugal spread of structural change at the nodes in degenerating mammalian nerves. *J. Anat. (Lond.)*, **87**, 185–191.

CAUSEY, G., AND STRATMANN, C. J., (1954); Recovery of degenerating mammalian nerve after prolonged stimulation. *J. Physiol. (Lond.)*, **123**, 234–240.

CAVANAGH, J. B., (1954); The toxic effects of triorthocresyl phosphate on the nervous system. *J. Neurol. Neurosurg. Psychiat.*, **17**, 163–172.

CHACKO, L. W., AND CERF, J. A., (1960); Histochemical localisation of cholinesterase in the amphibian spinal cord and alterations following ventral root section. *J. Anat. (Lond.)*, **94**, 74–81.

CHAMBERS, R., AND KAO, C. Y., (1952); The effects of electrolytes on the physical state of the nerve axon of the squid and of *Stentor*, a protozoon. *Exp. Cell Res.*, **3**, 564–573.

CHRIST, J. F., (1962); The early changes in the hypophysial neurosecretory fibres after coagulation. *Neurosecretion.* H. Heller and R. B. Clark, Editors. London, Academic Press (pp. 125–147).

CLOUET, D. H., AND WAELSCH, H., (1961); Amino acid protein metabolism of the brain. VIII. The recovery of cholinesterase in the nervous system of the frog after inhibition. *J. Neurochem.*, **8**, 201–215.

COOK, D. D., AND GERARD, R. W., (1931); The effect of stimulation on the degeneration of a severed peripheral nerve. *Amer. J. Physiol.*, **77**, 412–425.

COPPÉE, G., AND BACQ, Z. M., (1938); Dégénérescence, conduction et transmission synaptique dans le sympathique cervical. *Arch. int. Physiol.*, **47**, 312–320.

CRAIN, S. M., AND PETERSON, E. R., (1963); Bioelectric activity in long-term cultures of spinal cord tissues. *Science*, **141**, 427–429.

D'ARCY THOMPSON, W., (1942); *On Growth and Form.* London, Cambridge University Press.

DAVIDOVICH, A., AND LUCO, J. V., (1956); The synaptic transmission of sympathetic ganglia during Wallerian degeneration. Effect of length of degenerating nerve fibres. *Acta physiol. lat.-amer.*, **6**, 49–59.

DAVISON, A. N., AND DOBBING, J., (1961); Metabolic stability of body constituents. *Nature (Lond.)*, **191**, 844–848.

DENNY-BROWN, D., AND BRENNER, C., (1944); Lesion in peripheral nerve resulting from compression by spring clip. *Arch. Neurol. Psychiat.*, **52**, 1–19.

DE ROBERTIS, E., (1959); Submicroscopic morphology of the synapse. *Int. Rev. Cytol.*, **8**, 61–96.

DE ROBERTIS, E., (1962); Ultrastructure and function in some neurosecretory systems. *Neurosecretion.* H. Heller and R. B. Clark, Editors. London, Academic Press (pp. 3–20).

DE ROBERTIS, E., AND BLEICHMAR, H., (1962); Mitochondriogenesis in nerve fibres of the infrared receptor membrane of pit vipers. *Z. Zellforsch.*, **57**, 572–582.

DE ROBERTIS, E., AND SOTELO, J. R., (1952); Electron microscopy study of cultured nervous tissue. *Exp. Cell Res.*, **3**, 433–452.

DE ROBERTIS, E., AND VAZ FERREIRA, A., (1957a); Submicroscopic changes of the nerve endings in the adrenal medulla after stimulation of the splanchnic nerve. *J. biophys. biochem. Cytol.*, **3**, 611–614.

DE ROBERTIS, E., AND VAZ FERREIRA, A., (1957b); Electron microscope study of the excretion of catechol-containing droplets in the adrenal medulla. *Exp. Cell Res.*, **12**, 568–574.

DE WEBSTER, H. F., (1962); Transient, focal accumulation of axonal mitochondria during the early stages of Wallerian degeneration. *J. Cell Biol.*, **12**, 361–384.

DHAR, S. K., (1958); Cholinesterase in decentralized and axotomized sympathetic ganglia. *J. Physiol. (Lond.)*, **144**, 27–28.

DIAMOND, J., (1959); The effects of injecting acetylcholine into normal and regenerating nerves. *J. Physiol. (Lond.)*, **145**, 611–629.

DIEPEN, R., (1962); The difference between the neurosecretory pictures in various mammals. *Neurosecretion.* H. Heller and R. B. Clark, Editors. London, Academic Press (pp. 111–123).

DOBBING, J., (1961); The blood–brain barrier. *Physiol. Rev.*, **41**, 130–188.

DROZ, B., AND LEBLOND, C. P., (1962); Migration of proteins along the axons of the sciatic nerve. *Science*, **137**, 1047–1048.

DUNCAN, D., AND JARVIS, W. H., (1943); Observations on repeated regeneration of the facial nerve in cats. *J. comp. Neurol.*, **79**, 315–325.

EDSTRÖM, J. E., (1960); Extraction, hydrolysis and electrophoretic analysis of ribonucleic acid from microscopic tissue units (microphoresis). *J. biophys. biochem. Cytol.*, **8**, 39–46.

EDSTRÖM, J. E., EICHNER, D., AND EDSTRÖM, A., (1962); The ribonucleic acid of axons and myelin sheaths from Mauthner neurons. *Biochim. biophys. Acta (Amst.)*, **61**, 178–184.

EDWARDS, G. A., RUSKA, H., AND HARVEN, E., (1958a); Electron microscopy of peripheral nerves and neuromuscular junctions in the wasp leg. *J. biophys. biochem. Cytol.*, **4**, 107–114.

EDWARDS, G. A., RUSKA, H., AND HARVEN, E., (1958b); Neuromuscular junctions in flight and tymbal muscles of the *Cicada. J. biophys. biochem. Cytol.*, **4**, 251–255.

ERLANGER, J., AND SCHOEPFLE, G. M., (1946); A study of nerve degeneration and regeneration. *Amer. J. Physiol.*, **147**, 550–581.

ESTABLE, C., ACOSTA-FERREIRA, W., AND SOTELO, J. R., (1957); An electron microscope study of the regenerating nerve fibres. *Z. Zellforsch.*, **46**, 387–399.

EYZAGUIRRE, C., ESPILDORA, J., AND LUCO, J. V., (1952); Alterations of neuromuscular synapses during Wallerian degeneration. *Acta physiol. lat.-amer.*, **2**, 213–227.

FAWCETT, D. W., AND ITO, S., (1958); Observations on the cytoplasmic membranes of testicular cells, examined by phase contrast and electron microscopy. *J. biophys. biochem. Cytol.*, **4**, 135–142.

FELDBERG, W., (1943); Synthesis of acetylcholine in sympathetic ganglia and cholinergic nerves. *J. Physiol. (Lond.)*, **101**, 432–445.

FENG, T. P., JUNG, H. W., AND WU, W. Y., (1963); The contrasting trophic changes of the anterior and posterior latissimus dorsi of the chick following denervation. *Symposium on the Effect of Use and Disuse on Neuromuscular Functions*. E. Gutmann and P. Hník, Editors. Prague, Publishing House of the Czechoslovak Academy of Sciences, (pp. 431–441).

FISCHER, J., LODIN, Z., AND KOLOUSEK, J., (1958); A histoautoradiographic study of the effect of section of the facial nerve on the uptake of Methionine–^{35}S by cells of the facial nerve nucleus. *Nature (Lond.)*, **181**, 341–342.

FITZGERALD, M. J. T., (1961); Developmental changes in epidermal innervation. *J. Anat. (Lond.)*, **95**, 495–514.

FLAIG, J. V., (1947); Viscosity changes in axoplasm under stimulation. *J. Neurophysiol.*, **10**, 211–222.

FLEXNER, L. B., (1950); The cytological, biochemical and physiological differentiation of the neuroblast. *Genetic Neurology*. P. Weiss, Editor. Chicago, University of Chicago Press, Series B (pp. 194–198).

FRIEDE, R. L., (1959); Transport of oxydative enzymes in nerve fibres; a histochemical investigation of the regenerative cycle in neurons. *Exp. Neurol.*, **1**, 441–466.

FRIEDE, R. L., (1960); Histochemical demonstration of enzyme movements in injured nerve fibres. *J. Neuropathol. exp. Neurol.*, **19**, 143.

FUKUDA, T., AND KOELLE, G. B., (1959); The cytological localization of intracellular neuronal acetylcholinesterase. *J. biophys. biochem. Cytol.*, **5**, 433–440.

GAMBLE, H. J., (1957); Temperature effects in mammalian nerve regeneration. *Nature (Lond.)*, **180**, 146–147.

GAMBLE, H. J., (1958); Effect of a raised peripheral temperature upon the rate of regeneration in a mammalian peripheral nerve. *Nature (Lond.)*, **181**, 287.

GASSER, H. S., (1952); Discussion. The Neuron. *Cold Spr. Harb. Symp. quantit. Biol.*, **17**, New York, The biological Laboratory Cold Spring Harbor (p. 34).

GASTEIGER, E. L., HAAKE, P. C., AND GERGEN, J. A., (1960); An investigation of the distribution and function of homarine (N-methyl picolin acid). *Ann. N. Y. Acad. Sci.*, **90**, 622–636.

GEIGER, R. S., (1958); Subcultures of adult mammalian brain cortex *in vitro. Exp. Cell Res.*, **14**, 541–566.

GEIGER, R. S., AND STONE, W. G., (1962); The presence of cholinesterases in long term cultures and subcultures of adult mammalian brain cells. *Acta neurol. scand.*,Suppl. 1, **38**, 67–68.

GERARD, R. W., (1930); The response of nerve to oxygen lack .*Amer. J. Physiol.*, **9**, 498–541.

GERARD, R. W., (1932); Nerve metabolism. *Physiol. Rev.*, **12**, 469–592.

GERARD, R. W., AND TUPIKOVA, N., (1939); Nerve and muscle phosphates. *J. cell. comp. Physiol.*, **13**, 1–13.

GEREBTZOFF, M. A., (1962); Démonstration histochimique d'une localisation de l'acétylcholinesterase au noeud de Ranvier. *Arch. int. Physiol. Biochim.*, **70**, 418–420.

GERSCHENFELD, H. M., TRAMEZZANI, J. H., AND DE ROBERTIS, E., (1960); Ultrastructure and function in neurohypophysis of the toad. *Endocrinology*, **66**, 741–762.

GEY, G. O., SHAPRAS, P., AND BORYSKO, E., (1954); Activities and responses of living cells and their components as recorded by cinephase microscopy and electronmicroscopy. *Ann. N. Y. Acad. Sci.*, **58**, 1089–1095.

GLEES, P., (1948); The time factor in central nerve fibre degeneration. *Acta anat. (Basel)*, **6**, 447–450.

GODINA, G., (1960); Structure, growth and mutual relations between neurons. *Abstr. X Congr. int. Biol. cell.* (pp. 23–24).

GOLDBY, F., AND ROBINSON, L. R., (1961); Experimental degeneration in the ventral longitudinal bundles of the spinal cord of *Lacerta viridis*. *Cytology of Nervous Tissue*. Proceedings of the Anatomical Society of Great Britain and Ireland. London, Taylor and Francis (pp. 41–44).

GOLDSTEIN, L., (1960); Some properties of a protein component of the cell in constant migration between nucleus and cytoplasm. *Science*, **132**, 1492.

GOMBAULT, (1880–1881); Contribution à l'étude anatomique de la névrite parenchymateuse subaiguë et chronique. Névrite segmentaire périaxile. *Arch. Neurol.*, **1**, 11–38 and 177–190.

GOULD, R. P., AND HOLT, S. J., (1961); Observations on acid phosphatase and esterases in the rat sciatic nerve undergoing Wallerian degeneration. *Cytology of Nervous Tissue*. Proceedings of the Anatomical Society of Great Britain and Ireland. London, Taylor and Francis (pp. 45–48).

GUILLERY, R. W., (1961); Fibre degeneration in the efferent mamillary tract of the cat. *Cytology of Nervous Tissue*. Proceedings of the Anatomical Society of Great Britain and Ireland. London, Taylor and Francis (pp. 64–67).

GUTH, L., (1956); Regeneration in the mammalian peripheral nervous system. *Physiol. Rev.*, **36**, 441–478.

GUTMANN, E., (1958); *Die funktionelle Regeneration der peripheren Nerven*. Berlin, Akademie Verlag.

GUTMANN, E., (1962); *The Denervated Muscle*. Publishing House of the Czechoslovak Academy of Science, Prague.

GUTMANN, E., GUTTMAN, L., MEDAWAR, P. B., AND YOUNG, J. Z., (1942); The rate of regeneration of nerve. *J. exp. Biol.*, **19**, 14–44.

GUTMANN, E., AND HOLUBAR, J., (1950); The degeneration of peripheral nerve fibres. *J. Neurol. Neurosurg. Psychiat.*, **13**, 89–105.

GUTMANN, E., VODICKA, Z., AND ZELENÁ, J., (1955); Veränderungen im quergestreiften Muskel bei Durchtrennung in Abhängigkeit von der Länge des peripheren Stumpfes. *Physiol. bohemoslov.*, **4**, 200–204.

GUTTMAN, R., (1935); Differential oxygen uptake of regions of Limulus optic nerve as related to distance from the sense organ. *Biol. Bull. Marine biol. Lab.*, **69**, 356–360.

HAFTEK, J., (1963); *Rate of Elongation in Regenerating Axons of Peripheral Nerves*. Thesis, Medical Faculty, Warsaw.

HANZON, W., AND TOSCHI, G., (1959); Electron microscopy on microsomal fractions from rat brain. *Exp. Cell Res.*, **16**, 256–271.

HARRISON, R. G., (1910); The outgrowth of the nerve fibre as a mode of protoplasmic movement. *J. exp. Zool.*, **9**, 787–848; (reprinted in the same journal in 1959) **142**, 5–74.

HASSON, J., TERRY, R. D., AND ZIMMERMAN, H. N., (1958); Peripheral neuropathy in multiple sclerosis. *Neurology (Minneap.)*, **8**, 503–510.

HATTYASY, D., (1961); Continuous regeneration of the dentinal nerve-endings. *Nature (Lond.)*, **189**, 72–74.

HAY, E. D., (1960); The fine structure of nerves in the epidermis of regenerating salamander limbs. *Exp. Cell Res.*, **19**, 299–317.

HAYDEN, K., POMERAT, C. M., AND SMITH, MACDONALD, (1954); A note on the architecture of the mitochondrial cortex as seen in tissue cultures of nerve fibres. *Tex. Rep. Biol. Med.*, **12**, 470–473.

HEALD, P. J., (1961); Intracellular localization of cerebral phosphoproteins. *Regional Neurochemistry*. S. S. Kety and J. Elkes, Editors. London, Pergamon Press (pp. 89–101).

HEBB, C. O., (1957); Biochemical evidence for the neural function of acetylcholine. *Physiol. Rev.*, **37**, 196–220.

HEBB, C. O., (1963); Formation, storage, and liberation of acetylcholine. *Handbuch der experimentellen Pharmakologie*. G. B. Koelle, Editor. Berlin, Springer (Vol. 15, pp. 55–88).

HEBB, C. O., AND SILVER, A., (1961); Gradient of choline acetylase activity. *Nature (Lond.)*, **189**, 123–125.

HEBB, C. O., AND WAITES, G. M. H., (1956); Choline acetylase in antero- and retrograde degeneration of a cholinergic nerve. *J. Physiol. (Lond.)*, **132**, 667–671.

HEBB, C. O., AND WHITTAKER, V. P., (1958); Intracellular distribution of acetylcholine and cholinacetylase. *J. Physiol. (Lond.)*, **142**, 187–196.

HELLER, H., (1962); *Neurosecretion*. H. Heller and R. B. Clark, Editors. London, Academic Press (pp. XIII–XV).

HERMANS, J. J., (1952); Viscous flow through elastic capillaries. *Deformation and Flow in Biological Systems*. A. Frey-Wyssling, Editor. Amsterdam, North-Holland Publishing Company (pp. 344–351).

HESS, A., AND LANSING, A. I., (1953); The fine structure of peripheral nerve fibres. *Anat. Rec.*, **117**, 175–200.

HILD, W., (1951); Experimentell-morphologische Untersuchungen über das Verhalten der 'Neuro-secretorischen Bahn' nach Hypophysenstieldurchtrennungen, Eingriffen in den Wasserhaushalt und Belastung der Osmoregulation. *Virchows Arch. path. Anat.*, **319**, 526–546.

HILD, W., (1954); Das morphologische, kinetische und endokrinologische Verhalten von hypothala-mischem und neurohypophysärem Gewebe *in vitro. Z. Zellforsch.*, **40**, 257–312.

HILD, W., (1959); Myelin formation in cultures of mammalian central nervous tissue. *Biology of Myelin.* S. R. Korey, Editor. New York, Hoeber–Harper (pp. 188–200).

HILD, W., AND ZETLER, G., (1953); Experimenteller Beweis für die Entstehung der sogenannten Hypophysenhinterlappenwirkstoffe im Hypothalamus. *Pflügers Arch. ges. Physiol.*, **257**, 169–201.

HILLARP, N. A., AND OLIVECRONA, H., (1946); The role played by the axon and the Schwann cells in the degree of myelination of the peripheral nerve fibre. *Acta anat. (Basel)*, **2**, 17–32.

HOLMES, R. L., AND KNOWLES, F. G. W., (1960); Synaptic vesicles in the neurohypophysis. *Nature (Lond.)*, **185**, 710–711.

HOLMSTEDT, D., AND TOSCHI, G., (1959); Enzymic properties of cholinesterases in subcellular fractions from rat brain. *Acta physiol. scand.*, **47**, 280–283.

HOLTON, P., (1959); Further observations on substance P in degenerating nerve. *J. Physiol. (Lond.)*, **149**, 35–36.

HONJIN, R., NAKAMURA, T., AND IMURA, M., (1959); Electron microscopy of peripheral nerve fibres. III. On the axoplasmic changes during Wallerian degeneration. *Okajimas Folia anat. jap.*, **33**, 131–156.

HONJIN, R., TAKAHASHI, A., NAKAMURA, T., AND TANIGUCHI, H., (1962); Electron microscopy of nerve fibres. V. On the fine structure of the small myelinated nerve fibres in the peripheral nerve. *Okajimas Folia anat. jap.*, **38**, 387–409.

HUBER, G. C., (1900); Observations on the degeneration and regeneration of motor and sensory endings in voluntary muscle. *Amer. J. Physiol.*, **3**, 339–344.

HUGHES, A., (1953); The growth of embryonic neurites. A study on cultures of chick neural tissues. *J. Anat. (Lond.)*, **87**, 150–162.

HUGHES, A. F. W., AND LEWIS, P. R., (1961); Effect of limb ablation on neurons in *Xenopus* larvae. *Nature (Lond.)*, **189**, 333–334.

HUGHES, A., AND TSCHUMI, P. A., (1957); Transmission of trophic stimuli along developing nerve fibres. *Nature (Lond.)*, **180**, 999–1000.

HURSH, J. B., (1939); The properties of growing nerve fibres. *Amer. J. Physiol.*, **127**, 140–153.

HYDÉN, H., (1960); The neuron. *The Cell.* J. Brachet and A. E. Mirsky, Editors. New York and London, Academic Press (Vol. 4, pp. 215–323).

HYDÉN, H., AND REXED, B., (1943); Der Wachstumsmechanismus in den Schwannschen Zellen während der Nervenregeneration. *Z. mikr.-anat. Forsch.*, **54**, 352–357.

INUCE, S., (1960); Structural changes of nerve fibres in the early phases of limb regeneration in the adult newt with special references to fine structures of regenerating nerve fibres. *Gunma J. med. Sci.*, **9**, 302–328 (quot. *Biol. Abstr.*, **36**, 727–731, 1961).

JAHN, T. L., AND RINALDI, R. A., (1959); Protoplasmic movement in the foraminiferan *Allogromia laticollaris*; and a theory of its mechanism. *Biol. Bull. Marine biol. Lab.*, **117**, 100–118.

JHA, B. D., GOLDBY, F., AND GAMBLE, K. J., (1959); The effect of temperature on the maturation of regenerating peripheral nerves in the rat. *J. Anat. (Lond.)*, **93**, 436–447.

KAMIYA, N., (1959); Protoplasmic streaming. *Protoplasmalogia.* L. V. Heilbrun and F. Weber, Editors. Wien, Springer (Volume 8, 3a).

KATZ, B., (1962); The transmission of impulses from nerve to muscle and the subcellular unit of synaptic action. *Proc. roy. Soc. B*, **155**, 455–477.

KELSO, J. M., AND TURNER, J. S., (1955); Protoplasmic streaming in *Tradescantia*. I. The effects of indoleacetic acid and other growth-promoting substances on streaming. *Aust. J. biol. Sci.*, **8**, 19–38.

KISHIMOTO, V., AND AKABORI, H., (1959); Protoplasmic streaming of an internodal cell of *Nitella flexilis*. Its correlation with electric stimulus. *J. gen. Physiol.*, **42**, 1167–1183.

KOELLE, G. B., (1957); Histochemical demonstration of reversible anticholinesterase action at selective cellular sites *in vivo. J. Pharmacol. exp. Ther.*, **120**, 488–503.

KOENIG, E., AND KOELLE, G. B., (1961); Mode of regeneration of AChE in cholinergic neurons following irreversible inactivation. *J. Neurochem.*, **8**, 169–188.

KOENIG, H., (1958); The synthesis and peripheral flow of axoplasm. *Trans. Amer. neurol. Ass.*, **83**, 162–164.

KONORSKI, J., AND LUBIŃSKA, L., (1945); Rate of regeneration of peripheral nerves in mammals. *Bull. exp. Biol. Med.*, **2**, 14–17.

KONORSKI, J., AND LUBIŃSKA, L., (1946); Mechanical excitability of regenerating nerve fibres. *Lancet*, **250**, 609–610.

KOREY, S. R., AND ORCHEN, M., (1959); Relative respiration of neuronal and glial cells. *J. Neurochem.*, **3**, 277–285.

KOSTYUK, P. G., (1963); Functional presynaptic and postsynaptic changes during degeneration of central synapses. *Fed. Proc.*, **22**, Suppl., T1101–T1106.

KOSTYUK, P. G., AND SAVOSKINA, L. O., (1963); Functional changes in degenerating synaptic endings. *Fed. Proc.*, **22**, Suppl., T1107–T1111.

KREUTZBERG, G., (1962); Aktivitätsanstieg von Enzymen der Oxydoreduktion in Axonen des zentralen und peripheren Nervensystems nach Durchschneidung. *Acta neurol. scand.*, Suppl. 1, **38**, 53–54.

KREUTZBERG, G., (1963); Lokalisierter Oxydoreduktaseanstieg bei der Wallerschen Degeneration der peripheren Nerven. *Naturwissenschaften*, **50**, 96.

KREUTZBERG, G., AND PETERS, G., (1962); Enzymhistochemische Beobachtungen beim experimentellen Hirntrauma der Ratte. *Livre jubilaire du Dr. Ludo Van Bogaert*. Bruxelles, Acta Medica Belgica (pp. 454–462).

KREUTZBERG, G., UND WECHSLER, W., (1963); Histochemische Untersuchungen oxydativer Enzyme am regenerierenden Nervus ischiadicus der Ratte. *Acta neuropathol.*, **2**, 349–361.

KUHN, W., (1953); Spontane Aufteilung von Flüssigkeitszylindern in kleine Kugeln. *Kolloid Z.*, **132**, 84–99.

KURODA, K., (1958); Sur le courant protoplasmique dans le fragment de protoplasme d'un *Myxomycète*. *C. R. Soc. Biol. (Paris)*, **152**, 392–394.

LAJTHA, A., (1961a); Protein metabolism in nerve. *Chemical Pathology of the Nervous System*. J. Folch-Pi, Editor. Proc. III int. neurochem. Symp. London, Pergamon Press (pp. 268–276).

LAJTHA, A., (1961b); Observations on protein catabolism in brain. *Regional Neurochemistry*. S. S. Kety and J. Elkes, Editors. Oxford, Pergamon Press (pp. 25–36).

LANDAU, W. M., (1953); The duration of neuromuscular function after nerve section in man. *J. Neurosurg.*, **10**, 64–68.

LASSEK, A. M., (1946); The pyramidal tract. Speed of degeneration in axon following ablation of cells of origin in the monkey. *J. comp. Neurol.*, **85**, 45–51.

LEHMANN, H. J., AND ULE, G., (1963); Erregungsleitung in demyelinisierten Nervenfasern. *Naturwissenschaften*, **50**, 131–132.

LEVI, G., (1925); Ricerche sperimentali sovra elementi nervosi sviluppati 'in vitro'. *Arch. exp. Zellforsch.*, **2**, 244–272.

LEVI, G., (1934); Explantation, besonders die Struktur und die biologischen Eigenschaften der *in vitro* gezüchteten Zellen und Gewebe. *Ergebn. Anat. Entwickl.-Gesch.*, **31**, 125–707.

LEVI-MONTALCINI, R., AND ANGELETTI, P. U., (1962); Growth and differentiation. *Ann. Rev. Physiol.*, **24**, 11–56.

LEWIS, P. R., AND HUGHES, A. F. W., (1957); The acetylcholinesterase of developing neurons of *Xenopus laevis*. *Metabolism of the Nervous System*. D. Richter, Editor. London, Pergamon Press (pp. 511–514).

LEWIS, P. R., AND SHUTE, C. C. D., (1961); Intra-axonal localization of acetylcholinesterase in normal brains and distributional changes following tractotomy. *Cytology of Nervous Tissue*. Proceedings of the Anatomical Society of Great Britain and Ireland. London, Taylor and Francis (pp. 5–6).

LISSÁK, K., DEMPSEY, E. W., AND ROSENBLUETH, A., (1939); The failure of transmission of motor nerve impulses in the course of Wallerian degeneration. *Amer. J. Physiol.*, **128**, 45–56.

LUBIŃSKA, L., (1952a); On the arrest of regeneration of frog peripheral nerves at low temperatures. *Acta Biol. exp. (Warszawa)*, **16**, 65–71.

LUBIŃSKA, L., (1952b); Elasticity and distensibility of nerve tubes. *Acta Biol. exp. (Warszawa)*, **16**, 73–90.

LUBIŃSKA, L., (1954); Form of myelinated nerve fibres. *Nature (Lond.)*, **173**, 867–869.

LUBIŃSKA, L., (1956a); The physical state of axoplasm in teased vertebrate nerve fibres. *Acta Biol. exp. (Warszawa)*, **17**, 135–140.

LUBIŃSKA, L., (1956b); Outflow from cut ends of nerve fibres. *Exp. Cell Res.*, **10**, 40–47.

LUBIŃSKA, L., (1958a); Short internodes 'intercalated' in nerve fibres. *Acta Biol. exp. (Warszawa)*, **18**, 117–136.

LUBIŃSKA, L., (1958b); 'Intercalated' internodes in nerve fibres. *Nature (Lond.)*, **181**, 957–958.

LUBIŃSKA, L., (1961); Sedentary and migratory states of Schwann cells. *Exp. Cell Res. Suppl.*, **8**, 74–90.

LUBIŃSKA, L., AND ŁUKASZEWSKA, I., (1956); Shape of myelinated nerve fibres and proximo-distal flow of axoplasm. *Acta Biol. exp. (Warszawa)*, **17**, 115–133.

LUBIŃSKA, L., NIEMIERKO, S., AND ODERFELD, B., (1961); Gradient of cholinesterase activity in nerve fibres. *Nature (Lond.)*, **189**, 122–123.

LUBIŃSKA, L., NIEMIERKO, S., ODERFELD, B., AND SZWARC, L., (1962); Decrease of acetylcholinesterase activity along peripheral nerves. *Science*, **135**, 368–370.

LUBIŃSKA, L., NIEMIERKO, S., ODERFELD, B., AND SZWARC, L., (1963); The distribution of acetylcholinesterase in peripheral nerves. *J. Neurochem.*, **10**, 25–41.

LUBIŃSKA, L., NIEMIERKO, S., ODERFELD, B., AND SZWARC, L., (1964); Behaviour of acetylcholinesterase in isolated nerve segments. *J. Neurochem.*, **11**, 132–138.

LUBIŃSKA, L., NIEMIERKO, S., ODERFELD, B., SZWARC, L., AND ZELENÁ, J., (1963b); Bidirectional movements of axoplasm in peripheral nerve fibres. *Acta Biol. exp. (Warszawa)*, **23**, 239–247.

LUBIŃSKA, L., AND OLEKIEWICZ, M., (1950); The rate of regeneration of amphibian peripheral nerves at different temperatures. *Acta Biol. exp. (Warszawa)*, **15**, 125–145.

LUCO, J. V., AND EYZAGUIRRÉ, C., (1955); Fibrillation and hypersensitivity to acetylcholine in denervated muscle: Effect of length of degenerating nerve fibres. *J. Neurophysiol.*, **18**, 65–73.

LUFT, J. H., (1956); The fine structure of the electric organ of the electric eel and Torpedo ray. *J. biophys. biochem. Cytol. Suppl.*, **2**, 229–232.

LUMSDEN, C. E., (1952); Quantitative studies on lipolytic enzyme activity in degenerating and regenerating nerve. *Quart. J. exp. Physiol.*, **37**, 45–57.

McDONALD, W. I., (1961); Conduction velocity of cutaneous afferent fibres during experimental demyelination. *Proc. Univ. Otago med. Sch.*, **39**, 29–30.

McDONALD, W. I., (1962); Conduction in muscle afferent fibres during experimental demyelination in cat nerve. *Acta neuropathol.*, **1**, 425–432.

MACINTOSCH, F. C., (1938); L'effet de la section des fibres préganglionnaires sur la teneur en acétylcholine du ganglion sympathique. *Arch. int. Physiol.*, **47**, 321–324.

MACLENNAN, H., (1954); Acetylcholine metabolism of normal and axotomized ganglia. *J. Physiol., (Lond.)*, **124**, 113–116.

MAJNO, G., AND KARNOVSKY, M. L., (1958); A biochemical and morphologic study of myelination and demyelination. I. Lipid biosynthesis *in vitro* by normal nervous tissue. *J. exp. Med.*, **107**, 475–496.

MAJNO, G., AND KARNOVSKY, M. L., (1961); A biochemical and morphologic study of myelination and demyelination. III. Effect of an organo-phosphorus compound (Mipafox) on biosynthesis of lipid by nervous tissue of rats and hens. *J. Neurochem.*, **8**, 1–16.

MARINESCO, G., (1924); Recherches histo-chimiques sur le rôle des ferments oxydants dans les phénomènes de la vie à l'état normal et pathologique. *Ann. Anat. pathol. méd.-chir.*, **1**, 121–162.

MARSLAND, D., (1956); Protoplasmic contractility in relation to gel structure: temperature-pressure experiments on cytokinesis and amoeboid movement. *Int. Rev. Cytol.*, **5**, 199–227.

MAST, S. O., AND PROSSER, C. L., (1932); Effect of temperature, salts and hydrogen-ion concentration on rupture of the plasmagel sheet, rate of locomotion and gel/sol ratio in *Amoeba proteus. J. cell. comp. Physiol.*, **1**, 333–354.

MATSUMOTO, T., (1920); The granules, vacuoles and mitochondria in the sympathetic nerve fibres cultivated *in vitro*. *Johns Hopk. Hosp. Bull.*, **31**, 91–93.

MAXFIELD, M., (1953); Axoplasmic proteins of the squid giant nerve fiber with particular reference to the fibrous protein. *J. gen. Physiol.*, **37**, 210–216.

MELAMED, J., AND TRUJILLO-CENÓZ, O., (1963); Electron microscopic observations on reactional changes occurring in insect nerve fibres after transection. *Z. Zellforsch.*, **59**, 851–856.

MIANI, N., (1962); Evidence of a proximo-distal movement along the axon of phospholipid synthesized in the nerve cell body. *Nature (Lond.)*, **193**, 887–888.

MITCHELL, J. F., AND SILVER, A., (1963); The spontaneous release of acetylcholine from the denervated hemidiaphragm of the rat. *J. Physiol. (Lond.)*, **165**, 117–129.

MORGAN, J. A., THOMSON, J. D., AND HINES, H. M., (1948); Effect of repeated denervation upon neuromuscular function. *Amer. J. Physiol.*, **153**, 109–112.

MOSSA, S., (1927); Ulteriori studi sulla velocità di accrescimento dei neuriti coltivati '*in vitro*' in funzione della temperatura ambiente. *Arch. exp. Zellforsch.*, **4**, 188–205.

MURRAY, M. R., (1959); Factors bearing on myelin formation *in vitro*. *Biology of Myelin*. S. R. Korey, Editor. New York, Hoeber–Harper (pp. 201–229).

MURRAY, M. R., PETERSON, E. R., AND BUNGE, R. P., (1962); Some nutritional aspects of myelin sheath formation in cultures of central and peripheral nervous system. *Proc. IV. int. Congr. Neuropathol.*, **2**, 267–272.

NAGEOTTE, J., (1921); *L'Organisation de la Matière dans ses Rapports avec la Vie*. Paris, Alcan.

NAKAI, J., (1956); Dissociated dorsal root ganglia in tissue culture. *Amer. J. Anat.*, **99**, 81–129.

NAPIER, J. R., (1949); The significance of Tinel's sign in peripheral nerve injuries. *Brain*, **72**, 63–82.

NIEMIERKO, S., AND ZAWADZKA, I., personal communication.

NOLAND, L. E., (1957); Protoplasmic streaming. A perennial puzzle. *J. Protozool.*, **4**, 1–6.

OCHS, S., DALRYMPLE, D., AND RICHARDS, G., (1962); Axoplasmic flow in ventral root nerve fibres of the cat. *Exp. Neurol.*, **5**, 349–363.

OHMI, S., (1961); Electron microscopic study on Wallerian degeneration of the peripheral nerve. *Z. Zellforsch.*, **54**, 39–67.

PALAY, S. L., (1943); Neurosecretion. V. The origin of neurosecretory granules from the nuclei of nerve cells in fishes. *J. comp. Neurol.*, **79**, 247–276.

PALAY, S. L., (1953); Neurosecretory phenomena in the hypothalamo hypophysial system of man and monkey. *Amer. J. Anat.*, **93**, 107–141.

PALAY, S. L., (1956); Synapses in the central nervous system. *J. biophys. biochem. Cytol. Suppl.*, **2**, 193–202.

PALAY, S. L., (1960); The fine structure of secretory neurons in the preoptic nucleus of the goldfish (*Carassuis auratus*). *Anat. Rec.*, **138**, 417–443.

PALAY, S. L., AND PALADE, G. E., (1955); The fine structure of neurons. *J. biophys. biochem. Cytol.*, **1**, 69–88.

PARKER, G. H., (1933); The progressive degeneration in frog nerve. *Amer. J. Physiol.*, **106**, 398–403.

PARKER, G. H., AND PAINE, V. L., (1934); Progressive nerve degeneration and its rate in the lateral line nerve of the catfish. *Amer. J. Anat.*, **54**, 1–25.

PEASE, D. C., AND QUILLIAM, A., (1957); Electron microscopy of the Pacinian corpuscle. *J. biophys. biochem. Cytol.*, **3**, 331–342.

PETERSON, E. R., AND MURRAY, M. R., (1960); Modification of development in isolated dorsal root ganglia by nutritional and physical factors. *Develop. Biol.*, **2**, 461–476.

PITTS, R. F., AND MAST, S. O., (1934); The relation between inorganic salt concentration, hydrogen ion concentration and physiological processes in *Amoeba proteus*. II. Rate of locomotion, gel/sol ratio and hydrogen ion concentration in solutions of single salts. *J. cell. comp. Physiol.*, **4**, 237–256.

POMERAT, C. M., (1960); Cinematography indispensable tool for cytology. *Abstr. Xe Congr. int. Biol. cell. (Paris)*, (p. 5).

QUILLIAM, T. A., (1954); A quantitative study of certain neurohistological features of Pacinian corpuscle. *Amer. J. Physiol.*, **179**, 663.

RANSON, S. W., (1912); Degeneration and regeneration of nerve fibres. *J. comp. Neurol.*, **22**, 487–546.

RANVIER, L., (1878); *Leçons sur l'Histologie du Système Nerveux*. Paris, Savy.

RANVIER, L., (1882); Des modifications de structure qu'éprouvent les tubes nerveux en passant des racines dans la moelle épinière. *C. R. Acad. Sci.*, **95**, 1069–1072.

RÉNAUT, M. J., (1881); Recherches sur quelques points particuliers de l'histologie des nerfs. *Arch. Physiol. norm. pathol.*, **13**, 161–190.

REXED, B., (1944); Contributions to the knowledge of the post-natal development of the peripheral nervous system in man. *Acta psychiat.*, Suppl., **33**, 10–206.

REXED, B., AND REXED, U., (1951); Degeneration and regeneration of corneal nerves. *Brit. J. Ophthal.*, **35**, 38–49.

RHINES, R., (1959); Ultraviolet irradiation of small portions of nerve cell processes in tissue culture. *Exp. Neurol.*, **1**, 569–582.

ROBERTSON, D. J., (1956); The ultrastructure of a reptilian myoneural junction. *J. biophys. biochem. Cytol.*, **2**, 381–393.

ROBERTSON, D. J., (1960); The molecular structure and contact relationship of cell membranes. *Progress in Biophysics and Biophysical Chemistry*. J. A. V. Butler and B. Katz, Editors. London, Pergamon Press, **10**, (pp. 343–418).

ROSE, G. G., (1960); Cinematographic studies on microkinetospheres, the Golgi complex, and the endoplasmic reticulum. *Abstr. Xe Congr. int. Biol. cell. (Paris)*, 24.

ROSE, G. G., AND POMERAT, C. M., (1960); Phase contrast observations of the endoplasmic reticulum in living tissue cultures. *J. biophys. biochem. Cytol.*, **8**, 423–430.

ROSENBLUETH, A., AND DEL POZO, E. C., (1943); The centrifugal course of Wallerian degeneration. *Amer. J. Physiol.*, **139**, 247–254.

ROSSITER, R. J., (1961); The chemistry of Wallerian degeneration. *Chemical Pathology of the Nervous System*. J. Folch-Pi, Editor. London, Pergamon Press (pp. 207–227).

SAMORAJSKI, T., (1957); Changes in phosphatase activity following transection of the sciatic nerve. *J. Histochem. Cytochem.*, **5**, 15–27.

SAMUELS, A. J., BOYARSKY, L. L., GERARD, R. W., LIBET, B., AND BRUST, M., (1951); Distribution, exchange and migration of phosphate compounds in the nervous system. *Amer. J. Physiol.*, **164**, 1–15.

SATO, M., AND SCHNEIDER, D., (1954); Mikroskopisch-elektrophysiologische Untersuchung des Internodiums der markhaltigen Nervenfaser unter Einwirkung von Saponin und Elektrolyten. *Z. Naturforsch.*, **9b**, 644–654.

SAUNDERS, N., personal communication.

SAWYER, C. H., (1946); Cholinesterases in degenerating and regenerating peripheral nerves. *Amer. J. Physiol.*, **146**, 246–253.

SAWYER, C. H., AND HOLLINSHEAD, W. H., (1945); Cholinesterases in sympathetic fibres and ganglia. *J. Neurophysiol.*, **8**, 137–153.

SCHARRER, E., (1962); Concluding remarks. *Neurosecretion.* H. Heller and R. B. Clark, Editors. London, Academic Press (pp. 421–424).

SCHARRER, E. A., AND WITTENSTEIN, G. J., (1952); The effect of interruption of the hypothalamo-hypophysial neurosecretory pathway in the dog. *Anat. Rec.*, **112**, 387.

SCHLOTE, W., AND HAGER, H., (1960); Elektronenmikroskopische Befunde zur Feinstruktur von Axonveränderungen im peritraumatischen Bereich nach experimenteller Strangdurchtrennung am Rückenmark der weiszen Ratte. *Naturwissenschaften*, **47**, 448–451.

SCOTT, F. H., (1906); On the relation of nerve cells to fatigue of their nerve fibres. *J. Physiol. (Lond.)*, **34**, 145–162.

SEDDON, H. J., (1954); *Peripheral Nerve Injuries.* London, Her Majesty's Stationery Office.

SEDDON, H. J., MEDAWAR, P. B., AND SMITH, H., (1943); Rate of regeneration of peripheral nerves in man. *J. Physiol. (Lond.)*, **102**, 191–215.

SHAPIRO, H., (1937); The relative respiratory activity of sheath and axones in resting *Limulus* optic nerve. *J. cell. comp. Physiol.*, **9**, 381.

SHUTE, C. C. D., AND LEWIS, P. R., (1961a); Cholinergic nervous pathways in the forebrain. *Nature (Lond.)*, **189**, 332–333.

SHUTE, C. C. D., AND LEWIS, P. R., (1961b); The use of cholinesterase techniques combined with operative procedures to follow nervous pathways in the brain. *Bibl. anat. (Basel)*, **2**, 34–49.

SINGER, M., (1959); The acetylcholine content of the normal forelimb regenerate of the adult newt, *Triturus. Develop. Biol.*, **1**, 603–620.

SINGER, M., DAVIS, M. H., AND ARKOWITZ, E. S., (1960); Acetylcholinesterase activity in the regenerating forelimb of the adult newt, *Triturus. J. Embryol. exp. Morphol.*, **8**, 98–111.

SLOPER, J. C., ARNOTT, J. D., AND KING, B. C., (1960); Sulphus metabolism in the pituitary and hypothalamus of the rat. A study of radioisotope uptake after the injection of ^{35}S DL-cysteine, methionine and sodium sulphate. *J. Endocrinol.*, **20**, 9–23.

SNELL, R. S., (1957); Histochemical appearances of cholinesterases in the normal sciatic nerve and the changes which occur after nerve section. *Nature (Lond.)*, **180**, 378–379.

SPEIDEL, C. C., (1932); Studies of living nerves. I. The movements of individual sheath cells and nerve sprouts correlated with the process of myelinsheath formation in amphibian larvae. *J. exp. Zool.*, **61**, 279–317.

SPEIDEL, C. C., (1933); Studies of living nerves. II. Activities of ameboid growth cones, sheath cells, and myelin segments, as revealed by prolonged observation of individual nerve fibres in frog tadpoles. *Amer. J. Anat.*, **52**, 1–79.

SPEIDEL, C. C., (1935a); Studies on living nerves. III. Phenomena of nerve irritation, recovery, degeneration and repair. *J. comp. Neurol.*, **61**, 1–82.

SPEIDEL, C. C., (1935b); Studies of living nerves. IV. Growth, regeneration, and myelination of the peripheral nerves in salamanders. *Biol. Bull.*, **68**, 142–163.

SPEIDEL, C. C., (1950); Adjustments of peripheral nerve fibres. *Genetic Neurology.* P. Weiss, Editor. Chicago, Chicago University Press (p. 66).

STEWART, D. M., AND MARTIN, A. W., (1956); Hypertrophy of the denervated hemidiaphragm. *Amer. J. Physiol.*, **186**, 497–500.

STEWART, P. A., AND STEWART, B. T., (1961); Circular streaming patterns in a slime-mould plasmodium. *Nature (Lond.)*, **192**, 1206–1207.

STRONG, O. S., (1906); The mode of connection of the medullated nerve fibre with the cell body. *J. comp. Neurol.*, **16**, 397–401.

SUNDERLAND, S., (1947); Rate of regeneration in human peripheral nerves. Analysis of the interval between injury and onset of recovery. *Arch. Neurol. Psychiat.*, **58**, 251–295.

SUNDERLAND, S., AND BRADLEY, K. C., (1952); Rate of advance of Hoffman–Tinel sign in regenerating nerves. *Arch. Neurol. Psychiat.*, **67**, 650–654.

TARLOV, I. M., (1937); Structure of the nerve root. I. Nature of the junction between the central and the peripheral nervous system. *Arch. Neurol. Psychiat.*, **37**, 555–583.

TAYLOR, G. I., (1935); The formation of emulsions in definable fields of flow. *Proc. roy. Soc. A*, **146**, 501–523.

THIERY, J. P., (1960); Etude de l'ergastoplasme des plasmocytes à l'état vivant. *Abstr. Xe Congr. int. Biol. cell. (Paris)*, 24.

THOMSEN, E., (1954); Experimental evidence for the transport of secretory material in the axons of the neurosecretory cells of *Calliphora erythrocephala* MEIG. *Publ. Stazione Zool. (Napoli)*, Suppl., **24**, 48–49.

THOMPSON, C. M., AND WOLPERT, L., (1963); The isolation of motile cytoplasm from *Amoeba proteus*. *Exp. Cell Res.*, **32**, 156–160.

THORNBURG, W., AND DE ROBERTIS, E., (1956); Polarisation and electron microscope study of frog nerve axoplasm. *J. biophys. biochem. Cytol.*, **2**, 475–482.

TINEL, J., (1915); Le signe du 'fourmillement' dans les lésions des nerfs periphériques. *Presse méd.*, **23**, 388–389.

TITECA, J., (1935); Etude des modifications fonctionnelles du nerf au cours de la dégénérescence Wallérienne. *Arch. int. Physiol.*, **41**, 2–56.

TOSCHI, G., (1959); A biochemical study of brain microsomes. *Exp. Cell Res.*, **16**, 232–255.

VAN BREEMEN, V. L., ANDERSON, E., AND REGER, J. F., (1958); An attempt to determine the origin of synaptic vesicles. *Exp. Cell Res. Suppl.*, **5**, 153–167.

VAN CREVEL, H., (1958); The rate of secondary degeneration in the central nervous system. An experimental study in the pyramid and optic nerve of the cat. *Thesis*, Leiden (pp. 1–93).

VERA, C. L., AND LUCO, J. V., (1958); Synaptic transmission in spinal cord during Wallerian degeneration of dorsal root fibres. *J. Neurophysiol.*, **21**, 334–344.

VERHAART, W. J. C., AND VAN CREVEL, H., (1961); The degeneration rate of pyramidal axons. *Cytology of the Nervous Tissue*. Proceedings of the Anatomical Society of Great Britain and Ireland. London, Taylor and Francis (pp. 58–59).

VERNE, J., AND DROZ, B., (1960); Déplacement de la radioactivité dans le ganglion cervical supérieur après l'injection de ^{35}S-Méthionine. *Experientia (Basel)*, **26**, 77–78.

VIAL, J. D., (1958); The early changes in the axoplasm during Wallerian degeneration. *J. biophys. biochem. Cytol.*, **4**, 551–556.

VIGNAL, W., (1883a); Mémoire sur le développement des tubes nerveux chez les embryons des mammifères. *Arch. Physiol. norm. pathol.*, **15**, 513–535.

VIGNAL, W., (1883b); Accroissement en longueur des tubes nerveux, par la formation des segments intercalaires. *Arch. Physiol. norm. pathol.*, **15**, 536–548.

VON EULER, U. S., (1958); The presence of the adrenergic neurotransmitter in intraaxonal structures. *Acta physiol. scand.*, **43**, 155–166.

VON EULER, U. S., AND HILLARP, N. A., (1956); Evidence for the presence of noradrenaline in submicroscopic structures of adrenergic axons. *Nature (Lond.)*, **177**, 44–45.

WAELSCH, H., (1958); Some aspects of amino acid and protein metabolism of the neurons system. *J. nerv. ment. Dis.*, **126**, 33–39.

WAELSCH, H., (1962); Amino acid and protein metabolism. *Neurochemistry*. K. A. C. Elliot, I. H. Page and J. H. Quastel, Editors. Springfield, Charles C. Thomas (pp. 288–320).

WAELSCH, H., AND LAJTHA, A., (1961); Protein metabolism in the nervous system. *Physiol. Rev.*, **41**, 709–736.

WARSHAWSKY, H., AND DROZ, B., (1962); Reliability of the radioautographic technique for the detection of newly synthesized protein. *Anat. Rec.*, **142**, 289–290.

WECHSLER, W., UND HAGER, H., (1962); Elektronenmikroskopische Befunde zur Feinstruktur von Axonveränderungen in regenerierenden Nervenfasern des Nervus ischiadicus der weiszen Ratte. *Acta neuropathol.*, **1**, 489–506.

WEDDELL, G., (1942); Axonal regeneration in cutaneous nerve plexuses. *J. Anat. (Lond.)*, **77**, 49–62.

WEDDELL, G., AND GLEES, P., (1942); The early stages in the degeneration of cutaneous nerve fibres. *J. Anat. (Lond.)*, **76**, 65–93.

WEDDELL, G., AND ZANDER, E., (1951); The fragility of nonmyelinated nerve fibres. *J. Anat. (Lond.)*, **85**, 242–250.

WEISS, P., (1943); Nerve regeneration in the rat following tubular splicing of severed nerves. *Arch. Surg.*, **46**, 525–548.

WEISS, P., (1961); The concept of perpetual neuronal growth and proximo-distal substance convection. *Regional Neurochemistry*. S. S. Kety and J. Elkes, Editors. London, Pergamon Press (pp. 220–242).

WEISS, P., (1963); Self-renewal and proximo-distal convection in nerve fibres. *Symposium on the Effect of Use and Disuse on Neuromuscular Function.* E. Gutmann and P. Hník, Editors. Prague, Publishing House of the Czechoslovak Academy of Sciences (pp. 171–183).

WEISS, P., AND BURT, A., (1944); Effect of nerve compression on Wallerian degeneration *in vitro. Proc. Soc. exp. Biol. Med.,* **55**, 109–112.

WEISS, P., AND CAVANAUGH, M. W., (1959); Further evidence of perpetual growth of nerve fibres. Recovery of fibre diameter after the release of prolonged constrictions. *J. exp. Zool.,* **142**, 461–474.

WEISS, P., AND HISCOE, H. B., (1948); Experiments on the mechanism of nerve growth. *J. exp. Zool.,* **107**, 315–395.

WEISS, P., TAYLOR, A. C., AND PILLAI, P. A., (1962); The nerve fibre as a system in continuous flow: microcinematographic and electronmicroscopic demonstrations. *Science,* **136**, 330.

WETTSTEIN, R., AND SOTELO, J. R., (1963); Electron microscope study on the regenerative process of peripheral nerves of mice. *Z. Zellforsch.,* **59**, 708–730.

WILLIAMS, P. L., AND LANDON, D. N., (1963); Paranodal apparatus of peripheral myelinated fibres in mammals. *Nature (Lond.),* **198**, 670–673.

WILLIAMS, P. S., AND KASHEF, R., (1961); Asymmetry of the node of Ranvier in mammals — an experimental study. *J. Anat. (Lond.),* **95**, 610–611.

WILLIAMS, S. C., (1930); Regeneration of peripheral nerves in amphibia studied with the aid of a vital stain. *J. exp. Zool.,* **57**, 145–181.

WISLOCKI, G. B., AND SINGER, M., (1946); The occurrence and function of nerves in the growing antlers of deer. *J. comp. Neurol.,* **85**, 1–20.

WOLFE, D. E., POTTER, L. T., RICHARDSON, K. C., AND AXELROD, J., (1962); Localizing tritiated norepinephrine in sympathetic axons by EM autoradiography. *Science,* **138**, 440–441.

WYRWICKA, W., (1950); On the rate of regeneration of the sciatic nerve in white mouse. *Acta biol. exp. (Warszawa),* **15**, 147–153.

YONEZAWA, T., BORNSTEIN, M. B., PETERSON, E. R., AND MURRAY, M. R., (1962a); A histochemical study of oxidative enzymes in myelinating cultures of central and peripheral nervous tissue. *J. Neuropathol. exp. Neurol.,* **21**, 479–487.

YONEZAWA, T., BORNSTEIN, M. B., PETERSON, E. R., AND MURRAY, M. R., (1962b); Temporal and spatial distribution of oxidative enzymes (cytochrome oxidase compared with succinic dehydrogenase and diaphorases) during myelin formation and maintenance. *Proc. IV int. Congr. Neuropathol.,* **2**, 273–274.

YOUNG, J. Z., (1937); The structure of nerve fibres in Cephalopods and Crustacea. *Proc. roy. Soc. B,* **121**, 319–337.

YOUNG, J. Z., (1942); The functional repair of nervous tissue. *Physiol. Rev.,* **22**, 318–374.

YOUNG, J. Z., (1944a); Surface tension and the degeneration of nerve fibres. *Nature (Lond.),* **154**, 521–522.

YOUNG, J. Z., (1944b); Contraction, turgor and the cytoskeleton of nerve fibres. *Nature (Lond.),* **153**, 333–335.

YOUNG, J. Z., (1945); The history of the shape of a nerve-fibre. *Essays on Growth and Form.* W. E. Le Gros Clark and P. B. Medawar, Editors. Oxford, Clarendon Press (pp. 41–94).

YOUNG, J. Z., (1949); Narrowing of nerve fibres at the nodes of Ranvier. *J. Anat. (Lond.),* **83**, 55.

YOUNG, J. Z., AND MEDAWAR, P. B., (1940); Fibrin suture of peripheral nerves. Measurements of the rate of regeneration. *Lancet,* **239**, 126–129.

ZANDER, E., AND WEDDELL, G., (1951); Observations on the innervation of the cornea. *J. Anat. (Lond.),* **85**, 66–99.

ZELENÁ, J., AND LUBIŃSKA, L., (1962); Early changes of acetylcholinesterase activity near the lesion in crushed nerves. *Physiol. bohemoslov.,* **11**, 261–268.

ZELENÁ, J., AND SZENTÁGOTHAI, J., (1957); Verlagerung der Lokalisation spezifischer Cholinesterase während der Entwicklung der Muskelinnervation. *Acta histochem.,* **3**, 284–296.

DISCUSSION

ECCLES: I am very interested indeed in these convincing experiments showing that there is a streaming of organized particulate material in both directions along nerve fibres. Physiological experiments lead us to postulate the movement of trophic influences in both directions along nerve fibres; for example, from neuron to muscle and from muscle to neuron. The only misgiving I have is that the crush gives such a violent destruction of the axon. I, therefore, wish to ask if there has been any experimental investigation using more physiological and reversible methods to check the streaming movements, For example, a very localized freezing or cooling of a thin nerve trunk should be possible for at least 24 h, and following that there should be recovery giving a very good control of the results consequent on the temporary blockage. Another possible method of producing a very localized and reversible blockage is by a careful adjusted mechanical pressure applied by a clamp that can, for example, block conduction of impulses without being itself severe enough to cause degeneration.

LUBIŃSKA: So far we used only the mechanically interrupted axons. It is a very good suggestion to apply a localized freezing. It should permit to observe what happens to the accumulated material after resumption of flow.

Graded mechanical pressure is perhaps less suitable for this type of quantitative experiments since various fibres of the nerve would be affected differently according to their diameter and the position they occupy inside or on the surface of the nerve trunk.

GLEES: I would like to ask: how old was the culture of the chick embryo of the spinal motoneuron you showed? Which technique did you use and how long did the cell survive?

LUBIŃSKA: The film was from Dr. Nakai of Tokyo who kindly agreed to my showing it here. He used spinal ganglia and cord from chick embryo; the time of incubation was 7–12 days, after 6–7 days in culture.

HORSTFEHR: Do you think it will be possible to say that in the clear zone of the axon there is a higher dipole (e°) concentration than in the proximal (? e^+) and distal (?e $^-$) ends?

LUBIŃSKA: No attempt was made to analyze the results obtained in these terms.

VONEIDA: Would you comment on the possible attracting forces involved between a regenerating nerve fibre and its points of destination? I am referring particularly to the recently reported work of Attardi and Sperry in which surgically displaced regenerating optic nerve of the goldfish was found to retrace its original pathways into the tectum.

LUBIŃSKA: I have no idea how to explain these remarkable phenomena.

References p. 71

GUTMANN: There is one question which has always puzzled me, and that is the problem of the physiological significance of the intra-axonal streaming, and especially the rate of the processes. One is confronted with this question in studying the breakdown and re-synthesis of proteins in the nerve after functional activity. The normal protein content is restored in about 1 to 3 h. This is very difficult to explain without assuming local synthetic processes. There are, apparently due to the activity of Schwann cells, local processes of re-synthesis with a very high rate. In regenerating nerve the incorporation is about 6–700% higher than in normal nerves. This can partly be explained by the number of Schwann cells involved.

My main question is: do you think that the intra-axonal streaming has something to do with this type of processes?

LUBIŃSKA: Cytoplasmic streaming is essentially an intracellular phenomenon and goes on also in axons unaccompanied by Schwann cells. It is likely however, that Schwann cells may exert a modulatory influence on axoplasmic streaming either by metabolic contributions or by mechanical massaging. Rhythmic contractions of Schwann cells in culture were described by Pomerat (1959). Peterson (quoted by Murray, 1959) showed that nuclei of Schwann cells turn around the axons in cultures. There seem to be no investigations concerning the possible influence of the motility of Schwann cells on the translocation of materials inside the axons.

As to the physiological significance of intra-axonal streaming, migration of axonal materials was postulated on physiological grounds to explain the interdependence of various parts of the neuron long before the streaming was actually detected.

SINGER: Would you comment on Weiss' theory of peristaltic movements and can it explain your theory of bidirectional movement?

LUBIŃSKA: If I am not mistaken a full paper with analysis of the film and statement of the theory of peristalsis in nerve fibres has not yet appeared. It is difficult to form an opinion by simply watching Weiss' film. I saw there many wandering Schwann cells and axons breaking down into ovoids, both indicating the presence of degenerating fibres. Presumably the peristaltic waves were detected in non-degenerating fibres but no details are given in the abstract published in *Science*.

KREUTZBERG: May I underline the results of Prof. Lubińska by some histochemical investigations?

After cutting or crushing or freezing the nervus ischiadicus of the rat you get the same changes in oxidative enzymes (like DPN-diaphorase or succinic dehydrogenase) as Prof. Lubińska has shown it for AChE. Enzyme activity increases in both the peripheral and the proximal stumps. The same results were obtained after transection of the spinal cord.

In isolated pieces of peripheral nerves we found also an increase of oxidative enzyme when the isolated piece was longer than 1 cm. The accumulation was to be shown in the axons of both ends of the pieces.

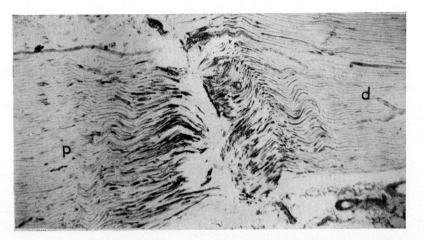

Fig. 1. N. ischiadicus of the rat. An accumulation of DPN-diaphorase is shown in the proximal (p) and the distal (d) stump, 24 h after transection of the nerve.

ECCLES: As a physiologist one is particularly interested in the fine machinery of the axoplasm that subserves movement of the particulate material in both directions. For example, is it possible that the neurofibrils provide a structural basis throughout the cross section of the axoplasm that is concerned in the propulsion?

LUBIŃSKA: It seems that at present the motile function cannot be assigned to any determined morphological structure. Some may be excluded, however. Since the streaming continues in axons separated from the perikaryon, its components cannot be the immediate source of propulsion. A finer analysis of factors involved in cytoplasmic streaming was made on other cellular material where it was shown, as in the previously quoted experiments of Allen, that the presence of the cell membrane is not essential for streaming. Thus Thompson and Wolpert (1963) describe the following behavior of gently homogenized amoebal cytoplasm contaminated very slightly with membranes. At 4° only Brownian movements of granules are visible. On addition of ATP under appropriate conditions sudden jerky displacements of granules appear distinct from Brownian motion. Progressively streams of granules become arranged in parallel lines moving in opposite directions through the bulk of cytoplasm. The rate of granules may be 80 μ/sec for distances of 600 μ. There is no net transfer of material in any direction. This type of movement resembles that seen in intact cells. These results, along with those described earlier, seem to indicate that the motility of cytoplasm is connected with its molecular organization rather than with cellular architecture on the microscopic level. Theories interpreting the bidirectional pattern of cytoplasmic streaming were proposed recently by Allen (1961), Kavanau (1962a, b), and Jahn and Rinaldi (1959).

HORSTFEHR: Will the progressive outflux of substances on the distal side of the axon be accompanied by an outflux on the proximal side or by an influx, or will there be simultaneous material changes on both sides?

References p. 71

LUBIŃSKA: In an excised nerve fibre the outflow is observed at both ends.

SCHADÉ: I was much impressed by the quantitative data of acetylcholinesterase. In view of the process of regeneration and the subsequent mechanisms of degeneration it would be of much interest to know about the amount and distribution of lactic dehydrogenase. Do you know any quantitative data on this subject or can you make a prediction about the localisation and distribution? One would expect the same distribution as AChE.

LUBIŃSKA: Several enzymes accumulate at the ends of interrupted nerve fibres and present in histochemical preparations a similar localization in the terminal region of axoplasm. As far as I know, there are no quantitative data on the subject except for acetylcholinesterase. Perhaps Dr. Kreutzberg who studied oxidative enzymes in cut and crushed nerves could answer your question better.

KREUTZBERG: Histochemically lactate dehydrogenase shows the same behavior as AChE. There is an increase in both stumps after cutting or crushing the peripheral nerve.

   Quantitative studies of the distribution of LDH in proximal and peripheral parts of normal nerves are unknown to me.

SINGER: If I understood your thesis correctly, you assume that the neuronal process resembles the cytoplasmic processes of other cells; in that there is bidirectional movement of protoplasm within it. However, you do recognize that the movement is predominantly proximodistal, but there is also a disto-proximal movement, perhaps to a lesser degree. This can be demonstrated particularly with crushing. At the moment you have no theory for the forces which cause the movement in one direction or the other direction at the same time, but I assume you believe that this bidirectional movement occurs at the same time. You also believe that the rate of movement can change at times and be relatively greater in one direction than the other? Would you care to comment on these thoughts?

LUBIŃSKA: Bidirectional movements of granules in the axons were described by many workers in tissue culture and by Speidel in growing cutaneous fibres *in vivo*. I think that there is no reason to assume the existence of a fundamentally different pattern of streaming along axons in the nerve trunks. This working hypothesis seems to be confirmed both by the biochemical experiments reported here and by the behavior of the proximal stump of cut nerves described by Ranson and Cajal. It is also helpful for interpretation of many aspects of neuronal biology such as reaction of the perikaryon to amputation of a part of its axon or, more generally, to the events occurring at the periphery.

   As to the question whether the movement in the proximo-distal direction predominates over that in the distal-proximal direction, it may be answered positively for growing and regenerating fibres. The answer is less certain for mature nerve fibres of stationary length where net transfer of bulk materials towards the nerve endings is not visible. Our experiments with AChE seem to indicate that more of this enzyme is carried in the proximo-distal than in the opposite direction. But, possibly, AChE which has a specific function at axon terminals and may be used up in some way there is not a best index for estimation of the amount of substances flowing in each direction. I would anticipate that other components which take part in the general metabolism of the nerve fibre without having a specialized function at the endings might behave differently in this respect and accumulate in similar amounts on both sides of the lesion during the period of survival of the cut fibres. We are trying to solve this problem experimentally.

If the interpretation proposed here is correct, various components would behave differently according to their state in the axoplasm and locus of utilization: (1) Substances dissolved in the axoplasm would not change appreciably in concentration near the cut ends of fibres; (2) Substances incorporated into structural particles would accumulate at the cut ends. The rate of accumulation would depend on the rate of streaming and on the amount of the investigated substance flown in each direction in unit time. It is only by sampling the rates of accumulation of many constituents that an estimate of the rate of streaming of axoplasm may be arrived at. We are in this respect in a much more difficult position than with neurons in culture where the rate of translocation of granules can be measured directly.

REFERENCES

KAVANAU, J. L., (1962a); On the genesis of cytoplasmic streaming. *Life Sciences*, **5**, 177–183.

KAVANAU, J. L., (1962b); Cytoplasmic streaming and non-equilibrium interfaces. *Exp. Cell Res.*, **27**, 595–598.

POMERAT, C. M., (1959); Rhythmic contractions of Schwann cells. *Science*, **130**, 1759.

THOMPSON, C. M., AND WOLPERT, L., (1963); The isolation of motile cytoplasm from *Amoeba proteus*. *Exp. Cell Res.*, **32**, 156–160.

Neurotrophic Relations in the Regeneration Process

E. GUTMANN

Institute of Physiology, Czechoslovak Academy of Sciences, Prague

CONTENTS

I. GENERAL ASPECTS OF NEUROTROPHIC RELATIONS

Interruption of a peripheral nerve initiates a complex chain of interrelated changes in the neurone and innervated tissues which ultimately may lead to complete loss of structural integrity. Profound changes in regulation of intercellular relationships are apparently initiated by nerve section, and are reversed by the regeneration process. We have to assume a very close metabolic relationship between nerve cell, nerve fibre and muscle cell and evidently this metabolic relationship is disturbed after nerve section and re-established during the regeneration process.

Intercellular relations or connections in the neuromuscular system are realized either in events which are of short duration, usually of fractions of a second — brief functional changes that occur with transmission of nerve impulse activity, synaptic facilitatory and inhibitory reactions and which are explained by membrane changes (*cf*. Eccles, 1957) — or in long term 'trophic' regulations which maintain and restore the structure and the functional capacity of the cells and which may not be identical with transmission of nerve impulses and junctional transmission. The evidence for such nervous mechanisms that mediate 'neurotrophic relations' is mostly indirect, derived from studies of (a) morphogenesis (Hamburger, 1954; Studitskii, 1959; Zelená, 1959), (b) denervation (Gutmann, 1959), (c) nerve cross-unions (Eccles, 1963) and (d) regeneration (Gutmann and Young, 1944; Desmedt, 1950, 1959).

The term 'neurotrophic relations', *i.e.* nervous mechanisms not regulated by nerve impulse activity, implies, that approaches will be used which are to some extent different from those of classical neurophysiology which explains nerve–muscle relations basically as direct results of nerve impulse transmission, liberation of a specific transmitter substance and excitation of the postsynaptic membrane. Another approach to the problem of nerve–muscle relations concerns long-term regulations and presupposes that in these relations mechanisms are operating which are relatively independent of nerve-impulse activity. These mechanisms have been vaguely defined as trophic and evidently need exact definition. It is understandable that the growing interest in these nervous mechanisms comes at a time when the problem of plasticity of the nervous system, being the basis of 'learning' and conditioning, is attacked at simpler levels of the mammalian central nervous system (*cf.* Sperry, 1945; Eccles, 1958, 1961b; and others) and also at a time when the general principles of the mode of operation of the central nervous system seem to have been established. The neurone theory, according to which each neurone acts as a unit in an excitatory or inhibitory manner by means of synaptic contacts, has played a central role in this development. The definition of the nerve impulse in peripheral nerve fibres and of neuromuscular transmission (*cf.* Katz, 1958) in exact physico-chemical terms (Hodgkin and Huxley, 1952; Castillo and Katz, 1956) and the probability that the same mechanisms are also operative in the central nervous system (Eccles, 1957, 1961a) have raised hopes that application of these general basic laws of the physiology of the nervous system would be sufficient for a uniform explanation of all coordinated behaviour of the whole nervous system including of course the neurological basis of learning and conditioning. In this sense the effect of use and disuse would be induced basically by increased or decreased synaptic efficacy and thus be the 'synaptic basis of learning' (Eccles, 1958, 1961b).

The original theory (Cajal, 1935) stresses especially the anatomical, genetic, functional and 'trophic' unity of the neurone. The characteristics of the so called trophic unit of the neurone were first defined by Waller (1852), who stated that the nerve when separated from its 'trophic centre', *i.e.* the nerve cell, degenerates, whereas the central stump connected with the nerve cell remains undisturbed. Shortcomings of this doctrine became already clear to the founder of the neurone theory and characteristically they apply to the nature of intercellular neurotrophic relations. Cajal (1935) draws attention to the changes in nerve cells following nerve section and to the difficulty of a concept ascribing the maintenance of a cell projection so distant from the nerve cell to 'nutrition' from the neurone only. Further difficulties were encountered later by extending the 'law of dynamic polarization' (Cajal, 1935), concerning the direction of conduction from cell to axon (axipetal), to all neurones. However, in spinal ganglion cells the perikaryon of the nerve cell is separated from the mechanisms of production and conduction of the nerve impulse and thus the primary trophic role of the perikaryon in the neurone, irrelevant of its relation to 'dynamic polarization', can not be neglected and its position in the neurone is related rather to outgrowth and metabolic maintenance processes than to conduction and polarization of the neurone (Bodian, 1962). This would suggest a certain independence of the function of response generation and transmission related to synapse bearing surfaces with respect to that of 'maintenance' related to the perikaryon (*cf.* Bodian, 1962). Denervation and reinnervation experiments also suggest a differentiation of a 'trophic' and 'specific' (associated with nerve impulse activity) function of the nerve cell (*cf.* Gutmann, 1962a,b).

Whatever the implications of such a far going differentiation may be, study and

References p. 106–112

elucidation of neurotrophic relations will be of great importance for an understanding of the plastic changes occurring also in the highest integrative functions of the central nervous system and it appears that we have to deal here also with neural influences not transmitted only by nerve impulses as such. These intercellular 'neurotrophic relations' can best be studied in the neuromuscular system as connections and target organs are well defined. It can, however, be expected that the implications of such studies will be equally applicable to interneuronal relations in the central nervous system. The choice of such different terms as neurobiotaxis (see Ariëns Kappers, 1932), resonance relations between nerve and muscle (Weiss, 1924), modulation (Weiss, 1955), repercussion (Golikov, 1950; Ufljand, 1950), only indicates that we have to deal with a difficult problem and that there is a long way to go before clarification of these problems will be achieved. It is apparently in face of these difficulties that conclusions are now arrived at, stating that the functional picture of the nerve cell is deficient in so far as it fails to account for the plastic and developmental phenomena (Eccles, 1957).

Generally, we define trophic functions as the mechanisms maintaining and restoring the structure and the functional capacity of tissues and we may consider them to be a kind of homeostatic system of the organism maintaining adequate conditions for functioning. For a long time the maintenance of the internal environment by self-regulatory mechanisms was thought to be the decisive or exclusive kind of homeostatic system. The principle of the constancy of the internal environment, the *milieu intérieur*, has been formulated first by Bernard (1865). We may recall his statement: 'La fixité du milieu intérieur est la condition de la vie libre, indépendante.'* This idea was further elaborated by Barcroft (1934) and Cannon (1939a), who also emphasized the maintenance of internal environment. Cannon stressed, however, the importance of special neural, *i.e.* adrenergic mechanisms. Lately, however, emphasis has shifted from 'intercellular fluid' regulation to intracellular regulation (Heilbrunn, 1956; Krebs, 1957); regulation of the *milieu intérieur* is no longer the dominant focus of such regulation studies. From these tendencies it is only a step to a more intensive interest in the physiology of intercellular regulations which for a long time has mostly been the concern of morphology and embryology only.

The study of neurotrophic relations thus appears to be an important aspect of the physiology of homeostatic regulations. 'Maintenance', being the result of a dynamic equilibrium between processes of degradation and synthesis, is continuously 'deranged' by repeated stimuli of the environment and will primarily entail the recovery processes which are either connected with or follow functional activity (or gross tissue damage in 'reparative regeneration'). In the recovery processes following physiological activity or tissue damage no qualitative differences are to be expected and essentially we have to deal with metabolic adaptations to changing requirements. In the study of neurotrophic relations we are concerned with the long-term metabolic interdependence of the innervated tissue and the neurone and with the regulations safeguarding it. This dependence, maintained by nervous 'trophic' mechanisms, is inter-

---

* 'Constancy of the internal environment is requisite for free, independent life.'

rupted by nerve section and restored during the process of regeneration. It is by these processes that structural dependence and relations are uncovered. However, structural relations are essentially metabolic relations. This is impressively exemplified for instance in the axon–Schwann cell relations (Geren, 1956). The difficulty of the study of 'trophic' (non-impulse) nervous control mechanisms affecting cellular metabolism and intercellular relations is due to the fact that these mechanisms cannot be analyzed succesfully until our knowledge of the regulation of cell metabolism is more complete. The nervous regulations are evidently superimposed on fundamental cellular control mechanisms (*cf*. Stadie, 1954) which concern not only regulation of the rate of metabolism by changing the enzyme-substrate system but also other reactions such as the effect of metabolic 'pace makers' (Krebs, 1957) and different feedback mechanisms in cellular metabolism.

It could be assumed that the mechanisms regulating neurotrophic functions will operate especially by controlling breakdown and synthesis of cellular constituents, especially of proteins. Regeneration (in the sense commonly used, *i.e.* following nerve interruption) is an important aspect of these studies since during this process the regenerating neurone has to synthesize not only its very long cell process, the axon, but apparently initiates and is responsible for the maintenance and recovery of proteins in the innervated tissues. A marked increase of synthetic processes after different stimuli can be seen in both recovery processes, *i.e.* during 'reparative' regeneration and after functional activity. During reinnervation of muscle, glycogen synthesis is first lowered (during the denevartion period), then raised above initial

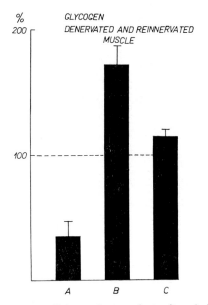

Fig. 1. Glycogen content of m. extensor digitorum longus of rats after administration of glucose during reinnervation, expressed as percentage of glycogen on the control side. (A) 10 days, (B) 20 days, (C) 30 days after crushing the nerve. (From Beránek *et al.*, 1954.)

levels and returns back to normal at later stages of reinnervation (Fig. 1) (Beránek *et al.*, 1954). In analogy, during muscle stimulation or other types of functional activity glycogen is broken down and returns to normal levels after an overshoot reaction (Fig. 2) (Gutmann *et al.*, 1954). These oscillations are suggestive of a feedback mechanism. A disturbance of these regulations apparently takes place in the denervated muscle. The accentuation of proteosynthesis both during the process of recovery after functional activity and during 'reparative' regeneration can also be

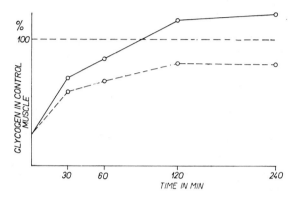

Fig. 2. Changes in glycogen resynthesis after direct stimulation (frequency 120/min, total number of stimuli 450) in normal (unbroken line) and denervated (broken line) m. tibialis in rats, expressed as percentage of the normal or denervated muscle of the control side. The initial values are those found immediately after stimulation of the muscle. Abscissa, time in minutes. Ordinate, percentage of glycogen resynthesis. (From Bass *et al.*, 1955.)

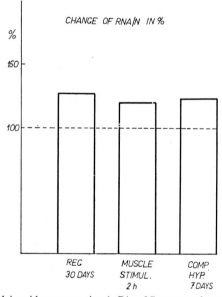

Fig. 3. Changes in ribonucleic acid concentration (γ P/mg N) expressed as percentage of concentration in the muscle of the control side, in reinnervated m. tibialis anterior of rats 30 days after crushing the nerve (reg), 2 h after direct stimulation of the muscle (muscle stimul.) and in muscle undergoing compensatory hypertrophy (7 days) after cutting the nerves of the control side (comp.hyp.).

seen in the changing ratio of ribonucleic acids to proteins (RNA/N) in a muscle after stimulation and during reinnervation and compensatory hypertrophy (Fig. 3). Increased RNA synthesis precedes proteosynthesis also in regenerating liver (Elliasohn *et al.*, 1951), after administration of growth hormone (Cater *et al.*, 1957) and after stimulation of muscle (Žák and Gutmann, 1960; Gutmann and Žák, 1961b). This change in RNA/N index during reinnervation and following stimulation of muscle demonstrates the considerable accentuation of proteosynthesis in both cases. These parallelities can, of course, be expected when both recovery processes are considered as homeostatic mechanisms inducing recovery of cellular constituents that are lost during functional activity or following nerve interruption.

Long-term regulations of the neurone concern especially the control of degradation and synthesis of proteins, *i.e.* change of their rates under different conditions. Thus a change in the general pattern of metabolism of proteins can be observed in all parts of the neuromuscular unit during denervation and reinnervation. In denervated muscle proteolytic activity (being a measure of the rate of degradation of proteins) increases and it returns to normal during reinnervation of the muscle (Fig. 4) (Hájek *et al.*, 1963)

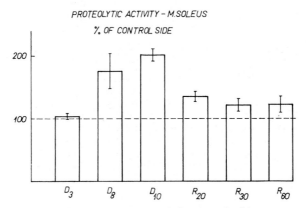

Fig. 4. Changes in proteolytic activity in soleus muscle in 3-month-old rats, expressed as percentage of proteolytic activity in the control muscle. Vertical lines, extinction values in per cent of control side. Abscissa, days after operation. D, denervation; R, reinnervation. (From Hájek *et al.*, 1963.)

The rate of proteosynthesis, as shown by the incorporation of ^{35}S-methionine into the proteins of denervated muscle, appears only slightly affected. However, there is an increase in free amino acids in the muscle, apparently caused by the changes in the denervated muscle membrane. These free amino acids cannot, however, be properly utilized, proteolytic activity is increased and thus atrophy takes place (Fig. 5) (Gutmann and Hájek, 1963). In the reinnervated muscle proteolytic activity returns only slowly to normal levels but there is increased proteosynthesis with normal utilization of free amino acids, which results in progressive 'muscle hypertrophy'. After nerve interruption different changes take place in the nerve cells and nerve trunk, these being apparently the result of an 'adaptive reaction' of the neurone to tissue damage and loss of proteins. In the nerve cell there is an increase in proteosynthesis (as measured by histoautoradiographic technique) already 3 days after nerve section,

followed by a decrease if reinnervation of the end organ does not take place (Fig. 6)
(Gutmann *et al.*, 1960). In the peripheral degenerating nerve trunk there is a considerable increase in proteosynthesis apparently due to the 'adaptive' reaction of
the proliferating Schwann cells connected with the regeneration process. This is

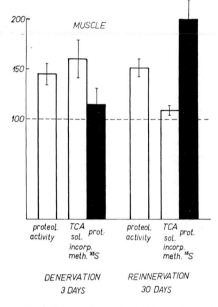

Fig. 5. Black columns: percentual changes in proteolytic activity and in specific activities of ^{35}S-
methionine in denervated (3 days after nerve section) and reinnervated (30 days after crushing the nerve)
m. tibialis anterior of rats, 1 h after i.v. injection of the labelled methionine (200 μC/100 g). Broken
line: proteolytic activity and specific activity of the same labelled compound in muscle of control side
taken as 100 %. TCA sol., trichloroacetic acid soluble fraction in the corresponding muscles. (From
Gutmann and Hájek, 1963.)

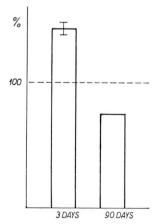

Fig. 6. Percentual change in number of grains in nerve cells of the spinal cord as shown by histoautoradiography, 3 and 90 days after cutting the sciatic nerve, compared with that of the normal
control side (100 %) in young rats. (From Gutmann *et al.*, 1960.)

followed by a decrease in the rate of proteosynthesis apparently related to the decrease in proliferation of Schwann cells (Fig. 7). These examples may suffice to show some aspects of the changing pattern of protein metabolism in the neuromuscular unit during denervation and reinnervation.

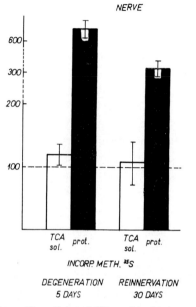

Fig. 7. Percentual changes of specific activity of ^{35}S-methionine in proteins of degenerated (5 days after section) and regenerated (30 days after crushing) sciatic nerve of rats after 1 h incubation in 5 ml Krebs–Ringer solution containing 1 μC/ml ^{35}S-methionine. Broken line: specific activity of the same labelled compound in nerve of control side as 100%. TCA sol.: Trichloroacetic acid soluble fraction in corresponding nerves. (From Gutmann and Hájek, 1963.)

Study of neurotrophic relations between the nerve and muscle cells during regeneration concerns both the dependence of the neurone on changes in terminal organs and that of the terminal organs on changes in the neurone. Evidently neuroembryological studies concerning the factors controlling early stages of neurone development, nerve growth and establishment of neurotrophic relations between nerve cells and terminal structures should be especially helpful. It has been stressed that ontogenetic and regenerative nerve growth have most of their basic mechanisms in common and that experimental evidence obtained in one field can often be directly applied to the other (Weiss, 1950). Neuroembryology, though taking its starting point from classical embryology in its inquiry into the causal factors of embryonic development is lately increasingly contacting neurophysiology (*cf.* Hamburger, 1954), and is in fact asking most impertinent questions. However, it has to be seen whether and how far these experiences can be applied to the physiology of neuromuscular relations as exemplified in the processes of degeneration and regeneration.

An attempt will be made to apply some of these experiences of neuroembryology to the study of the physiology of neurotrophic relations in the regeneration process. No complete discussion of these complex problems can, of course, be expected.

Morphogenesis or better neurogenesis can be said to comprise at least these phenomena: (1) cellular differentiation, (2) tissue organization, (3) growth, and (4) establishment of tissue relations.

These phenomena are, of course, interrelated, though neurogenesis follows a rather regular sequence of steps from the proliferating activity near the lumen of the central canal to extensive cell and axon growth and establishment of synaptic connections (Hamburger, 1956). Differentiation used in the narrow sense of the establishment of cytological specialization of neurones reveals itself in marked qualitative diversity of the neural elements (*cf.* Weiss, 1950). Specific enzymatic patterns are established (*cf.* Flexner, 1950). The differentiation implies a change in the kind of protein produced and it seems that the heterogeneity of RNA will be an important factor in the establishment of 'discriminating precision exerted by neuronal proteins' (*cf.* Gale, 1959). This specialization, initiated apparently by the succession of synthetic activity from RNA to proteins, increases with decrease of mitotic activity (Løvtrup, 1959).

However, this differentiation in embryonic cells is controlled to a large extent by the presence of other cell types, *i.e.* by cellular interactions and knowledge of the mechanisms active in these interactions will, of course, be very important for the understanding of the nature of neurotrophic relations. By interaction of one cell type with others the protein-forming system of the differentiating cell becomes modified (Herrmann, 1959) and we may recall in this connection that different cell strains cultivated *in vitro* have virtually identical nutritional requirements as those *in vivo* and that only *in vivo* the difference in metabolic requirements can be established (see Eagle, 1958). Cells are not isolated and cellular interactions are essential already during embryonic differentiation, establishment of the genetic characteristics of the neurone and also for tissue formation. Since Spemann (1938) it was thought that the localization and initiation of specific cellular differentiations are due to contact interactions with adjacent material, to 'embryonic inductions'. Only lately a hopeful attack on the chemical nature of the agents responsible for induction has been undertaken. There is now evidence for induction occurring 'at a distance' by 'diffusible agents', the material responsible for induction being released from inducing cells and bringing about the characteristic changes in the reacting cell system (Twitty, 1953; Twitty and Niu, 1954; Niu, 1956). Differentiation of pigment induced by phenylalanine in cells normally not synthetizing pigment may serve as an example for such chemically defined intercellular relations (Wilde, 1956). A further step was the discovery of a diffusible growth promoting agent, found in mouse sarcoma, snake venom and finally also in sympathetic nerve cells themselves. This nerve-growth stimulating agent induced a vigorous hyperplasia of sympathetic ganglia (Bueker, 1948; Levi-Montalcini and Hamburger, 1951; *cf.* Levi-Montalcini and Angeletti, 1960). The hyperplastic responses in the ganglia could also be induced *in vitro* after transplantation of tumour pieces onto allantoic membrane of 4-day-old embryos and the effects of these extra-embryonic tumours on the host were identical with those of intra-embryonic tumours. They do not only increase the number of cells and cause cellular hypertrophy but also accelerate the rate of differentiation and fibre growth, *i.e.* also control cell growth and rate of differentiation (Hamburger, 1956). These tissue culture experiments showed that neuroblasts can be affected directly by the tumour agent without the mediation of axons. Such a 'long distance diffusion effect' could also be shown for thyroxin on the growth of the mesencephalic V. nucleus in amphibians (Kollros and McMurray, 1955). The isolation of the nerve-growth stimulating factor is proceeding (Cohen and Levi-Montalcini, 1956; see Levi-Montalcini and Angeletti, 1960), and all these findings should in the end help in the chemical definition of processes of induction and of intercellular relations generally.

It is, of course, too early to decide whether in the transmission of inducing mechanisms metabolic precursors, inducing substrates for adaptive enzymes, or gene-like units inducing synthesis of proteins are responsible (see Edds, 1959), or whether transmission of sterically distinct molecular patterns from one cell surface to another is an important mechanism (Weiss, 1955; Tyler, 1955). Even the frequency of transmission of metabolic units could be effective (see Edds, 1959). Similar mechanisms may, of course, operate during the regeneration process. The problem is extremely complicated, but it can be concluded that intercellular control systems are apparently transmitted by different specific substances conveyed axonally and extra-axonally and that these substances will be isolated and identified. There is now hope that these basic findings of the study of intercellular relations will sooner or later be applied to the study of nerve–muscle cell relations in adult life.

So far we have considered especially the mechanisms of induction or 'neuralizing agents' which involve a chemical interaction between the inductor and the reacting system. In these intrinsic correlations in neurogenesis we are essentially concerned only with differentiation in the nervous tissue itself, the possibility of neural differentiation being present in all ectodermal tissue. Originally it was thought that there might be a non-specific chemical stimulus applied to the cell surface for all neuralization (Holtfreter, 1948). However, there is not only a specific pattern of neuronal metabolism and regionally specific organization imparted on non-specific neural tissue but there are, as shown before, also distinct chemical systems, acting 'at a distance' by diffusible mechanisms. The problem of intercellular relations in neurogenesis is of course not exhausted by the study of induction concerning nervous tissue itself. In neurogenesis the interactions of nervous and non-nervous tissues are the main field of neurotrophic relations, applicable to regeneration studies. It is in these intercellular correlations that the dependence of the nervous system on peripheral structures and that of peripheral structures on the nervous system are materialized and demonstrated. Neurones establish contact with other neurones or non-nervous structures and in this way double bonds or a double dependence (Young, 1946) are established which are realized by transmission of nerve impulse and non-impulse ('trophic') activity. Both types of connections are important for the maintenance of the neurone, and both operate with a different time sequence already during the embryonic period.

The neurone and the peripheral tissues are dependent on their connections. A disturbance of these connections implies disturbance of neurotrophic relations and is followed by changes, (a) in neurones deprived of synapses terminating on their cell bodies (transneuronal effects), (b) in neurones deprived of their terminal connections with non-nervous tissues, so called 'retrograde degeneration', (c) in non-nervous tissues deprived of their innervation (denervation effects), and (d) in neurones and non-nervous tissues produced by alteration in reactivity to hormones (hormonal effects on 'decentralized' neurones and denervated tissues). Some main aspects of these four changes of neurotrophic relations will be discussed first in morphogenesis and then in the regeneration process.

II. CHANGES OF NEUROTROPHIC RELATIONS DURING MORPHOGENESIS

Transneuronal effects

Transneuronal effects have been shown in many systems and only few examples will be quoted. They concern the changes in sensory columns of the spinal cord after changes at the periphery (Hamburger, 1934; Barron, 1945), in the optic (Harrison, 1929; Larsell, 1931) and the acoustic vestibular systems (Levi-Montalcini, 1949). The 'rebound on secondary units' (Weiss, 1955) is very marked, much more so than in the adult and it seems to be established that formation of synaptic connections on the surface of the neuroblast or on its dendrites is a necessary condition for the completion of its growth and differentiation and for the maintenance of its structural integrity (*cf.* Hamburger, 1954).

Changes in neurones

Changes in the peripheral field of innervation of a nerve have very marked effects on development of the primary nerve centres (see Hamburger, 1954). This 'peripheral rebound on primary neurones' (Weiss, 1955) was first studied in detail in the excessive development of spinal ganglia in trunk segments when the peripheral field had been increased by a grafted limb (Detwiler, 1920). Many experiments on extension of the peripheral field produced by implantation of supernumerary limbs have been performed (see Weiss, 1955), the result being hyperplasia due to increased proliferation and subsequent neural differentiation of the supernumerary cells. Connections with nerve fibres need nct be necessary for these effects of the peripheral field which evidently controls differentiation, proliferation and maintenance of the nerve centres. It must be assumed that 'neurotrophic' agents, required for nerve growth and differentiation, are provided by the peripheral tissues. However, the mechanisms remain unclear. Some clues are provided by the effect of the neurotrophic agent of sarcoma, which selectively stimulates growth and differentiation of sympathetic and sensory neurones (Bueker, 1948; Levi-Montalcini and Hamburger, 1951). Extra-axonal mechanisms are apparently operating to a great extent. Normally a certain regularity and constancy of relative growth rates (*cf.* D'Arcy Thompson, 1942), constituting differential rates of tissues, are maintained probably by genetically fixed patterns, but these can be deranged by factors leading to an unbalance of neurotrophic relations and uncovering remarkable growth potentialities of nerve cells.

The effect of a decrease of the peripheral field on development of nerve centres is even more dramatic. Massive cell degeneration of neuroblasts takes place after limb extirpation (Hamburger and Levi-Montalcini, 1949). It is interesting that reactions were also discovered in cells which have no direct fibre connections with the periphery, indicating that some peripheral influences will act indirectly (see Hamburger, 1954). In other cases, however, a marked effect was shown on differentiation of neurones in the ventral horn mediated axonally and it was concluded that the trophic stimulus from the limb travels to the cord along afferent fibres (Hughes and Tschumé, 1957). The susceptibility of neurones differs but on the whole it can be said, that the metabolic equilibrium of neurotrophic relations during development is a very labile one. It is probable that the constant centrifugal flow of axoplasm along the axon (Weiss and Hiscoe, 1948; and others) has a steep gradient related to tremendous proteosynthesis during early growth and any change of it apparently leads to severe disbalance. Increased susceptibility to humoral factors ('diffusible agents') may also be an important mechanism. Many of these effects will concern neurones which have not yet established functional connections with accordingly less differentiated end organs and it is possible that this factor will also change the 'rebound' on primary neurones and explain the quicker and greater susceptibility of nerve cells to changes of the peripheral field during development.

Denervation changes

In the early stages of development muscle cells differentiate independently of nerves and it seems that in the differentiation of embryonic extrafusal muscle fibres the presence of a nerve supply is not necessary (see Boyd, 1960). The differentiation of myoblasts, development of the myotube stage and myofibrils may occur without the influence of nerve fibres. However, dependence on nerves is very marked in differentiation of the receptor organs (Zelená, 1959). Denervation does not stop early differentiation of the myoblasts but later, of course, leads to denervation atrophy and degeneration and these effects are the more severe, the earlier nerve interruption has been performed (see Zelená, 1962). Differentiation of the end-plate structure is dependent on innervation and differentiation of the subneural apparatus and accumulation of nuclei does not occur until after innervation (Couteaux, 1947) and acetylcholinesterase (AChE) appears at the time of contact with the muscle fibres (Zelená and Szentágothai, 1957). The entire length of the foetal muscle is uniformly sensitive to acetylcholine and only after birth retraction of the AChE-sensitive area takes place (Ginetzinski and Shamarina, 1942; Diamond and Miledi, 1959). The development of the neuromuscular synapse is apparently responsible for the slow retraction of the sensitive area and also for the increasing rate of spontaneous subthreshold depolarizations corresponding progressively to the adult miniature end-plate potentials.

Interruption of neurotrophic relations may affect also morphogenetic processes, differentiation of muscle cells in adult life. Arrest of muscle cells at the myoblastic stage following denervation in regenerating muscle of adult animals has been described (Studitskii and Striganova, 1951) and there is evidence that this trophic effect

References p. 106–112

of nerve on muscle regeneration occurs independently of transmitted nerve impulse activity (Studitskii, 1959). Differentiation of muscle cells in adult animals is considerably retarded in regenerating autotransplanted muscle if the latter is deprived of innervation (see Studitskii, 1959; Zhenevskaya, 1963) and only the motor component of innervation was shown to be responsible (Zhenevskaya, 1963). However, there are also some negative findings on the effect of innervation on muscle regeneration (Saunders and Sissons, 1953). Interesting findings on the effect of innervation on morphogenetic processes in peripheral tissues concern the regeneration of salamander limbs, which do not regenerate in the absence of nerve supply (see Singer, 1956). Analysis of this phenomenon has provided important data on the dependence of growth on nerves in morphogenesis. Apparently we have to deal with a 'trophic' action, not dependent on nerve impulse transmission, since sensory nerve supply disconnected from the central nervous system can by itself evoke growth (Singer, 1943) and it appears that acetylcholine is not the transmitter responsible for this growth action (see Singer, 1956). The quantity of nerve fibres was the most important factor and could induce regenerative growth also in frogs (Singer, 1954). Thus nerves do not seem to be necessary for early cell differentiation, but are needed for the regeneration of differentiated tissues and their absence during morphogenesis leads to severe and fast proceeding atrophy and degeneration at later stages of development. Moreover, there is evidence that many of these morphogenetic actions are transmitted by non-impulse mechanisms of the nerves.

Hormonal effects

In adult life many metabolic changes in neurones and peripheral tissues are described which are produced by alteration of reactivity to mediators and hormonal agents. These changes were summed up by Cannon (1939b) in the Law of Denervation and concern especially the 'supersensitivity of denervated structures' (Cannon and Rosenblueth, 1949) to acetylcholine. The change of sensitivity to acetylcholine during development depending on innervation suggests an interaction between neural and humoral factors. Little is known about these interactions concerning other humoral and hormonal effects during morphogenesis. However, the importance of hormonal effects is shown very clearly during development in the mechanisms of hormonal control of insect metamorphosis.

Neurotrophic relations are regulated at least partly by hormonal effects in these morphogenetic mechanisms. The neurosecretory cells of the brain stimulate the prothoracic gland which produces ecdyson which in turn is released into the haemolymph and induces the development of the imago (Karlson, 1963). Secretion of neurosecretory cells activates another hormone, the juvenile hormone of the corpora alata. It is released into the haemolymphe and is indispensable for larval development. Both 'long distant mechanisms' controlling metamorphoses represent hormonal neurotrophic relations partly transmitted by axons. It is interesting to quote here the effect of the moulting hormone, activated by neurosecretory cells of the brain, which provokes rapid synthesis of nucleic acids and proteins in the course of a few hours and which may induce development of cross-striated muscle fibres in the ventral abdominal muscle (Wigglesworth, 1957). It remains to be seen whether this neuro-secretory activity is not perhaps a universal mechanism by means of which a 'trophic activity' of the neuron is effected. The axonal transport mechanism realized and connected with neurosecretion brings to mind the growth phenomena observed in the peripheral nerve and, of course, the general problem of neurosecretory activity of neurones. The secretory activity of these cells and the conveyance of its effects through 'long distance humoral chains' was demonstrated in the hypothalamic nuclei (Scharrer and Scharrer, 1954). The neurosecretory material, produced in these cells, is transported along the axons to the posterior lobe of the pituitary and from there released into the blood and acting at distant target organs. It is possible that also in motoneurones comparable neurosecretory mechanisms are operating (Ortmann, 1960). Although the capacity of these neurones both to conduct impulses and to carry on neurosecretion is still poorly understood (Ortmann, 1960), the existence of neurosecretory activities consisting in the elaboration of a distinct chemical substance acting as a mediator between the nervous and endocrine systems has been proved unequivocally. Nervous impulses are transformed into hormonal activity and a concept that these cells unite two main integrating systems — nervous and endocrine — has thus been elaborated (Scharrer and Scharrer, 1954). A primary neurosecretory activity of nerve cells can be imagined and later development leads apparently to differentiation of neural and hormonal mechanisms. Anyhow, the findings indicate that in neurotrophic relations hormonal long-distance effects, partly transmitted by axons can not be excluded.

We may conclude, that the double dependence between the neurone and peripheral tissues during development is a very marked one, the dramatic degenerative changes in neuroblasts following the loss of the peripheral field being of special importance. In many of these interactions neurotrophic, non-impulse mechanisms are participating; however, the differentiation of nervous and humoral mechanisms remains a difficult task of these studies.

III. CHANGES OF NEUROTROPHIC RELATIONS DURING THE REGENERATION PROCESS

The neurotrophic relations between nerve and muscle cells established during develop-ment persist throughout life but undergo changes during postnatal ontogeny. The interdependence of neurone and periphery, safeguarded by the trophic functions of the neurone shown in neurogenesis is also convincingly demonstrated during the regeneration process. However, this relation is in some aspects different from that operating during neurogenesis. This is to be expected as in postnatal regeneration following nerve section, we have to deal not with a primary establishment of inter-cellular relations but with an adaptive homeostatic reaction of the organism to tissue damage, a process of recovery by which tissues are again included and integrated into normal reflex actions of the organism. The process of outgrowth of axons and their myelinization is of course only a part, though the basic one, of this process. Con-comitant changes occur in all parts of the neuromuscular unit during the regeneration process and therefore the definition of four main changes in neurotrophic relations which will be used in elucidating the process of morphogenesis is a schematic one. However, it has the advantage of enabling an analytic approach to the study of the regeneration process.

Transneural effects

The problem of changes in neurons deprived of synapses terminating on their cell bodies (*i.e.*, of transneural relations) is essentially a problem of regeneration of central nerve fibres and is out of the scope of the present paper. Very little information seems to be available on transneural effects during the regeneration process of peripheral nerves in adult life. A suggestion of their existence, however, is given by the observation that after section of the truncus sympathicus no myelinization of the n. caroticus int. (the postganglionic fibre) is found (Szentágothai and Rajkovits, 1955). Otherwise transneural effects are much more pronounced in early development.

Changes in the neurone

The neurone has remarkable potentialities of repeated regeneration (Duncan and Jarvis, 1943; Gutmann, 1948) and discussion of the changes in the neuromuscular unit taking place during repeated regeneration affords a good model convincingly showing the necessity of studying the regeneration process in all parts of the units concerned.

The rate of regeneration as demonstrated by the onset of recovery does not seem to be significantly altered even after eight repeated nerve interruptions and subsequent

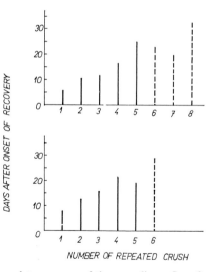

Fig. 8. Time necessary for complete recovery of the spreading reflex after its onset during 8 and 6 recoveries respectively after repeated crushing of the peroneal nerve at increasing distances from m. peroneus longus. Broken lines mean that no full recovery was achieved and indicate time at which the highest degree of spreading was obtained. (From Gutmann, 1948.)

regenerations but the degree of recovery, as demonstrated by the time necessary for adequate functional recovery, is decreasing significantly and no normal function is recovered after such repeated nerve interruptions (Gutmann, 1948). This is due to the fact that changes in neurone and terminal structures (partly irreversible) occur and that no normal neurotrophic relations can be established any longer under such conditions (Figs. 8, 9). Analysis of these deficiencies helps to uncover the basic principles of neurotrophic relations and the limitations of the recovery processes during regeneration.

This is a question of practical importance as knowledge of these limitations should help in the treatment of neuromuscular disorders. The deficiency in recovery of function may be due to changes in the neurone, the nerve fibres or in the terminal organs. An isolated approach will not be helpful. We have to do with a disturbance of neurotrophic relations and on such a basis correct questions, if not answers, should be formulated. After a single crush complete recovery of function occurs relatively early (Gutmann, 1942) and normal muscle fibre size is recovered already after 12 weeks though normal maturation of nerve fibres is achieved much later (Gutmann and Sanders, 1943). After repeated crushing and reinnervation recovery becomes progressively deficient (Fig. 8). This cannot be due to deficiency of the growth process, the rate of functional regeneration being normal even after the eighth interruption of the nerve (Fig. 9).

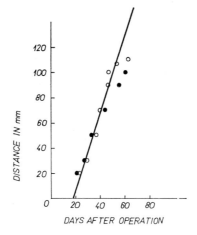

Fig. 9. Recovery times plotted against level of lesions in 69 animals in which the peroneal nerve was interrupted by crushing it at varying distances from m. peroneus longus. Regression line arithmetically calculated. Circles represent successive recoveries in two animals in which the peroneal nerve was crushed 6 times (solid circles) and 8 times (open circles). (From Gutmann, 1948.)

An analysis of the different factors involved led to the conclusion that with a denervation period of 8 months, achieved by repeated crushing of the nerve, the deficiency in formation of new endings is the most important factor. There is an abnormal pattern of innervation. New end plates are formed (Gutmann and Young, 1944) which may be functionally deficient and a deficiency of neurone function not reflected by a change in rate of growth is suggested. With longer periods of dener-

References p. 106–112

vation atrophy, or after delayed suturing of the nerve the degree of muscle atrophy becomes apparently the decisive factor limiting the degree of functional recovery (Gutmann, 1948).

The morphological changes occurring in a nerve cell following section of a nerve have originally been described as 'primäre Reizung' (Nissl, 1892); later, in view of the dispersion of the ribonucleic acids which are the chemical correlates of the Nissl substance, as 'retrograde degeneration' (Marinesco, 1896; Bielschovsky, 1935). The first term is nearer to the truth as there is in fact an increasing proteosynthesis in the nerve cells. There is an increase in volume and in proteins, 'chromatolysis' apparently being due to a change in physical condition of RNA particles (Brattgärd et al., 1958). There is an increase in incorporation of ^{35}S-methionine already 3 days following nerve section (Fig. 6) (Gutmann et al., 1960). Changes in cell volume are connected with changes of concentration of cell constituents and earlier experiments, using staining reactions or ultraviolet microspectography, are, or have to be, reinterpreted (Nicholson, 1924; Gersh and Bodian, 1943; and others). There is thus a high protein production in regenerating neurones (see Hydén, 1943, 1960), which is not surprising if we consider regeneration as an adaptive process during which the neurone has to recover a very long cell projection requiring 1000% more of protein synthesis than the perykaryon does. From this point of view it is understandable that the 'chromatolytic' reaction is the more pronounced the nearer the lesion is to the nerve cell (Geist, 1933; Romanes, 1946). The cell reaction varies with the age of the animal. Nerve section in early stages of postnatal development results in severe degenerative changes (Romanes, 1946), i.e. in cell changes reminding of the reactions during neurogenesis. On the other hand in old age the increase of proteosynthesis after nerve section is missing or delayed (Fig. 10) (Gutmann et al., 1962) and this is related to delayed

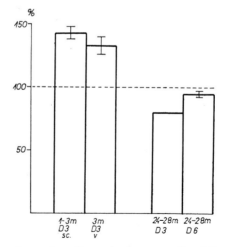

Fig. 10. Percentual changes in number of granules in nerve cells of the spinal cord, as shown by histoautoradiography in 1–3-month-old rats, 3 days after cutting the sciatic nerve (D3, Sc.), 3 days after cutting the ventral roots only (D3, v.), 3 days after cutting the sciatic nerve in old animals (D3, 24–28 m), and 6 days after cutting the sciatic nerve in old animals (D6, 24–28 m.). (From Gutmann et al., 1962.)

outgrowth of the axons (Drahota and Gutmann, 1961). A decline of the trophic function of the nerve cell in old age has therefore been assumed (Drahota and Gut-mann, 1961, 1962). In young animals increased requirements of proteosynthesis due to increased functional activity and growth may be too consuming during the regeneration process and under these conditions a poor maturation of nerve fibres indicating deficiencies of proteosynthesis in the nerve cell could be observed (Fig. 11) (Gutmann and Jakoubek, 1963).

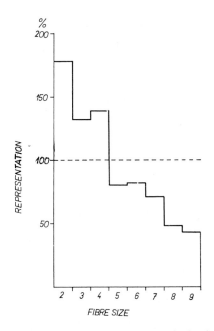

Fig. 11. Diameter of nerve fibres in 30-day-old rats which were submitted to intensive motor activity 35 days after crushing the sciatic nerve, expressed as percentage of the average frequency of diameters of the corresponding size groups (2 μ steps) in the controls. From Gutmann and Jakoubek, 1963.)

The increased proteosynthesis in nerve cells during the normal regeneration process is of course related to the continuous axon growth, implying peripheral transportation of new material in the axon. The observed nucleoprotein gradient from the nucleus outward in the cytoplasm supports the view, that axoplasmic proteins are manu-factured in the nerve cell soma and transported peripherally (Hydén, 1943). Further evidence of this process is provided by many findings (Hydén, 1943; Young, 1946; Gutmann and Sanders, 1943; Weiss and Hiscoe, 1948; Lubińska, 1952, 1956a, b; Ochs and Burger, 1958; Vodička, 1958; and many others).

If connection with the end organ is not reestablished secondary atrophy of the nerve cells will take place. Incorporation of ^{35}S-methionine into the nerve cells is decreased 90 days following nerve section (Gutmann et al., 1960) and during later stages destruction of nerve cells will occur. However, the restitutional capacity of the neurones is remarkable (Duncan and Jarvis, 1943; Bowden and Gutmann, 1944; Gutmann, 1948), the stimulus for the renewed proteosynthesis being the loss of proteins. After nerve section decline of fibre diameter and of conduction velocity takes place (Fig. 12), and this can be avoided to a certain extent if regeneration is induced by crushing the central stump of the sectioned nerve (Gutmann and Holubář, 1948, 1951) (Fig. 13). This reaction may be considered as part of the basic adaptive mechanism of the regeneration process (see Gutmann, 1958). This concept stresses

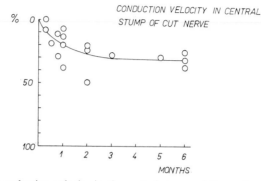

Fig. 12. Changes of conduction velocity in the central stump of the sectioned nerve expressed in per cent of the values of the control nerve (circles: changes in different animals). (From Gutmann and Holubář, 1948.)

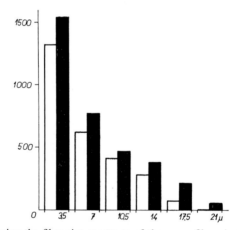

Fig. 13. Histogram showing the fibre size spectrum of the nerve fibres in the central stump of the peroneal nerve 12 months after nerve section (clear), and in the central stump of peroneal nerve which had been cut 12 months previously and which had also been crushed above the point of section (shaded). (From Gutmann and Holubář, 1951.)

the evolutionary basis of the regeneration process, expressed by Darwin, and underlines development of regeneration capacity as a reaction to repeated tissue destruction (see Studitskii and Striganova, 1951).

Many reactions of the nerve cell during the regeneration process are evidently not due to nerve impulse activity. A comparative study of electrophysiological and metabolic changes in neurones following nerve section draws attention to a dissociation of synaptic and trophic function. After section of the postganglionic sympathetic nerve fibres almost complete failure of synaptic transmission through the ganglion takes place (Brown and Pascoe, 1954) and the monosynaptic reflex cannot be elicited for several weeks after section of motor axons (Downman *et al.*, 1953). During this time there is considerably increased proteosynthesis. Whatever the explanation of these remarkable functional changes is, a dissociation between synaptic (essentially membrane) and trophic (essentially intracellular) cell activities can be observed. An increase of proteosynthesis occurs both after combined section of ventral and dorsal root and after section of ventral root only (Fig. 10). Impulse activity through afferent fibres is therefore not necessary for the reaction of increased proteosynthesis.

In these neurotrophic relations we have apparently to deal with nervous regulations not following the classical pattern of reflex actions. The signal ('the trophic impulse') is probably an intracellular one and may proceed antidromically. For instance, the spinal ganglion cell has no synaptically activated dendrites associated with the cell body (see Bodian, 1962). All these facts will make it necessary to reformulate or extend the classical reflex theory from the point of view of the trophic functions of the nerve cell.

The factors involved in nerve maturation provide important data on the effect of terminal connections on nerve cell and fibre metabolism. Fibres disconnected from the muscle remain smaller in diameter (Weiss *et al.*, 1945; Sanders and Young, 1946; Aitken *et al.*, 1947). It can be assumed that no signals transmitted through afferent nerve fibres are involved. Maturation of the axon reflects the balance between the rate of proteosynthesis in the neurone (partly genetically determined) and the effect on proteosynthesis initiated and signalized by establishment of neuromuscular connection (see Guth, 1956). We do not know what signals are involved in the control of maturation, *i.e.* proteosynthesis of the neurone. Some diffusible agents from terminal organs may also be active since regenerating fibres connected with a denervated muscle show a more complete maturation process than those connected to a normal muscle (Aitken, 1949). The maturation process is a very prolonged one, taking 300 days after crushing (Gutmann and Sanders, 1943), but after nerve section no recovery of normal diameter or conduction velocity is achieved. Evaluation of the factors responsible for these deficiencies will be helpful in the analysis of neurotrophic relations. Fibre size is affected by decreased (for instance in tenotomy) and increased (for instance in nerve fibres to muscles, whose synergists are denervated) activity (Gutmann and Vrbová, 1952; Edds, 1949, 1950a, b). However, neuromuscular inactivity cannot be the only factor inducing changes of proteosynthesis in the neurone since increase as well as decrease of maturation can occur in unconnected nerve fibres.

Important intercellular relations between neurone and Schwann cell are uncovered in the regeneration process. The increased mitotic activity of the Schwann cells after nerve interruption is a very marked phenomenon which has its maximum 15–20 days after section (Talantow, 1940; Abercrombie and Johnson, 1942, 1946). After completion of reinnervation this proliferation of the Schwann cells is again inhibited (Abercrombie *et al.*, 1949). There is also an increased incorporation of ^{14}C-leucin (Takahashi *et al.*, 1961) and of ^{35}S-methionine (Gutmann and Hájek, 1963) into the degenerated nerve. Proteosynthesis increases by 600% and decreases with reinnervation (see Fig. 7) (Gutmann and Hájek, 1963), suggesting that inhibitory mechanisms are mediated by the regenerating neurone and/or its cell process, the axon. The Schwann cell reacts with increased activity to tissue damage just as the neurone itself, but it is included in the process of myelinization during the regeneration process under the control of the axon. These complicated intercellular relations are now becoming clearer. Electron microscopical findings show a very close structural relation between the axon, the myelin sheath and Schwann cells and demonstrate that the myelin sheath is formed by a process of infolding of the Schwann cell surface, initiated at the time when the Schwann cell envelopes the outgrowing axon (see Geren, 1956). Thus previous data on the radial repeating concentric units of the myelin sheath, assumed on the basis of X-ray diffraction (Schmidt *et al.*, 1935), were explained. The infolding of the Schwann cell with the increase of the number of layers during development (Geren and Raskin, 1953) suggests a continuous synthesis of myelin by the Schwann cell, evidently under control of the axon. It remains to be shown how this control is mediated by the nerve cell itself. Schwann cell and myelin sheath are apparently a physiological unit (Kornmüller, 1947), a *physiologische Reaktionseinheit*, and this is reflected by the close correlation of length of segment (Schwann cell distance), conduction velocity and latent period of excitation in nerve fibres (Kornmüller, 1947) and correspondingly of myelin thickness. Increase of proteosynthesis in the Schwann cells is related to increase of proteosynthesis in nerve cells and reflects an 'adaptive recovery reaction' after nerve section. This will not surprise in view of the neural origin of the Schwann cells (Kohn, 1905). As in the neurone, decrease of this activity will occur if no neuromuscular connections are established (Abercrombie and Johnson, 1946).

It has been suggested that three sites of proteosynthesis in the neurone may be distinguished, *i.e.* in the Schwann cell, in the axon and in the neurone itself, the latter being related to the flow of axoplasm from the cell body along the axon (Waelsch and Lajtha, 1961). The data on nerve metabolism suggest that local synthesis of proteins in the Schwann cells under the control of the neurone or its cell process, the axon, may be a very important factor enabling neurotrophic relations.

When comparing the reactions of the neurones during morphogenesis and regeneration it can be said that the very labile and often dramatic degenerative changes in neuroblasts or immature neurones cannot be found in adult regeneration processes. Neurotrophic relations in neurogenesis and regeneration differ also in respect to nerve fibre growth. There is a marked ability to select conforming pathways after transection of mixed nerves to a young differentiating limb (*cf.* Taylor, 1943) and peripheral connections seem to be established only between fibres and end organs that match (*cf.* Weiss, 1950), whereas a lack of selectivity is observed during later regenerative outgrowth. No neurotactic influences can be assumed and the principle of contact guidance (*cf.* Weiss, 1950, 1955) is sufficient to explain growth directions. No evidence of specificity of pathways has been found in regeneration. Sensory nerve fibres will regenerate equally rapidly into former motor pathways as into sensory ones (Gutmann, 1945; Weiss and Edds, 1945). The marked selectivity found in first development may be due to genetically fixed mechanisms operating in the process of induction.

Denervation effects

Denervation entails dramatic changes in the peripheral tissues which may lead to the complete replacement of the muscle by fatty or connective tissue. Before this occurs, regeneration will resume metabolic connections and often completely restore normal structure and metabolism of the peripheral tissues.

Evidence for these long-term regulatory functions of the neurone responsible for these changes is provided especially by comparison of disuse and denervation atrophy. If the disturbance due to denervation has specific characteristics, not reproducible by disuse alone, we must assume a specific 'trophic' influence of the nervous system, lack of this influence leading to specific denervation muscle atrophy. Disuse should imply a complete absence of nerve impulses and junctional transmission. In this sense experiments on denervation atrophy and its differentiation from disuse atrophy are of great theoretical interest. If all consequences of denervation could be reproduced by mere lack of nerve impulses and junctional transmission then it would be unnecessary to postulate an independent 'trophic mechanism of the nervous system' (see Gutmann, 1962b).

Three changes after denervation have been considered specific and not reproducible by disuse alone: (*a*) the increased sensitivity to ACh (Ginetzinsky and Shamarina, 1942; Axelsson and Thesleff, 1959; Miledi, 1960b); (*b*) fibrillation (Langley, 1916; Denny-Brown and Pennybacker, 1938; Tower, 1939); (*c*) electrical excitability changes described repeatedly since Erb (1868). Changes in properties of the muscle fibre membrane are apparently of great importance and may be directly responsible (*e.g.*, Nicholls, 1956; Harris and Nicholls, 1956; Drahota *et al.*, 1957; Drahota and Hudlická, 1960).

The question arises whether these changes represent the primary link in denervation atrophy and many attempts have been made to correlate the changes in membrane characteristics with those of sensitivity to ACh. For instance, amplitude of motor endplate potentials is proportional to the input resistance of the muscle fibre (Katz and Thesleff, 1957) and with respect to the increase of membrane resistance of denervated muscle fibres, it was suggested that mean size of ACh quanta responsible for the motor endplate potentials is smaller at the denervated endplates (see Miledi, 1960b). These correlations are important as they may give a clue to the primary regulatory influence of the nerve fibres transmitting 'trophic' functions. The possibility that the continuous liberation of microquanta of ACh (Fatt and Katz, 1952) represents a primary mechanism in these functions seemed a tempting hypothesis. In this connection an explanation of the mechanism by which the spread of ACh-sensitivity in denervated muscle takes place and of the nervous factor controlling spread of ACh receptors in muscle fibres should be of great importance.

Thesleff (1960), on the basis of experiments with *Botulinum* toxin which suppresses the normal acetylcholine action and leads to spread of sensitivity to ACh, assumed that the regulatory influence restricting the ACh sensitive area to the endplate region is ACh itself. However, retraction of the ACh sensitive area of a denervated muscle occurs before recovery of neuromuscular transmission (Miledi, 1960a). It is therefore improbable that the spontaneous liberation of ACh from motor nerve terminals is the responsible regulatory factor restricting the ACh-sensitive zone to the endplate region. Moreover, ACh continuously applied to denervated isolated muscles does not abolish their supersensitivity (Miledi, 1960b) and we may have to deal with autogenous sensitization in 'isolated' structures deprived of nervous influences. Neither increased sensitivity to ACh (John and Thesleff, 1961) nor fibrillation activity (Tower, 1937; Eccles, 1941) can be reproduced by disuse. Regulation by ACh cannot be the causative factor, as fibrillation activity is not arrested by curare (Rosenblueth and Luco, 1937). During regeneration restoration of endplate structures (Gutmann and Young, 1944), recovery of weight (Gutmann, 1942), changes of electrical time constants both of the strength-duration curve and of accomodation (Desmedt, 1950, 1959), all take place before recovery of neuromuscular transmission. Thus the regulatory influence of the nerve fibre — the 'trophic' influence not connected with transmission of nerve impulse activity — reveals itself gradually and relatively independently of nerveimpulse activity and this applies also to the 'receptor controlling factor' which is not the transmitter substance itself (Miledi, 1960a).

Moreover, there are also 'specific' intracellular changes in a denervated muscle which probably are not connected with changes of the membrane characteristics. At this place we may quote only the considerable increase of deoxyribonucleic acid (DNA) content in denervated muscle (Fig. 14) which can be correlated with loss of neuromuscular transmission (Gutmann and Žák, 1961a). This change cannot be reproduced by continuous novocaine application to the nerve using a drip infusion. A 3-days novocain block also does not reproduce the other changes observed at this time after denervation (Fig. 15).

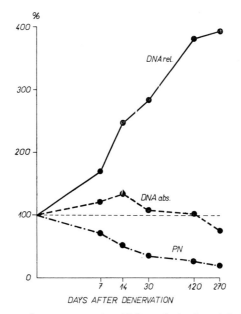

Fig. 14. Percentage of non-collagenous proteins (PN), and absolute (whole muscle) and relative (γ P/mg N) content of deoxyribonucleic acid (DNA) in m. tibialis anterior of rats following denervation. Abscissa, days after denervation. (From Gutmann and Žák, 1961.)

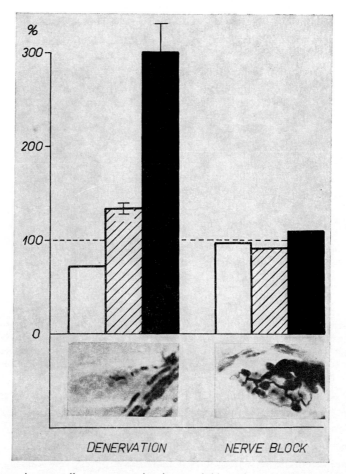

Fig. 15. Changes in non-collagenous protein nitrogen (white columns), relative content of DNA (γ P/mg N; hatched columns) and glycogen content (black columns) in m. extensor digitorum longus of rabbits expressed in percentages of control side, 72 h after nerve section and novocain blockade. (From Gutmann and Žák, 1961.)

It is possible to agree with Tower (1937) who stated that 'both, activity impulse and some other as yet unrecognized trophic agent must operate between nerve and muscle beyond the motor endplate' and that 'inactivation of skeletal muscle reproduces part, but not the whole of the reaction to denervation in muscle'.

Convincing evidence of 'trophic' non-impulse activities is produced by experiments in which the nerve is cut high on one side and low on the other. Degeneration of endplates and decline of muscle glycogen synthesis (Gutmann *et al.*, 1955), fibrillation activity (Luco and Eyzaguirre, 1955) and increase of proteolytic activity (Hájek *et al.*, 1963) appear earlier when the nerve is sectioned nearer to the muscle (Fig. 16). These experiments convincingly show that these long-term 'trophic' influences do exist and affect muscle metabolism independently of transmission of nerve impulses. We can therefore assume an action of substances conveyed intracellularly by the nerve and the sooner exhausted after nerve section the smaller the degenerating nerve stump is.

What is the nature of this long-term control mechanism suggested by denervation effects?

Is the action of a transmitter, *i.e.* is the spontaneous emission of microquanta of ACh (Fatt and Katz, 1952) the decisive mechanism?

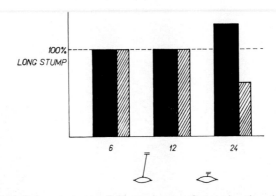

Fig. 16. Proteolytic activity in m. extensor digitorum longus after cutting the sciatic nerve near to the entry into the muscle as compared with proteolytic activity in the contralateral muscle after cutting the nerve high up in the thigh (100%; black columns). Hatched columns: per cent of degenerated endplates in m. tibialis anterior with short nerve stump. (From Hájek *et al.*, 1963).

It could be assumed that the regulating system concerned with the maintenance and recovery of structure and functional capacity will operate especially by controlling the breakdown and synthesis of proteins. Regeneration experiments provide interesting clues for the nature of the nervous control of degradation of muscle proteins. During denervation proteolytic activity in muscle increases progressively. During the process of reinnervation normal proteolytic activity is recovered (see Fig. 4). Increase of proteolytic activity in the denervated muscle starts with interruption of the metabolic connection between nerve and muscle cell and this is heralded by the first signs of degeneration of endplates. The longer the peripheral stump of the sectioned nerve, the later the break up of this connection and the rise of proteolytic activity. Chemical systems maintaining the structure and inhibiting degradation of proteins are, as shown before, exhausted earlier in a muscle with a short nerve stump. These data suggest the existence of an inhibitory system in the nerve and it remains to be seen what relations this system has to the inhibiting influence of the motor nerve controlling spread of receptors beyond the synaptic region (see Miledi, 1960a).

The metabolism of a denervated muscle exhibits the characteristics of an uninhibited system, due to loss of regulations mediated by the nerve. This is suggested by the 'uninhibited' increase of DNA, increase of degradation of proteins, a breakdown of the control of chemical sensitivity to ACh and a tendency to spontaneous activity resulting in fibrillation activity. There is also increased blood flow, oxygen and glucose consumption, glucose being utilized by wrong metabolic pathways for lipid synthesis (Bass and Hudlická, 1960). There is increased incorporation of ^{32}P into phosphorus esters, especially the phosphates of ATP and ADP, suggesting a disturbance of oxidative phosphorylation (Bass and Vítek, 1963). All this becomes regulated during development and regeneration.

We may point out in this connection that the reactivity of denervated muscle has often been compared with that of muscle at early stages of ontogenetic development or with muscle reactivity at lower evolutionary levels. Dedifferentiation or return of the denervated muscle to an embryonic state has been assumed (Orbeli, 1945). Thus embryonic muscle tissue exhibits spontaneous activity which disappears when nerve fibres reach the muscle and spontaneous bursts of action potentials and hypersensitivity to ACh are exhibited by foetal muscle before innervation (Diamond and Miledi, 1959). Contraction times of muscles shorten during ontogenetic development (Koshtoyantz and Ryabinowskaya, 1935) and the slow, spontaneous, rhythmic contractions of the flight muscles of insects disappear gradually during development (Voskresenskaya, 1959).

Studies of denervation effects prove the existence of 'trophic' non-impulse activity of the nerve cell regulating metabolism of peripheral tissues. It is improbable that the chemical system operating these functions, would act only by inhibitory mechanisms. However, the problem of the nature of the regulatory system cannot be solved by denervation studies alone.

Hormonal effects

A cursory remark should be made about the hormonal effects on the regeneration process. Mostly negative evidence is reported of the effect of hormones on the rate of regeneration (see Guth, 1956). However, there is a marked change in chemical sensitivity of denervated muscle and apparently of 'decentralized' neurones, which returns to normal during the regeneration process. Although the increased sensitivity of denervated structures has been demonstrated especially clearly in relation to ACh and adrenalin in organs which are under sympathetic control the reaction is of much wider significance (see Cannon and Rosenblueth, 1949). The increase in sensitivity to acetylcholine observed in cells in the denervated superior cervical ganglion (Cannon and Rosenblueth, 1936) may serve as an example of these changes in reactivity. There is marked alteration in reactivity of denervated muscle, both to transmitters (ACh) and humoral agents (see Gutmann, 1959), this being a general phenomenon formulated as the 'Law of Denervation' by Cannon and Rosenblueth (1949).

Humoral and motoneurone influences on muscle metabolism are apparently coordinated in normal circumstances, disturbed during denervation and recovered on reinnervation. However, the basic trophic function is operated by the motoneurone. The hormonal effects are of secondary nature and are probably inhibited by the motoneurone.

IV. THE NATURE OF THE TROPHIC FUNCTION OF THE NERVE CELL

The study of neurotrophic relations will, of course, remain unsatisfactory until direct analysis of the chemical systems involved will be possible. A direct search for the chemical systems by means of which trophic functions operate is necessary and will also be decisive for the study of the specificity of neural metabolism and of the nervous mechanisms controlling metabolism of peripheral tissues. Denervation studies

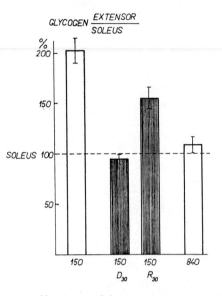

Fig. 17. Glycogen content (expressed in per cent of glycogen content of m. soleus in normal 150-day-old animals), of denervated (D_{30}, 30 days of denervation) and reinnervated m. extensor digitorum longus (R_{30}, 30 days after crushing the sciatic nerve) and of normal muscles of 840-day-old rats. (From Drahota and Gutmann, 1963.)

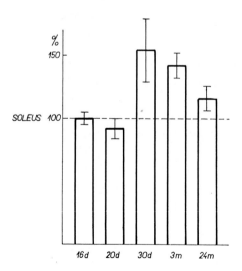

Fig. 18. Proteolytic activity in m. extensor digitorum longus expressed in per cent of proteolytic activity in m. soleus in rats, 16, 20, 30 days, 3 and 24 months old (From Hájek *et al.*, 1963.)

suggest the existence of inhibitory systems, but is is improbable that regulations mediating trophic functions would act only by such mechanisms.

Regeneration studies will again prove helpful. The reinnervated muscle shows a marked accentuation of synthetic processes, demonstrated by increase in glycogen synthesis above initial levels (Beránek *et al.*, 1954), increased uptake of potassium (Drahota *et al.*, 1957) and increase in RNA concentration (Drahota and Gutmann, 1961). This can also be observed in the muscle following its stimulation but overshoot reactions found in normal muscles are missing in the denervated muscle.

An interesting example is offered by the changes taking place in protein and nucleic acid metabolism in the denervated muscle. After muscle stimulation RNA and protein content decrease and resynthesis of RNA but not of protein takes place in the recovery phase (Gutmann and Žák, 1961b). This was interpreted as a lack of precursors of nucleic acid metabolism normally supplied by the nerve. Such findings are, of course, only unsatisfactory steps in the chemical definition of physiological regulations. At this juncture, combination of regeneration and induction studies is to be expected.

During neurogenesis and regeneration neurones establish a marked specificity in metabolism which is apparently conveyed to the innervated muscles.

Studies of comparative muscle physiology show a high degree of specificity of metabolism in different muscles according to their functional adaptation, especially in the metabolic differences between red and white muscles (see Needham, 1926; Yakovlev and Yakovleva, 1953; and others). These metabolic differences are linked to differences in contraction time and develop progressively under the influence of the nervous system. All muscles are slow at birth and differentiate into fast and slow types during the first weeks of postnatal life (Koshtoyants and Ryabinowskaya, 1935; Buller *et al.*, 1960a). Moreover, a slow muscle can be transformed into a fast muscle if the nerve fibre from a phasic motoneurone has been made to innervate a slow muscle (Buller *et al.*, 1960b). The study of the corresponding metabolic differentiation of muscle, its loss and recovery during the regeneration process contributes to the elucidation of the nature of the neural mechanisms influencing the metabolism of muscle. Phasic, 'quick' muscles, *e.g.* m. extensor digitorum longus (adapted to anaerobic metabolism) contain more potassium (Drahota, 1960), more glycogen (Fig. 17) (Drahota and Gutmann, 1963), and have higher proteolytic activity (Fig. 18) (Hájek *et al.*, 1963) than 'slow', tonic muscles *e.g.* the soleus muscle. However, the latter muscle has a higher concentration of ribonucleic acids (RNA/N) and deoxyribonucleic acids (DNA/N) (Fig. 19) (Gutmann and Krejči, 1963). These differences develop progressively during postnatal development (Fig. 20), are lost with denervation and recovered during reinnervation (Fig. 17), the neurone again resuming its modulating influence on muscle metabolism (Drahota and Gutmann, 1963). The differences disappear in old age (Figs. 17, 18), suggesting a decline of the trophic function of the nerve cell in old age. Similarly as in the experiments of Buller *et al.* (1960b) who showed that a slow muscle can be transformed into a fast muscle by cross-union, the soleus muscle gained the metabolic pattern of the extensor digitorum longus muscle when innervated from the motoneurone pool originally innervating the latter (Fig. 21).

References p. 106–112

The mechanism proper leading to this change in metabolic pattern has still to be elucidated. In the studies concerning transformation of muscle speed the differentiation process also proceeded in muscles reinnervated from an isolated spinal segment (Buller *et al.*, 1960a, b) and it was concluded that specific nerve influences, independent of impulse activity were effected by the nerve cell and determined the speed of contraction (Buller *et al.*, 1960a, b). So far we have not been able to reproduce conclusively corresponding metabolic differentiation in muscles reinnervated from a

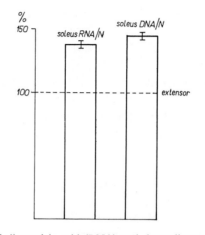

Fig. 19. Concentrations of ribonucleic acid (RNA) and deoxyribonucleic acid (DNA) referred to nitrogen content (γ P-RNA/mg N and γ P DNA/mg N) of m.soleus of rats expressed as percentages of these concentrations in m. extensor digitorum longus. (From Gutmann and Krejčí, 1963.)

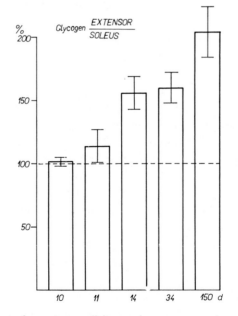

Fig. 20. Glycogen content of m. extensor digitorum longus expressed as percentage of glycogen content of m. soleus of rats, 10, 11, 14, 34 and 150 days after birth. (From Drahota and Gutmann, 1963.)

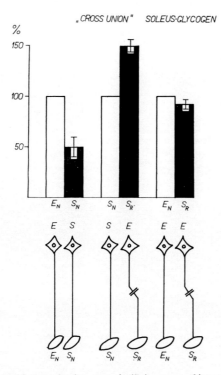

Fig. 21. Glycogen content: (a) of normal soleus muscle (S_N) expressed in per cent of glycogen content of normal extensor muscle (E_N); (b) of cross-reinnervated soleus muscle (S_R) expressed in per cent of normal soleus muscle (S_N); (c) of cross-reinnervated soleus muscle (S_R) expressed in per cent of normal extensor muscle (E_N). The diagram shows the experimental situation produced by the reinnervation from foreign nerve sources, *i.e.* by peroneal nerve supply (E) to soleus muscle (S_R). (From Drahota and Gutmann, 1963.)

'quiescent' spinal cord. However, the specificity of the neuromuscular connections recovered in the regeneration process is very high indeed. A specific pattern of innervation reveals itself also in cross-reinnervation of a muscle by sensory nerve fibres. The nerve fibres form a plexus characteristic for the pattern of skin innervation (Fig. 22), do not connect with endplates and are, of course, not able to restore normal metabolic conditions (Gutmann, 1945). On the other hand, motor nerve fibres are able to restore the structure of muscle fibres which had undergone extreme atrophy, the muscle fibres often consisting of thin strands of sarcoplasm with long rows of nuclei (Figs. 23, 24) (Gutmann and Young, 1944; Gutmann, 1945). A high degree of recovery of muscle fibre size can also be observed in muscle fibres innervated from a foreign motor nerve source, *e.g.* in experiments in which crossing of the peroneal and tibial nerves was performed, although function was practically missing. In such cross-union experiments limitations of central adaptation capacity are very marked (Sperry, 1941). A high degree of specificity of the neurones concerned is revealed in these experiments and it is also shown that the neurones are able to maintain or recover a relatively good trophic state of the muscle fibres.

Here we are not primarily concerned with the functional recovery after heterogenous

References p. 106–112

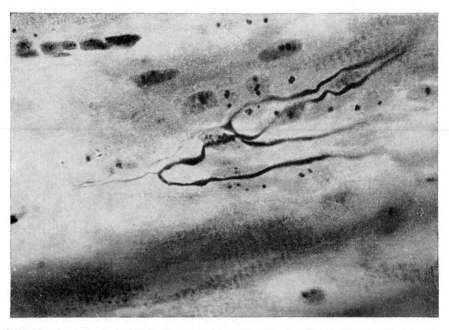

Fig. 22. Plexiform terminal endings of sensory nerve fibres innervating m. peroneus longus. (From Gutmann, 1945.)

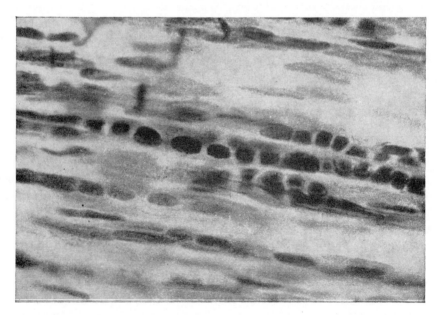

Fig. 23. Atrophic muscle fibres after 20 months of denervation and 6 months of reinnervation achieved by cross-union of the sural with the tibial nerve. (From Gutmann, 1945.)

regeneration (*i.e.* reinnervation of end-organs by nerves not originally meant for their innervation), which is apparently only very little affected by primary motor or sensory

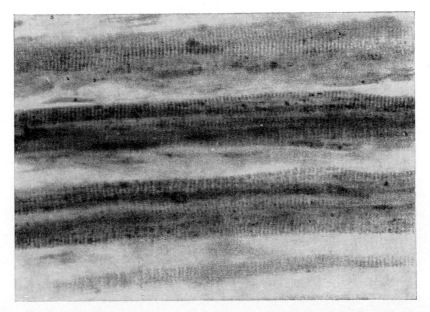

Fig. 24. Muscle fibres reinnervated by a cross-union of n. fibularis with n. tibialis, 6 months after nerve suture performed after a period of 20 months of denervation. (From Gutmann, 1945.)

nuclei and involves predominantly the action of higher levels of nervous integration (Sperry, 1945), but with neurotrophic mechanisms whose importance is very much underestimated if defined as 'various growth regulating and other local physiological and biochemical phenomena' (Sperry, 1945). It may be that we are dealing here also with another example of dissociation between synaptic and trophic function of the nerve cell. Experiments on heterogenous reinnervation raise the question of both the plastic properties of individual synapses and of patterns of synaptic activation (a problem we are not primarily concerned with here) and that of 'trophic' plasticity, *i.e.* changes concerning the maintenance and recovery of tissues by means of non-impulse activities.

A 'dissociation' between functional and 'trophic' readaptation is, however, not surprising. Functional readaptation or plasticity would imply a change in synaptic connections on the neurone and concerns therefore especially the effect of cellulipetal signalization and the pattern of activation of motoneurones. There is a marked specificity of synaptic connections, *e.g.* plastic changes in the organisation of mono-synaptic reflexes ensuing after cross-uniting motoneurones and muscle afferents are very small indeed (Eccles, 1963). There is thus little evidence for the process of 'myotypic' specification, a 'modulating influence' from muscle to nerve as postulated by Weiss (1924, 1955), at least in mammals. Functional readaptation seems to be affected at supraspinal levels.

Plasticity of neurotrophic mechanisms is, however, very great. Regeneration demonstrates these mechanisms which are apparently mediated by a continuous growth process or proximo-distal transport of axonal material towards the muscle (*cf.* Weiss, 1955). The normal uninterrupted axon, however, also displays this growth process.

References p. 106–112

Section of one cutaneous nerve results in 'local extension' of nerve fibres of the adjacent normal nerves into the denervated areas of the skin (Weddell *et al.*, 1941). This growth process is evidently an expression of changes in neurotrophic relationship between neighbouring neurones. Growth cones of the axons (see Fig. 25) are an expression of the continuous regeneration which reflects changes in proteosynthesis

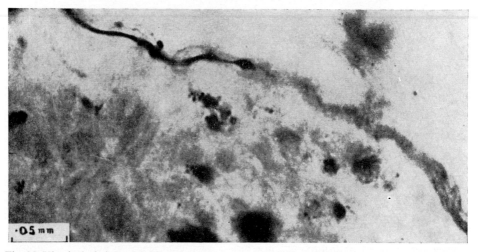

Fig. 25. Histological picture of skin 3 weeks after section of the sural nerve in the rabbit. The growth cone of the neighbouring axon points in the direction of the denervated area in the intermediary zone. The axon can be seen penetrating towards the Schwann cell sheath. (From Weddell *et al.*, 1941.)

of the neurone. This 'long-term' nervous mechanism seems to be analogous, but not identical with the process of reflex coordination taking place in 'phasic' reciprocal innervation.

The process of 'collateral regeneration' was determined with greater detail in muscle by Van Harreveld (1945), Hoffman (1950) and Edds (1950a). In the search for the stimulus of this collateral branching, chemical agents, possibly released from degenerating nerves, were thought to be responsible. Such suggestions comply with the concept of neurobiotaxis which has, however, remained an unsatisfactory approach to the problem of neurotrophic relations, both in mechanisms of nerve-to-nerve and nerve-to-end-organs connections. No evidence for specific 'attraction' forces postulated by Cajal (1929) has been put forward (see Weiss, 1950).

Thus neurones retain their growth potency throughout life, but are adjusted in response to central and peripheral changes. Lack of adequate peripheral connections will reduce proteosynthesis in the neurone and change of neurotrophic balance between two neurones will induce increased proteosynthesis as can be demonstrated in collateral regeneration. Regenerating neurones, not able to reinnervate old endplates, due to long-lasting atrophy, will grow along the atrophic muscle fibres and form new endplates (Gutmann and Young, 1944). Changing demands on proteosynthesis will thus be reflected in changes in growth as a basic mechanism in neurotrophic relations between neurone and terminal organ. The physiological implications of such a concept may be especially important in respect to mechanisms of learning (see Weiss, 1950).

Thus we arrive at a concept which recognizes a relatively independent trophic control function of the perikaryon of the neurone related to continuous metabolic maintenance and recovery of the neurone itself and of the innervated structure. This maintenance and recovery process can be visualized in growth or proximo-distal transport which sustains metabolic connection between neurone and terminal organ. This function is best demonstrated in neurosecretory mechanisms, in the transport of neurosecretory material which is stored in the glandular system. Definition of the chemical compounds transported and their action on peripheral organs has been succesful in some cases. Assumption that such mechanisms are basic for neurotrophic relations (and suggestion of neurosecretion is given also in motor nerve cells; *cf.* Ortmann, 1960) will, however, not substitute the chemical definition of the systems involved. We are still confronted with the question of the nature of the chemical systems signalizing and mediating the metabolic 'long-term' connections. Description of 'traffic routes' will not solve a problem of metabolic relationships. Similarly as in neurogenic induction the question of what chemical substances are transmitted and how they are acting will have to be answered. In some neurosecretory mechanisms, especially concerning the antidiuretic hormone, such questions are being solved successfully and detailed chemical analysis of the substances and feedback ('rebound') effects is proceeding. In neuromuscular relations comparable studies are concerned only with the ACh-AChesterase mechanism which is involved in the synaptic functions and which, as we have seen, can not explain all basic neurotrophic relations.

We may conclude, that there is conclusive evidence now for a trophic function of the nerve cell and for the importance of neurotrophic (non-impulse) relations exemplified in the regeneration process. The following main problems, however, have still to be solved: (*a*) a more exact definition of the trophic function of the nerve cell; (*b*) differentiation of synaptic and trophic functions of the neurone; (*c*) definition of the chemical systems effecting neurotrophic relations; (*d*) analysis of the physiological regulation of neurotrophic relations.

SUMMARY

A survey is given of (a) general aspects of neurotrophic relations, (b) neurotrophic relations during morphogenesis and regeneration, and (c) the nature of the trophic function of the nerve cell. Neurotrophic relations in the neuromuscular system are discussed as intercellular homeostatic functions realized by long-term mechanisms not directly connected with nerve impulse activity, which maintain and recover structure and functional capacity of cells. The dependence of the neurone on changes in terminal organs and that of the terminal organs on changes in the neurone are demonstrated and compared in the processes of neurogenesis and regeneration. Different changes are demonstrated: (a) in neurones following loss of synapses terminating on their cell bodies (transneuronal effects); (b) in neurones after loss of their terminal connections with non-nervous tissue ('retrograde degeneration'); (c) in non-nervous tissue deprived of innervation (denervation effects); (d) in neurone and non-nervous tissue due to alteration of reactivity to transmitters and hormonal agents.

The changes in the control of breakdown and synthesis of proteins in the neuro-muscular unit are especially stressed and examples of the changing pattern of metabolism of proteins and nucleic acids following interruption and resumption of neurotrophic relations are given. Denervation and reinnervation studies are then used to demonstrate the existence of a relatively independent trophic function of the nerve cell and to differentiate changes in denervated muscle caused by disuse from those due to loss of the trophic influence of the nerve cell. Finally an attempt is made to define more exactly the nature of the trophic function of the nerve cell by showing its differentiating effect on metabolism of muscles with different function. Evidence is discussed for the concept of a relatively independent trophic function of the nerve cell regulating long term connections with the muscle cell and questions requiring further research are indicated.

REFERENCES

ABERCROMBIE, M., AND JOHNSON, M. L., (1942); The outwandering of cells in tissue cultures of nerves undergoing Wallerian degeneration. *J. exp. Biol.*, **19**, 266–278.

ABERCROMBIE, M., AND JOHNSON, M. L., (1946); Quantitative histology of Wallerian degeneration. I. Nuclear population in rabbit sciatic nerve. *J. Anat. (Lond.)*, **80**, 37–47.

ABERCROMBIE, M., JOHNSON, M. L. AND THOMAS, G. A., (1949); The influence of nerve fibres on Schwann cell migration investigated in tissue culture. *Proc. roy. Soc. B*, **136**, 448–460.

AITKEN, J. T., (1949); The effect of peripheral connexions on the maturation of regenerating nerve fibres. *J. Anat. (Lond.)*, **83**, 32–43.

AITKEN, J. T., SHARMAN, M., AND YOUNG, J. Z., (1947); Maturation of regenerative nerve fibres with various peripheral connexions. *J. Anat. (Lond.)*, **81**, 1–22.

D'ARCY W. THOMPSON, (1942); *On Growth and Form*. Cambridge University Press.

ARIËNS KAPPERS, C. U., (1932); Principles of develoment of the nervous system. *Cytology and Cellular Pathology of the Nervous System*. W. Penfield, Editor. New York, Hoeber (p. 43–90).

AXELSSON, J., AND THESLEFF, S., (1959); A study of supersensitivity in denervated mammalian skeletal muscle. *J. Physiol. (Lond.)*, **147**, 178–193.

BARCROFT, J., (1934); *Features in the Architecture of Physiological Function*. Cambridge University Press.

BARRON, D. H., (1945); The role of the sensory fibres in the differentiation of the spinal cord in sheep. *J. exp. Zool.*, **100**, 431–443.

BASS, A., AND HUDLICKÁ, O., (1960); Utilization of oxygen, glucose, unesterified fatty acids, carbon dioxide and lactic acid in normal and denervated muscle *in situ*. *Physiol. bohemoslov.*, **9**, 401–407.

BASS, A., AND VÍTEK, V., (1963); Metabolism of high energy phosphates in the denervated muscle. *Physiol. bohemoslov.*, in the press.

BERÁNEK, R., GUTMANN, E., AND VRBOVÁ, G., (1954); Changes in the synthesis of glycogen during recovery of function of denervated and tenotomized muscles. *Physiol. bohemoslov.*, **3**, 47–52.

BERNARD, C., (1865); *Introduction à l'Etude de la Médecine Expérimentale*. Paris, Ballière et Fils.

BIELSCHOWSKY, M., (1935); Allgemeine Histologie und Histopathologie des Nervensystems. *Handbuch der Neurologie*. O. Bumke and O. Foerster, Editors. (p. 35–226).

BODIAN, D., (1962); The generalized vertebrate neuron. *Science*, **137**, 323–326.

BOWDEN, R. E. M., AND GUTMANN, E., (1944); Denervation and re-innervation of human voluntary muscle. *Brain*, **67**, 273–313.

BOYD, J. D., (1960); Development of striated muscle. *The Structure and Function of Muscle, Vol. I.* G. H. Bourne, Editor. New York, Academic Press (p. 63–85).

BRATTGÄRD, S. O., EDSTRÖM, J. E., AND HYDÉN, H., (1958); The productive capacity of the neuron in retrograde reaction. *Exp. Cell Res.*, Suppl. 5, 185–200.

BROWN, G. L., AND PASCOE, J. E., (1954); The effect of degenerative section of ganglionic axons on transmission through the ganglion. *J. Physiol. (Lond.)*, **123**, 565–573.

BUEKER, E. D., (1948); Implantation of tumours in the hind limb field of the embryonic chick and the developmental response of the lumbosacral nervous system. *Anat. Rec.*, **102**, 369–390.

BULLER, A. J., ECCLES, J. C., AND ECCLES, R. M., (1960a); Differentiation of fast and slow muscles in the cat hind limb. *J. Physiol. (Lond.)*, **150**, 339–416.

BULLER, A. J., ECCLES, J. C., AND ECCLES, R. M., (1960b); Interactions between motoneurons and muscles in respect of the characteristic speeds of their responses. *J. Physiol. (Lond.)*, **140**, 417–434.

CAJAL, S. R., (1929); *Studies in Vertebrate Neurogenesis.* L. Guth, Translator. Springfield, Ill., Thomas (1960).

CAJAL, S. R., (1935); Die Neuronenlehre. *Handbuch der Neurologie.* O. Bumke and O. Foerster, Editors. Berlin, Springer (p. 887–994).

CANNON, W. B., (1939a); *The Wisdom of the Body.* New York, Norton.

CANNON, W. B., (1939b); A law of denervation. *Amer. J. med. Sci.*, **198**, 737–750.

CANNON, W. B., AND ROSENBLUETH, A., (1936); Sensitization of sympathetic ganglion by preganglionic denervation. *Amer. J. Physiol.*, **116**, 408–413.

CANNON, W. B., AND ROSENBLUETH, A., (1949); The supersensitivity of denervated structures. *A Law of Denervation.* New York, McMillan.

CASTILLO, J., DEL., AND KATZ, B., (1956); Biophysical aspects of neuromuscular transmission. *Progr. Biophys. biophys. Chem.*, **6**, 121–170.

CATER, D. B., HOLMES, B. E., AND MEE, L. K., (1957); The effect of growth hormone upon cell division and nucleic acid synthesis in the regenerating liver of the rat. *J. Biochem.*, **66**, 482–489.

COHEN, S., AND LEVI-MONTALCINI, R., (1956); A nerve growth stimulating factor isolated from snake venom. *Proc. nat. Acad. Sci. (Wash.)*, **42**, 571–574.

COUTEAUX, R., (1947); Contribution à l'étude de la synapse myoneurale. *Rev. canad. Biol.*, **6**, 563–687.

DENNY-BROWN, D., AND PENNYBACKER, J. B., (1938); Fibrillation and fasciculation in voluntary muscle. *Brain*, **61**, 311–334.

DESMEDT, E. J., (1950); Etude expérimentale de la dégénérescence Wallérienne et de la réinnervation du muscle squelettique. *Arch. int. Physiol.*, **58**, 23–68, 125–156.

DESMEDT, E. J., (1959); The physio-pathology of neuromuscular transmission and the trophic influence of motor innervation. *Amer. J. phys. Med.*, **38**, 248–261.

DETWILER, S. R., (1920); On the hyperplasia of nerve centres resulting from excessive peripheral loading. *Proc. nat. Acad. Sci. (Wash.)*, **6**, 96–101.

DIAMOND, J., AND MILEDI, R., (1959); The sensitivity of foetal and new-born rat muscle to acetylcholine. *J. Physiol. (Lond.)*, **149**, 50.

DOWNMAN, C. N. B., ECCLES, J. C., AND McINTYRE, A. K., (1953); Functional changes in chromatolysed motorneurones. *J. comp. Neurol.*, **98**, 9–36.

DRAHOTA, Z., (1960); Changes in the potassium content of various muscles immediately after denervation. *Physiol. bohemoslov.*, **9**, 1–4.

DRAHOTA, Z., AND GUTMANN, E., (1961); The influence of age on the course of reinnervation of muscle. *Gerontologia (Basel)*, **5**, 88–109.

DRAHOTA, Z., AND GUTMANN, E., (1962); The effect of age on compensatory and 'postfunctional hypertrophy' in cross-striated musle. *Gerontologia (Basel)*, **6**, 81–90.

DRAHOTA, Z., AND GUTMANN, E., (1963); Long-term regulatory influence of the nervous system on some metabolic differences in muscles of different function. *Physiol. bohemoslov.*, **12**, 339–348.

DRAHOTA, Z., GUTMANN, E., AND VRBOVÁ, G., (1957); Changes in potassium in normal, denervated and reinnervated muscle. *Physiol. bohemoslov.*, **6**, 77–84.

DRAHOTA, Z., AND HUDLICKÁ, O., (1960); The effect of denervation on ^{42}Potassium uptake by the rat muscle *in vitro*. *Nature (Lond.)*, **186**, 396–397.

DUNCAN, D., AND JARVIS, W. H., (1943); Observation on repeated regeneration of the facial nerve in cats. *J. comp. Neurol.*, **79**, 315–327.

EAGLE, H., (1958); The growth requirements and metabolic activities of human and animal cell in cultures. *Biochemistry of Morphogenesis.* IV. International Congress of Biochemistry. New York, London, Pergamon Press (p. 1–19).

ECCLES, J. C., (1941); Disuse atrophy of skeletal muscle. *Med. J. Aust.*, **2**, 160–164.

ECCLES, J. C., (1957); *The Physiology of the Nerve Cell.* Baltimore, Johns Hopkins Press.

ECCLES, J. C., (1958); Problems of plasticity and organization at simplest levels of mammalian nervous system. *Persp. Biol. Med.*, **1**, 379–396.

ECCLES, J. C., (1961a); The mechanism of synaptic transmission. *Ergebn. Physiol.*, **51**, 299–430.

ECCLES, J. C., (1961b); The effects of use and disuse on synaptic function. *Brain Mechanisms and Learning.* J. F. Delafresnaye, Editor. Oxford, Blackwell (p. 335–348).

Eccles, J. C., (1963); Specificity of neural influence on speed of muscle contraction. *Effect of Use and Disuse on Neuromuscular Functions*. E. Gutmann and P. Hník, Editors, Prague, Publ. House Czechosl. Ac. Sci. (p. 111–128).

Eccles, J. C., (1963); Specificity of monosynaptic innervation of motoneurones. *The Effect of Use and Disue on Neuromuscular Functions*. E. Gutmann and P. Hník, Editors. Prague, Publ. House Czechosl. Ac. Sci. (p. 229–246).

Edds, M. V., Jr., (1949); Experiments on partially deneurotized nerves. II. Hypertrophy of residual fibres. *J. exp. Zool.*, **112**, 29–47.

Edds, M. V., Jr., (1950a); Collateral regeneration of residual motor axons in partially denervated muscles. *J. exp. Zool.*, **113**, 517–552.

Edds, M. V., Jr., (1950b); Hypertrophy of nerve fibres to functionally overloaded muscles. *J. comp. Neurol.*, **93**, 259–275.

Edds, M. V., Jr., (1959); Embryonic systems for the study of biochemistry of morphogenesis. *Biochemistry of Morphogenesis*. W. J. Nickerson, Editor. New York, London, Pergamon Press (p. 210–220).

Elliason, N. A., Hammarsten, E., Reichard, P., Aquivist, S., Thorcell, B., and Ehrensvärd, G., (1951); Turnover rates during formation of proteins and polynucleotides in regenerating tissues. *Acta chem. scand.*, **5**, 431–444.

Erb, W., (1868); Zur Casuistik der Nerven- und Muskelkrankheiten. *Dtsch. Arch. klin. Med.*, **4**, 242.

Fatt, P., and Katz, B., (1952); Spontaneous subthreshold activity at motor nerve endings. *J. Physiol. (Lond.)*, **117**, 109–128.

Flexner, L. B., (1950); The cytological, biochemical and physiological differentiation of the neuroblast. *Genetic Neurology*. E. Weiss, Editor. Chicago, University of Chicago Press (p. 194–198).

Gale, E. F., (1959); Protein synthesis in subcellular systems. *Biochemistry of Morphogenesis*. W. J. Nickerson, Editor. New York, London, Pergamon Press (p. 156–165).

Geist, F. D., (1933); Chromatolysis of efferent neurons. *Arch. Neurol. Psychiat. (Chic.)*, **21**, 88–103.

Geren, B., (1956); Structural studies of the formation of the myelin sheath in peripheral nerve fibres. *Cellular Mechanisms in Differentiation and Growth*. D. Rudnick, Editor. Princeton, N. J., Princeton University Press (p. 213–220).

Geren, B. B., and Raskin, J., (1953); Development of the fine structure of the myelin sheath in sciatic nerves of chick embryos. *Proc. nat. Acad. Sci. (Wash.)*, **39**, 880–884.

Gersh, I., and Bodian, D., (1943); Some chemical mechanisms in chromatolysis. *J. cell. comp. Physiol.*, **21**, 253–279.

Ginetzinski, A. G., and Shamarina, N. M., (1942); Tonomotor phenomena in the denervated muscle. (In Russian.) *Usp. sovr. Biol.*, **15**, 283–294.

Golikov, N. V., (1950); *Physiological Lability and its Changes in Basic Nerve Processes*. (In Russian.) Leningrad, Lenin State University Publishing House.

Guth, L., (1956); Regeneration in the mammalian peripheral nervous system. *Physiol. Rev.*, **36**, 441–478.

Gutmann, E., (1942); Factors affecting recovery of motor function after nerve lesions. *J. Neurol. Psychiat.*, **5**, 81–95.

Gutmann, E., (1945); The reinnervation of muscle by sensory nerve fibres. *J. Anat. (Lond.)*, **79**, 1–43.

Gutmann, E., (1948); Effect of delay of innervation on recovery of muscle after nerve lesions. *J. Neurophysiol.*, **11**, 279–294.

Gutmann, E., (1958); *Die funktionelle Regeneration der peripheren Nerven*. Akademie Verlag. Berlin,

Gutmann, E., (1959); Metabolic reactions of denervated and reinnervated muscle. *Amer. J. phys. Med.*, **38**, 104–117.

Gutmann, E., (1962a); The trophic function of the nervous system. *Advances in Biological Sciences*. Prague, Publ. House Czechosl. Ac. Sci. (p. 215–233).

Gutmann, E., (1962b); Denervation and disuse atrophy in cross-striated muscle. *Rev. canad. Biol.*, **21**, 353–315.

Gutmann, E., and Hájek, I., (1963); unpublished observations.

Gutmann, E., and Holubář, J., (1948); Changes in central stump of the interrupted nerve. (In Czech.) *Cas. Lék. čes.*, **87**, 648–659.

Gutmann, E., and Holubář, J., (1951); Atrophy of nerve fibres in the central stump following section and the possibilities of its presentation. *Arch. int. Studi neurol.*, **1**, 1–11.

Gutmann, E., and Jakoubek, B., (1963); Effect of increased motor activity on regeneration of the peripheral nerve in young rats. *Physiol. bohemoslov*, **12**, 463–468.

Gutmann, E., Jakoubek, B., Rohliček, V., and Skaloud, V., (1962); Effect of age on proteosynthesis in spinal motoneurones following nerve interruption as shown by histoautoradiography of ³⁵S labelled methionine. *Physiol. bohemoslov.*, **11**, 437–442.

GUTMANN, E., JAKOUBEK, B., AND ŠKALOUD, J., (1960); The incorporation of methionine ³⁵S into spinal motoneurones during immobilization and denervation of the limb. (In Czech.) *Čsl. Fysiol.*, **9**, 416–417.

GUTMANN, E., AND KREJČÍ, L., (1963); unpublished observations.

GUTMANN, E., AND SANDERS, F. K., (1943); The recovery of fibre size and numbers during nerve regeneration. *J. Physiol. (Lond.)*, **101**, 489–518.

GUTMANN, E., VODIČKA, Z., AND VRBOVÁ, G., (1954); The significance of the nervous system for glycogen supercompensation in skeletal muscle. *Physiol. bohemoslov.*, **3**, 182–188.

GUTMANN, E., VODIČKA, Z., AND ZELENÁ, J., (1955); Changes in cross striated muscle after the nerve interruption depending on the length of the nerve stump. (In Russian.) *Physiol. bohemoslov.*, **4**, 200–204.

GUTMANN, E., AND VRBOVÁ, G., (1952); The physiology of the tenotomized muscle. (In Russian.) *Physiol. bohemoslov.*, **1**, 205–220.

GUTMANN, E., AND YOUNG, J. Z., (1944); The reinnervation of muscle after various periods of atrophy. *J. Anat. (Lond.)*, **78**, 15–43.

GUTMANN, E., AND ŽÁK, R., (1961a); Nervous regulation of nucleic acid level in cross-striated muscle. Changes in denervated muscle. *Physiol. bohemoslov.*, **10**, 493–500.

GUTMANN, E., AND ŽÁK, R., (1961b); Nervous regulation of nucleic acid level in cross-striated muscle. Resynthesis of nucleic acids and proteins in normal and denervated muscle. *Physiol. bohemoslov.*, **10**, 501–509.

HÁJEK, I., GUTMANN, E., AND SYROVÝ, I., (1963); Changes of proteolytic activity in denervated and reinnervated muscle. *Physiol. bohemoslov.*, in the press.

HAMBURGER, V., (1934); The effects of wing bud extirpation on the development of the central nervous system in chick embryos. *J. exp. Zool.*, **68**, 449–494.

HAMBURGER, V., (1954); Trends in neuroembryology. *Biochemistry of the Developing Nervous System.* New York, Academic Press (p. 52–73).

HAMBURGER, V., (1956); Developmental correlations in neurogenesis. *Cellular Mechanisms in Differentiation and Growth.* D. Rudnick, Editor. Princeton, N. J. Princeton University Press (p. 191–212).

HAMBURGER, V., AND LEVI-MONTALCINI, R., (1949); Proliferation, differentiation and degeneration in the spinal ganglia of the chick embryo under normal and experimental conditions. *J. exp. Zool.*, **111**, 457–501.

HARRIS, E. J., AND NICHOLLS, J. G., (1956); The effect of denervation on the rate of entry of potassium into frog muscle. *J. Physiol. (Lond.)*, **131**, 473–476.

HARRISON, R. G., (1929); Correlation in the development and growth of the eye studied by means of heteroplastic transplantation. *Wilhelm Roux' Arch. Entwickl.-Mech. Org.*, **120**, 1–55.

HEILBRUNN, E. T., (1956); *The Dynamics of Living Protoplasma.* New York, Academic Press.

HERRMANN, H., (1959); The embryonic cell as a protein forming system. *Biochemistry of Morphogenesis.* W. J. Nickerson, Editor. New York, London, Pergamon Press (p. 171–185).

HODGKIN, A. L., AND HUXLEY, A. F., (1952); A quantitative description of membrane current and its application to conduction and excitation in nerve. *J. Physiol. (Lond.)*, **117**, 500–544.

HOFFMAN, H., (1950); Local reinnervation in partially denervated muscle; a histophysiological study. *Aust. J. exp. Biol. med. Sci.*, **28**, 383.

HOLTFRETER, J., (1948); Concepts on the mechanism of embryonic induction and its relation to parthenogenesis and malignancy. *Symp. Soc. exp. Biol.*, **2**, 17–49.

HUGHES, A., AND TSCHUMÉ, P. A. (1957); Transmission of trophic stimuli along developing nerve fibres. *Nature (Lond.)*, 999–1000.

HYDÉN, H., (1943); Protein metabolism in the nerve cell during growth and function. *Acta physiol. scand.*, **6**, Suppl. XVII, 1–136.

HYDÉN, H., (1960); The Neuron. *The Cell*, Vol. IV. J. Brachet-Mirski, Editor. New York, Academic Press (p. 215–323).

JOHN, T. R., AND THESLEFF, S., (1961); Effects of motor inactivation on the chemical sensitivity of skeletal muscle. *Acta physiol. scand.*, **51**, 136–141.

KARLSON, P., (1963); Morphogenese und Metamorphose der Insekten. *Induktion und Morphogenese.* Berlin, Springer (p. 101–118).

KATZ, B., (1958); Microphysiology of the neuromuscular junction. A physiological 'quantum of action' at the myoneural junction. *Bull. Johns Hopk. Hosp.*, **102**, 275–295.

KATZ, B., AND THESLEFF, S., (1957); On the factors which determine the amplitude of the 'miniature end plate potential'. *J. Physiol. (Lond.)*, **137**, 267–278.

KOHN, A., (1905); Ueber die Entwicklung des peripheren Nervensystems. *Anat. Anz.*, **27**, 145.

KOLLROS, J. J., AND MCMURRAY, V. M., (1955); The mesencephalic v.nucleus in *Anuräus*. I. Normal development in *Rana pipiens*. *J. comp. Neurol.*, **102**, 47–64.

KORNMÜLLER, A. E., (1947); *Die Elemente der nervösen Tätigkeit*. Stuttgart, Thieme.

KOSHTOYANTZ, C., UND RYABINOVSKAYA, A., (1935); Beitrag zur Physiologie der Skelettmuskeln der Säugetiere in verschiedenen Stadien ihrer individuellen Entwicklung. *Pflüg. Arch. ges. Physiol.*, **235**, 416–421.

KREBS, H. A., (1957); Control of metabolic processes. *Endeavour*, **16**, 125–132.

LANGLEY, J. N., (1916); Observations on denervated muscle. *J. Physiol. (Lond.)*, **50**, 335.

LARSELL, O., (1931); The effect of experimental excision of one eye on the development of the optic lobe and opticus layer in larvae of the tree-toad (*Hyla regilla*). *J. exp. Zool.*, **58**, 1–20.

LEVI-MONTALCINI, R., (1949); The development of acoustico-vestibular centers in the chick embryo in the absence of the afferent root fibres and of descending fibre tracts. *J. comp. Neurol.*, **91**, 209–242.

LEVI-MONTALCINI, R., AND ANGELETTI, P. U., (1960); Biological properties of a nerve growth promoting protein and its antiserum. *IV. International Neurochemical Symposium*, New York, London, Pergamon Press (p. 362–377).

LEVI-MONTALCINI, R., AND HAMBURGER, V., (1951); Selective growth-stimulating effects of mouse sarcoma on the sensory and sympathetic nervous system of the chick embryo. *J. exp. Zool.*, **116**, 321–362.

LØVTRUP, S., (1959); Biochemical indices of embryonic differentiation. *Biochemistry and Morphogenesis*, W. J. Nickerson, Editor. New York, London, Pergamon Press (p. 105–125).

LUBIŃSKA, L., (1952); Elasticity and distensibility of nerve tubes. *Acta Biol. exp. (Łodź)*, **16**, 73–90.

LUBIŃSKA, L., (1956a); Outflow from cut of nerve fibres. *Exp. Cell Res.*, **10**, 40–47.

LUBIŃSKA, L., (1956b); The physical state of axoplasm in teased vertebrate nerve fibres. *Acta Biol. exp. (Łodź)*, **17**, 135–140.

LUCO, J. V., AND EYZAGUIRRE, C., (1955); Fibrillation and hypersensitivity to ACh in denervated muscle. Effect of length of degenerating nerve fibres. *J. Neurophysiol.*, **18**, 65–73.

MARINESCO, G., (1896); Considérations générales sur l'histologie et la biologie de la cellule nerveuse. *Semaine méd. (Paris)*, **50**.

MILEDI, R., (1960a); Properties of regenerating neuromuscular synapses in the frog. *J. Physiol. (Lond.)*, **154**, 190–205.

MILEDI, R., (1960b); The acetylcholine sensitivity of frog muscle fibres after complete or partial denervation. *J. Physiol. (Lond.)*, **151**, 1–23.

NEEDHAM, D. M., (1926); Red and white muscle. *Physiol. Rev.*, **6**, 1.

NICHOLLS, J. G., (1956); The electrical properties of denervated skeletal muscle. *J. Physiol. (Lond.)*, **131**, 1–15.

NICHOLSON, F. M., (1924); Morphological changes in nerve cells following injury to their axons. *Arch. Neurol. Psychiat. (Chic.)*, 680–697.

NISSL, F., (1892); Ueber die Veränderungen der Ganglienzellen am Facialiskern des Kaninchens nach Ausreissung des Nervs. *Allg. Z. Psychiat.*, **48**, 197–198.

NIU, M. C., (1956); New approaches to the problem of embryonic induction. *Cellular Mechanisms in Differentiation and Growth*. D. Rudnick, Editor. Princeton, N. J., Princeton University Press (p. 150–171).

OCHS, S., AND BURGER, E., (1958); Movement of substance proximo-distally in nerve axons as studied with spinal cord injection of radio active phosphorus. *Amer. J. Physiol.*, **194**, 499–507.

ORBELI, L. A., (1945); The evolution of the neuro-muscular system. (In Russian.) *Trudy Inst. Fiziol. (Mosk.)*, **1**, 3–12.

ORTMANN, R., (1960); Neurosecretion. *Handbook of Physiology. Sect. 1, Neurophysiology*, Vol. II. J. Field *et al.*, Editors. Washington, American Physiological Society (1039–1067).

ROMANES, G. J., (1946); Motor localization and the effects of nerve injury on the ventral horn cells of the spinal cord. *J. Anat. (Lond.)*, **80**, 117.

ROSENBLUETH, A., AND LUCO, J. V., (1937); A study of denervated mammalian skeletal muscle. *Amer. J. Physiol.*, **126**, 39–57.

SANDERS, F. K., AND YOUNG, J. Z., (1946); The influence of peripheral connexion on the diameter of regenerating nerve fibres. *J. exp. Biol.*, **22**, 203–212.

SAUNDERS, J. H., AND SISSONS, H. A., (1953); The effect of denervation on the regeneration of skeletal muscle after injury. *J. Bone Surg.*, **35**, 113–130.

SCHARRER, E., AND SCHARRER, B., (1954); Hormones produced by neurosecretory cells. *Recent Progr. Hormone Res.*, **10**, 183–240.

SCHMIDT, F. O., BEAR, R. S., AND CLARK, G. L., (1935); X-ray diffraction studies on nerve. *Radiology*, **25**, 131–142.

SINGER, M., (1943); The nervous system and regeneration of the forelimb of adult *Triturus*. II. The role of the sensory supply. *J. exp. Zool.*, **92**, 453–493.

SINGER, M., (1954); Induction of regeneration of the forelimb of the postmetamorphic frog by augmentation of the nerve supply. *J. exp. Zool.*, **126**, 419–471.

SINGER, M., (1956); The influence of nerves on regeneration. *Regeneration in Vertebrates. Conference Series.* C. S. Thornton, Editor. Chicago, University of Chicago Press (p. 59–80).

SPEMANN, H., (1938); *Embryonic Development and Induction.* Yale University Press. New Haven,

SPERRY, R. W., (1941); The effect of crossing nerves to antagonistic muscles in the hind limb of the rat. *J. comp. Neurol.*, **76**, 283–321.

SPERRY, R. W., (1945); The problem of central nervous reorganization after nerve regeneration and muscle transposition. *Quart. Rev. Biol.*, **20**, 311–369.

STADIE, W. C., (1954); Current concepts of the action of insulin. *Physiol. Rev.*, **34**, 52–100.

STUDITSKII, A. N., (1959); *Experimental Surgery of Muscles*, (In Russian) Moscow, Publ. House Acad. Sci. U.S.S.R.

STUDITSKII, A. N., AND STRIGANOVA, A. R., (1951); *Recovery Processes in Cross-Striated Muscle.* (In Russian) Moscow, Publ. House Acad. Sci. U.S.S.R.

SZENTÁGOTHAI, J., UND RAJKOVITS, K., (1955); Die Rückwirkung der spezifischen Funktion auf die Struktur der Nervenelemente. *Acta morph. Acad. Sci. hung.*, **5**, 253–274.

TAKAHASHI, Y., NOMURA, M., AND FURUSAWA, S., (1961); *In vitro* incorporation of ^{14}C amino-acids into proteins of peripheral nerve during Wallerian degeneration. *J. Neurochem.*, **7**, 97–102.

TALANTOV, (1940); cited by Ostrowerchow, G. E., (1952); *Wiederherstellungsoperationen bei Schädigung der Extremitätennervenstämme.* Moscow, Publ. House of Medical Sciences.

TAYLOR, A. C., (1943); Selectivity of nerve fibres from dorsal and ventral roots in the development of the frog limb. *J. exp. Zool.*, **96**, 159–185.

THESLEFF, S., (1960); Effects of motor innervation on the chemical sensitivity of skeletal muscle. *Physiol. Rev.*, **40**, 734–752.

TOWER, S. S., (1937); Trophic control of non-nervous tissues by the nervous system. *J. comp. Neurol.*, **67**, 241–269.

TOWER, S. S., (1939); Persistence of fibrillation in denervated muscle and its non-occurrence in muscle and its non-occurrence in muscle after tenotomy. *Arch. Neurol. Psychiat. (Chic.)*, **47**, 219.

TWITTY, V. C., (1953); Intercellular relations in the development of amphibian pigmentation. International Symposium on the Cellular Basis of Differentiation. *J. Embr. exp. Morph.*, **1**, 263–268.

TWITTY, V. C., AND NIU, M. C., (1954); The motivation of cell migration, studied by isolation of embryonic pigment cells singly and in small groups *in vitro. J. exp. Zool.*, **125**, 541–573.

TYLER, A., (1955); Ontogeny of immunological properties. *Analysis of Development.* D. H. Willier, P. A. Weiss and V. Hamburger, Editors. Philadelphia, Saunders (p. 556–573).

UFLJAND, J. M., (1950); Repercussion in injuries of peripheral nerves. *Problems of Neuromuscular Physiology.* Leningrad, State Publ. House of Medical Literature (p.1).

VAN HARREVELD, A., (1945); Reinnervation of denervated muscle fibres by adjacent functioning motor units. *Amer. J. Physiol.*, **144**, 477–493.

VODIČKA, Z., (1958); Transport of substances within the nerve. *Symposium on Nervous Regulation of Metabolism and Active Transport of Ions.* Prague, Publ. House Czechosl. Ac. Sci. (p. 125–131).

VOSKRESENSKAYA, A. K., (1959); *Functional Properties of the Neuromuscular Apparatus of Insects.* (In Russian.) Moscow, Publ. House Acad. Sci. U.S.S.R.

WAELSCH, H., AND LAJTHA, A., (1961); Protein metabolism in the nervous system. *Physiol. Rev.*, **41**, 709.

WALLER, A., (1852); Sur la réproduction des nerfs et sur la structure et les fonctions des ganglions spinaux. *Arch. Anat., Physiol. wiss. Med.*, 392–401.

WEDDLL, G., GUTTMANN, L., AND GUTMANN, E., (1941); The extension of nerve fibres into denervated areas of skin. *J. Neurol. Psychiat.*, **4**, 206–225.

WEISS, P., (1924); Die Funktion transplantierter Amphibienextremitäten. Aufstellung einer Resonanztheorie der motorischen Nerventätigkeit auf Grund abgestimmter Endorgane. *Wilhelm Roux' Arch. Entwickl.-Mech. Org.*, **102**, 635–672.

WEISS, P., (1950); An introduction to genetic neurology. *Genetic Neurology.* E. Weiss, Editor. Chicago, University of Chicago Press.

WEISS, P., (1955); Nervous system (Neurogenesis). *Analysis of Development*. D. H. Willier, P. A. Weiss and V. Hamburger, Editors, Philadelphia, Saunders (p. 346–401).

WEISS, P., AND EDDS, M. V., JR., (1945); Sensory-motor nerve crosses in the rat. *J. Neurophysiol.*, **8**, 173–193.

WEISS, P., EDDS, M. V., JR., AND CAVANAUGH, M., (1945); The effect of terminal connexions on the calibre of nerve fibres. *Anat. Rec.*, **92**, 215–233.

WEISS, P., AND HISCOE, H. B., (1948); Experiments on the mechanism of nerve growth. *J. exp. Zool.*, **207**, 315–395.

WIGGELSWORTH, V. B., (1957); The action of growth hormones in insects. *Symp. Soc. exp. Biol.*, **11**, 204–227.

WILDE, C. E., (1956); The *Urodele* neuroepithelium. III. The presentation of phenylalanine to the neural crest by archenteron roof mesoderm. *J. exp. Zool.*, **133**, 409–440.

YAKOVLEV, N. N., AND YAKOVLEVA, E. S., (1953); Biochemical and morphological changes under the influence of systematic functional loading. *Usp. sovr. Biol.*, **35**, 134.

YOUNG, J. Z., (1946); Effect of use and disuse on nerve and muscle. *Lancet*, **2**, 109–112.

ŽÁK, R., AND GUTMANN, E., (1960); Lack of correlation between synthesis of nucleic acids and proteins in denervated muscle. *Nature (Lond.)*, **185**, 766–767.

ZELENÁ, J., (1959); The influence of innervation on the development of the muscle. (In Czech.) Prague, Babák's Series, Vol. 12.

ZELENÁ, J., (1962); The effect of denervation on muscle development. *The Denervated Muscle*. E. Gutmann, Editor. Prague, Czechoslovak Academy of Sciences.

ZELENÁ, J., UND SZENTÁGOTHAI, J., (1957); Verlagerung der Lokalisation spezifischer Cholinesterase während der Entwicklung der Muskelinnervation. *Acta histochem. (Jena)*, **3**, 284–296.

ZHENEVSKAYA, R. P., (1963); Experimental histologic investigation of striated muscle tissue. *Rev. canad. Biol.*, **21**, 457–470.

DISCUSSION

LUBIŃSKA: I would like to ask whether you think that the neurotrophic influence is actually effectuated by specific molecules.

GUTMANN: This is a question which has to be answered by future research. Neurotrophic influences (*i.e.* long term metabolic influences not connected with nerve-impulse activity) could of course be mediated by subthreshold liberation of mediators acting on the cell membranes but embryological studies suggest that even direct interactions may take place. Even large molecular material can be taken up by embryonic cells, specific molecules may be released from inducing cells which effect reacting cell systems — and there are the data on incorporation of immunologically detectable proteins into embryonic cells. (For lit. see *e.g.* Herrmann, 1959).

Studies on embryonic induction show actions of specific molecules and I think they suggest the possibility of corresponding mechanisms in intercellular relations also in adult life.

SINGER: Do I understand you correctly that you assume that there are substances which come out of the nerve fiber and these have the trophic quality and impress themselves on peripheral tissues, and that these same substances are responsible for the maintenance of the fiber itself?

GUTMANN: The nerve cell maintains structure and metabolism of its cell process *i.e.* the axon, and it influences also maintenance of innervated tissue. Both 'trophic' or 'maintenance' processes must be dependent on substances produced by the nerve cell but I suppose it is not yet possible to answer definitely the question whether we have to deal with exactly the same substances or chemical systems in both processes.

GLEES: You see the same neurotrophic influences in the interdependence between retina and lateral geniculate body. When you cut the optic nerve the lateral geniculate body atrophies in a very short time from the 3rd day onwards. The cells are reduced in number and the nuclear–cytoplasm relationship shows rapid alterations. We might assume that there is only 1 type of synapse, the so-called retinal synapse of the retinal geniculate body. There is some evidence of other synapses too, but these are not sufficient to keep up the integrity of the postsynaptic neuron. So here too one might presume a more general influence besides impulse transmission. Do you like to comment about this?

GUTMANN: May I say that I agree with your suggestion. Intercellular relations between nerve and muscle cell are realized not only by impulse transmission, and the same, I think, must apply also for interneuronal relationships. We need more data on these mechanisms and your data are very interesting from this point of view. In nerve–muscle relationships the study is easier, the innervation being mostly not a multiple one.

SINGER: Would you say Dr. Glees, in those circumstances where the major part of the innervation of a central nucleus is from one source, there you do get transneuronal degeneration? It is known also for certain nuclei within the thalamus, whereas I suppose the posterior horn cell does not show this because its innervation is multiple.

ECCLES: The manner in which the cross-union of nerves to soleus and extensor digitorum longus changes the glycogen and potassium contents of the muscles prompts me to ask if you have investigated the myoglobin contents. Some years ago we cross-united the nerves to red and pale muscles and were surprised to find that there had been a partial conversion of red to pale and of pale to red, and this led us to investigate the speeds of muscle contraction, and to find that these also had been changed in accord with the nerve innervation. But to my knowledge there has been no quantitative investigation of their myoglobin contents.

My second comment concerns the finding that there is a loss of trophic influence of nerve on muscle in old animals. At least in one case this is not so. The cross-union of nerves to fast and slow muscles in adult cats results in a transformation of the fast muscle to a slowly contracting muscle, and *vice versa* for the slow to fast, that is at least as remarkable as that occurring in young animals.

My third comment concerns the changes brought about by axonal section of motoneurons. Our original suggestion that there was a large depression of monosynaptic innervation is only partly true. The most striking change in excitability occurs in the soma-dendritic membrane which exhibits patches of evanescent increases in excitability. As a consequence the depressed monosynaptic excitation results in local responses that sum with one another and so often result in the discharge of an impulse down the axon after a considerable delay. Thus, in addition to the remarkable changes in metabolism of nerve cells during the axon-reaction, there are also changes in the excitability of the surface membranes.

GUTMANN: Your observations on changes of the colour of the muscle in cross-unions of nerves are very interesting. As you say, changes in myoglobin concentration should be expected and their study would prove very fruitful. I do not know of a quantitative study of these changes. Concerning the second question I have to stress that the animals in our experiments were very old indeed with little further life expectation. I would not expect metabolic changes, suggesting a loss of the trophic influence of nerve on muscle in adult cats.

HORSTFEHR: May the reduction of conduction velocity of the axon after cutting be related to changes of the pH value inside the axon?

GUTMANN: This is a possibility. We may expect reduction in oxygen supply and concomittant a shift of pH values to lower levels.

GLEES: Could I ask Dr. Eccles one question? We should of course not reject the possibility of impulse transmission. Could you say whether the impulse transmission is different in red muscle from white muscle? Could you stimulate electrically with the old impulse frequency in your crossed-union experiments? Would you then be able to turn a white into a red muscle and *vice versa*? Is the firing rate of these moto-neurons different?

ECCLES: The firing is different. We have done and tried to answer this question by preventing all firing, and then nothing happens. We have also tried to stimulate by controlled frequencies of firing. It is just a remote possibility that firing rate may do it, but I think highly improbable. I am much more in favor of Dr. Gutmann's general story that this is a trophic influence and not firing rate. This would also line up with the changes found in glycogen and potassium and all other components.

SINGER: I would like to ask Dr. Gutmann the following. You know how loosely the term 'trophic' has been used and still is used. Would you like to give us a short definition so that we don't go astray in the rest of our conference on the meaning of 'trophic'?

GUTMANN: For neurotrophic relations I would suggest: 'nervous non-impulse mechanisms maintaining (and recovering) metabolism and structure of tissues'. This is still a broad definition but it reflects the level of present research.

Proximo-Distal Movement of Phospholipid in the Axoplasm of the Intact and Regenerating Neurons

N. MIANI

Department of Anatomy, University of Padua, Padua (Italy)

As is well known, Weiss and Hiscoe (1948) reported that the axoplasm of the peripheral nerve fibre is maintained in constant proximo-distal motion and that the source of the axonal constituents is in the nucleated cell space. Several observations have recently been pointed out to substanciate this concept. Three methods of investigation have been especially employed: (*1*) Radioactive tracer methods (Samuels *et al.*, 1951; Waelsch, 1958; Koenig, 1958; Weiss, 1961; Lajtha, 1961; Ochs *et al.*, 1962); (*2*) Analysis of neuroplasmic enzymes, *i.e.* cholinesterase (Sawyer, 1946; Lubińska *et al.*, 1961; Koenig and Koelle, 1961; Clouet and Waelsch, 1961; Lubińska, 1963) and cholineacetylase (Hebb and Waites, 1956; Hebb and Silver, 1961); (*3*) Observations on isolated nerve cells in tissue culture (Levi and Godina, 1959; Weiss *et al.*, 1962). Most of these investigations appeared to support the hypothesis of Weiss and Hiscoe (1948), although some technical difficulties made the interpretations of the data obtained from them rather laborious. The radioactive tracer methods especially suffer from the basic handicap that a high amount of injected radioactive material becomes rapidly fixed in the nucleated structures of the nerve (Schwann cells, connective tissue cells and cells of the blood vessel walls, Droz and Leblond, 1962; Weiss, 1961) so that the somato-axonal stream of labelled material becomes poorly discernible.

During the last three years I have carried out a variety of experiments (Miani, 1960, 1962a, 1963) whose main objects were: (*1*) To develop a procedure for labelling the nerve cell body electively with a phospholipid precursor *in vivo*; (*2*) To obtain evidence of proximo-distal movement along the axis cylinder of phospholipids synthesized in the perikaryon; (*3*) To determine the nature of phospholipids of the axon. Here is a brief account of them.

Labelling the nerve-cell body with ^{32}P-orthophosphate

The cell bodies of the somatal and visceral efferent components of the vagal and hypoglossal nerves of the rabbit were labelled by placing 1 μl of radioactive phosphate on the calamus scriptorius of the IVth ventricle under direct vision. The procedure was repeated every 15 min up to $2\frac{1}{2}$ h and so a total amount of 200 ± 20 μC of ^{32}P was deposited. All through the experiment, the IVth ventricle was carefully kept free of cerebrospinal fluid by a continuous drainage of the cisterna magna with cotton.

Under these experimental conditions the radioactivity concentrated for long in the structures surrounding the calamus, while negligible amounts of ^{32}P that had left the brain were found in the blood as well as in the nucleated structures of the peripheral nerves (Miani, 1963).

Evidence of proximo-distal movement along the axis cylinder of phospholipids synthesized in the perikaryon

Shortly after labelling the bulb, ^{32}P-phospholipids appeared in the vagal and hypoglossal nerves. Measurements of labelled phospholipids along each nerve were made by dividing it into several segments of 6 mm length and analysing separately the radioactivity in the lipid fraction prepared according to the procedure of Folch *et al.*, 1957. The radioactivity was therefore expressed as counts/min/6 mm of vagal nerve and as counts/min/6 mm of hypoglossal nerve, respectively.

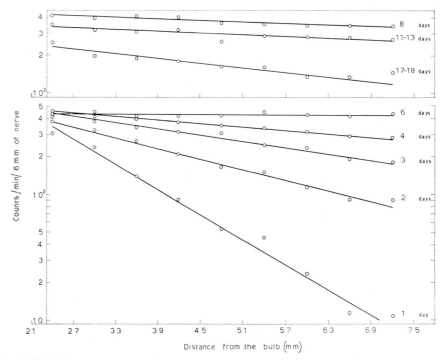

Fig. 1. ^{32}P-lipid content in successive segments of the cervical vagus at different time intervals after labelling the bulb with ^{32}P-orthophosphate. Each point plotted on a semilogarithmic scale includes the right and left nerves and is the mean value of 10 tracer experiments.

At 1 day after labelling the bulb, the cervical vagus showed a rather steep gradient of radioactivity, falling out exponentially in the proximo-distal direction (Fig. 1). The radioactivity in the distal segments quickly increased until labelled phospholipids became uniformly distributed all along the nerve (6th day). Their concentration then declined somewhat, although the fall was slightly higher at the lower than at the upper nerve segments. At 1 day after labelling the bulb, the hypoglossal nerve showed also a steep proximo-distal gradient of radioactivity, but, unlike the vagal nerve, the increase in radioactivity with time neither reached the equilibrium nor came to a stop even after 18 days.

The exponential form of the outflow suggests that several labelled phospholipids in downward transit exchange on the way unlabelled and stationary phospholipids of the system. In other words, the amount of labelled phospholipids in any arbitrary segment of the vagal and hypoglossal nerves would be made up of two portions at least: that which has locally exchanged phospholipids in the system, and that in downward transit. As a result of the present series it seems that the rate of exchange is much higher in the vagal than in the hypoglossal nerve, because the radioactive equilibrium is reached much earlier in the former (6 days) than in the latter (near to the 18th day). Since exchange activity is a variable before the radioactive equilibrium is reached in the system, the rate of motion of labelled phospholipids along the vagal

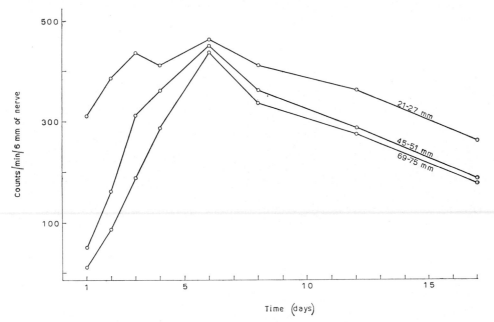

Fig. 2. ^{32}P-lipid content in the upper, middle and low segments of the cervical vagus at different time intervals after labelling the bulb with ^{32}P-orthophosphate. Data have been taken from Fig. 1.

nerve is to be estimated from 6 days after labelling the bulb as indicated in Fig. 2. Calculations made on the basis of the slope of the descending linear portion of all 3 curves indicated a relatively slow rate of transit of 2.91 mm/day. This figure, however, is of limited significance for two reasons at least: (1) Labelled phospholipids of the axon are not homogeneous (see below); (2) The motion of labelled phospholipids as calculated above is the resulting motion of more motions whose nature and number are at present unknown. A component motion of remarkable significance can be measured from the radioactivity-time curves of Fig. 1, i.e. that of the fast-moving phospholipids. The rate of the fast-moving phospholipids along the vagal nerve is the

References p. 126

distance covered by labelled phospholipids in front of the radioactive column in the
unit time (day). For the vagus it is of the order of 72 mm/day (this value is correct
compared with that of 41 mm/day elsewhere reported, Miani, 1962a) and of 39–45
mm/day in the hypoglossal nerve.

The foregoing results have been substantiated by experiments in which the radioactive tracer test was combined with constriction experiments. The first series was
designed to determine whether degeneration and regeneration of the axons affected
the peripheral flow of the labelled phospholipids. For the purpose, the right vagus
and hypoglossus were crushed from 1–57 days before the tracer experiment and the

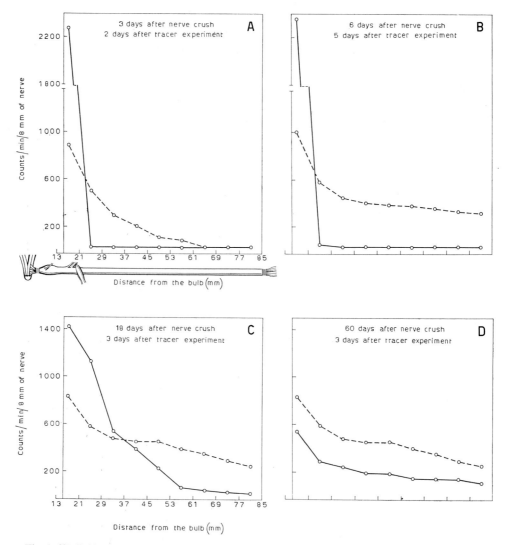

Fig. 3. ^{32}P-lipid content in successive segments of regenerating (heavy line) and intact (broken line)
cervical vagus. Crushing the nerve preceded labelling the bulb at different time intervals. Each point
is the mean value of 12 experiments.

radioactivity in crushed as well as in intact contralateral nerves was usually measured 2 or 3 days later.

At 3 days after nerve crush, the concentration of labelled phospholipids was minimum in the degenerating stump while, coincidently, the concentration of labelled phospholipids just above the constriction rose much compared with the control. This occurred to both the vagal (Fig. 3) and hypoglossal nerves. As the time interval between crushing the nerve and labelling the bulb increased, the radioactive column of the central stump invaded anew the distal one and return proceeded *pari passu* at the regenerating axons, *i.e.* at the rate of about 1 mm/day and 4 mm/day in the cervical vagus (Evans and Murray, 1954a, b) and in the hypoglossal nerve (Gutman *et al.*, 1942; Brattgård *et al.*, 1957), respectively. These series of experiments therefore prove (*1*) that labelled phospholipids are only in the growing axons and (*2*) that in those, labelled phospholipids move proximo-distally.

The second series of experiments was designed to determine how the normal distribution of labelled phospholipids throughout the length of the nerve was altered after

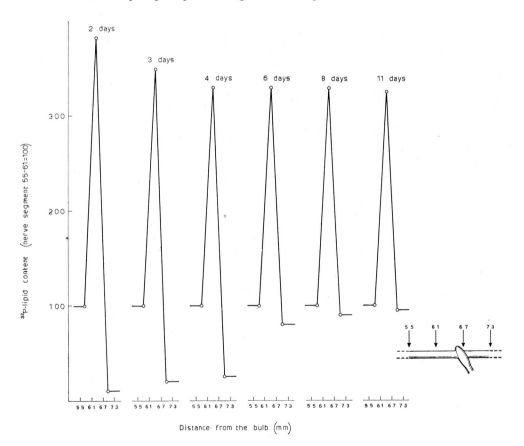

Fig. 4. Amount of labelled phospholipids in the nerve segments immediately above and below the constriction of the vagus. Data are expressed as percentage of the amount of labelled phospholipids in the last nerve segment but one in the central stump. Each curve is the mean value of 8 or 11 experiments.

nerve crush. The right vagus was crushed at the lower cervical level from 1–11 days after labelling the bulb with ^{32}P, and the re-distribution of the radioactivity above the constriction was examined 20 h later. The result of a complete experiment from nerves crushed 11 days after labelling the bulb is shown in Fig. 5. It may be seen that the surplus is confined to the terminal 5 mm of the central stump. The more proximal

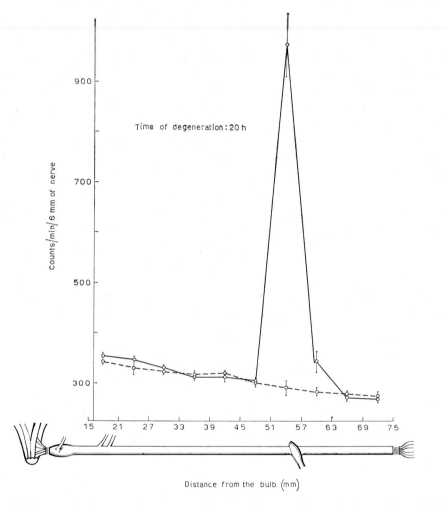

Fig. 5. ^{32}P-lipid content in successive segments of the central stump of the cervical vagus (heavy line) and of intact contralateral controls (broken line). The nerves were crushed 11 days after labelling the bulb with ^{32}P-orthophosphate, and the re-distribution of the radioactivity above the constriction was examined 20 h later. Each point is the mean value of 9 experiments.

parts of the nerve demonstrated no changes compared to the intact contralateral controls. The same occurred to nerves crushed within 1–10 days after tracer experiment. Accordingly, only 3 nerve segments have been considered in Fig. 4, i.e. the terminal nerve segment of the central stump plus the nerve segments immediately above and below it. At 2 days after labelling the bulb with ^{32}P, the amount of labelled phospholipids just above the constriction is 3.8 times higher than that in the reference nerve segment immediately more proximal. The peak then lowers somewhat up to 4 days, but for the time intervals from 4–11 days the peak remains stationary.

These series of experiments therefore reveal the following facts: (*1*) Labelled phospholipids flow for long down the axon under the present conditions; (*2*) The flow per hour becomes constant after 4 days from labelling the bulb, *i.e.* when the vagus is going to reach the equilibrium; (*3*) Labelled phospholipids are continuously synthesized within the confines of the bulb and then conveyed down the axon. As a matter of fact, it is possible to interrupt the traffic of ^{32}P-lipids at any arbitrary point of the cervical vagus, as well as at any time after labelling the bulb, without the increase of label'ed phospholipids just above the constriction, being accompanied by depletion of them in the more proximal part of the nerve.

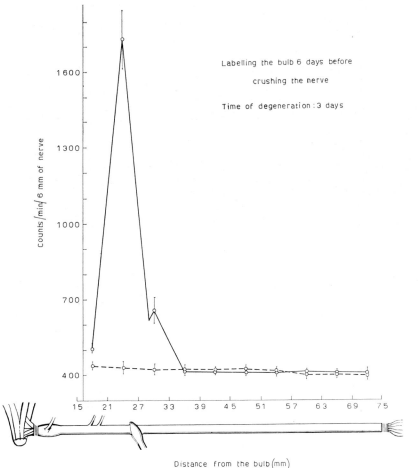

Fig. 6. ^{32}P-lipid content in successive segments of degenerating (heavy line) and intact (broken line) cervical vagus. The nerves were crushed 6 days after labelling the bulb with ^{32}P-orthophosphate, and the re-distribution of the radioactivity below the constriction was examined 3 days later. Each point is the mean value of 9 experiments.

It seemed of interest, finally, to determine whether or not motion of labelled phospholipids could occur in the peripheral stump of the cervical vagus during the first 3 days after crushing the nerve. Times longer than 3 days have not been studied because the extensive histological changes in the degenerating stump might complicate the results. Crushing of the right vagus at the upper cervical level took place 6 days after labelling the bulb and the re-distribution of labelled phospholipids below the contriction was examined 1, 2 and 3 days later. Fig. 6 summarizes experiments of 3 days of degeneration. It appears that there is no significant difference in radio-activity between degenerating and intact contralateral controls (P>0.05), with the

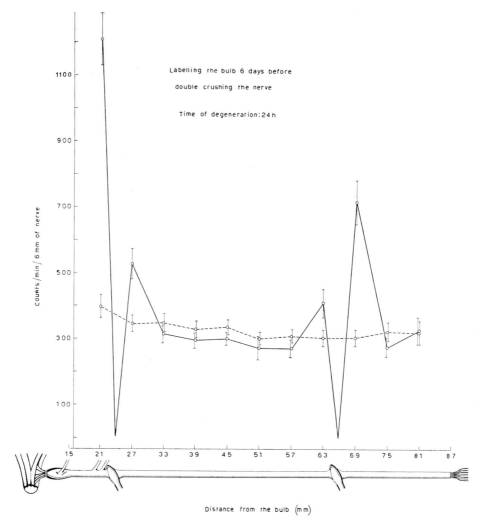

Fig. 7. ^{32}P-lipid content in successive segments of degenerating (heavy line) and intact (broken line) cervical vagus. The nerves were crushed in 2 points several centimetres apart 6 days after labelling the bulb with ^{32}P-orthophosphate, and the re-distribution of the radioactivity was examined 1 day later. Each point is the mean value of 9 experiments.

exception of a slight piling up of labelled phospholipids in the nerve segment immediately below the constriction. The right vagus of another group of rabbits was simultaneously crushed at the upper and lower cervical levels 6 days after the tracer experiment and the radioactivity in crushed as well as in intact contralateral nerves was measured 1 day later. It may be seen in Fig. 7 that increases of labelled phospholipids were confined to the nerve segments immediately above and below both the upper and lower constrictions. The first proximal surplus related to the terminal 5 mm of the central stump (see above) is much higher than the following three related to the peripheral stump. The nerve segments lying between the peaks presented a slight fall in radioactivity compared with the intact antimeric controls. All in all, the 3rd series of experiments indicates that there is not a proximo-distal depletion of labelled phospholipids in the degenerating stump of the vagus. Small amounts of them move and the direction of the motion is simultaneously from proximal to distal and *vice versa*.

Nature of the labelled phospholipids in the axon

A further step in the analysis of the labelled phospholipids in transit along the axon was to individualize them. For this purpose, pieces of intact cervical vagus, 72 mm long, and of hypoglossus, 32 mm long, were removed at different time intervals

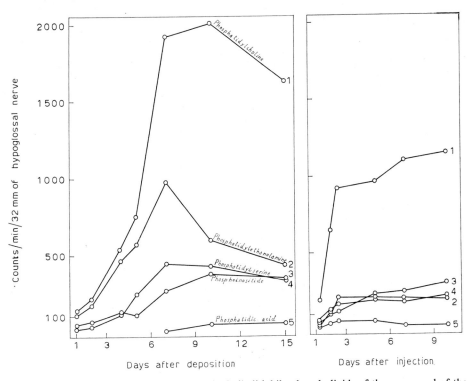

Fig. 8. Comparison of ^{32}P-content in individual alkali-labile phospholipids of the axons and of the nucleated structures of the hypoglossal nerve at different time intervals after labelling the bulb with ^{32}P-orthophosphate or after injection of ^{32}P-orthophosphate. Each point is the mean value of 10–12 experiments.

after labelling the bulb with ^{32}P and individual alkali-labile phospholipids or individual plasmalogens were obtained from each lipid sample according to the procedure referred to elsewhere (Miani, 1962b). Additional information about the metabolic
activity of the nucleated structures of the vagal and hypoglossal nerves (henceforward
designed as 'myelin sheaths') was obtained by replacing in the above procedure
labelling the bulb by an intraperitoneal injection of 1.4 μC of radioactive phosphate/
g body weight. In fact, injected radioactive material becomes rapidly fixed in the
myelin sheaths of the nerves (Weiss, 1961; Droz and Leblond, 1962).

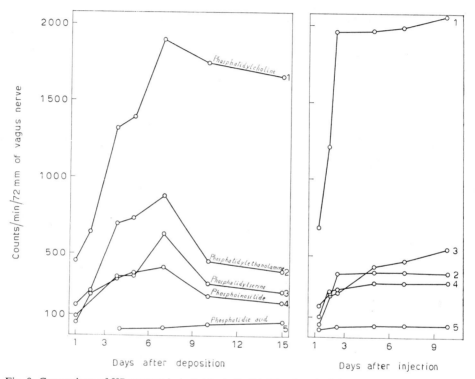

Fig. 9. Comparison of ^{32}P-content in individual alkali-labile phospholipids of the axons and of the
nucleated structures of the vagus at different time intervals after labelling the bulb with ^{32}P-ortho-
phosphate or after injection of ^{32}P-orthophosphate. Each point is the mean value of 10–12 experiments.

The following phospholipids have been individualized in the axons of the vagal
and hypoglossal nerves: phosphatidylcholine, phosphatidylethanolamine, phospha-
tidylserine and phosphoinositide. Data on phosphatidic acid were rather equivocal
owing to its relatively low activity. Serine plasmalogen, ethanolamine plasmalogen
and choline plasmalogen also migrated along the axons. Finally, phospholipids stable
to alkali and mercury (phosphosphingosides) were in motion in the neuroplasm.
Examining comparatively Figs. 8 and 9, it is noted that the relative amounts of
radioactivity in individual alkali-labile phospholipids of the axon were very different
from those of the myelin sheath. Differences were also apparent between the axonal
phospholipids of the hypoglossal (Fig. 8) and those of the vagal nerve (Fig. 9). As a

matter of fact, in the myelin sheaths of both nerves the molecular ratios of ^{32}P-phosphatidylcholine : ^{32}P-phosphatidylethanolamine : ^{32}P-phosphatidylserine : ^{32}P-phosphoinositide approximated 5 : 1 : 1 : 1 both in short- and long-term experiments. On the contrary, in the axons of hypoglossal and vagal nerves the ratios were 5 : 4 : $1\frac{1}{2}$: 1 and 5 : 2 : $1\frac{1}{2}$: 2, respectively, in short-term experiments. As the time increased up to 10 days, the value for both nerves became approximately 5 : 1 : 1 : 1. For the alkali-stable phospholipids of the axons of the vagal and hypoglossal nerves, whose data have been reported elsewhere (Miani, 1963), the radioactivity was highest for choline plasmalogen and total phosphosphingosides, followed by serine plasmalogen and ethanolamine plasmalogen in decreasing order of activity. These radioactivities are similar in proportion to those obtained by the myelin sheath, although the maximum of the radioactivity was reached much earlier in the plasmalogens and phosphosphingosides of the axon than in those of the myelin sheath of the vagal nerve. Information concerning the significance of individual phospholipids of the axon is completely lacking at present.

SUMMARY

There is a considerable degree of certainty that most of the labelled phospholipids of the hypoglossal and vagal nerves are inside the axon under the present conditions. Two groups of experiments substantiate this concept: the first has shown that in the distal part of the crushed nerves labelled phospholipids are only in the newly regenerating axons; the second one has indicated that in intact nerves the Schwann cells and the connective tissue cells of the peri- and endo-neurium synthesize negligible amounts of ^{32}P-lipids as the cells are only supplied with negligible amounts of ^{32}P either by the blood and lymphatic vessels or by the endoneural space.

As far as the source of labelled phospholipids of the axon is concerned, the results hitherto presented are all consistent with the concept of a primary synthesis of them in the perikaryon. The rate of migration towards the periphery of the fast-moving phospholipids is of the order of 72 mm/day and of 39–41 mm/day in the cervical vagus and hypoglossal nerve, respectively. The resultant velocity of all motions of the phospholipids in the vagus is of the order of 2.91 mm/day. Taking the present data in conjunction with those of Weiss and Hiscoe (1948), the fact emerges that the fast-moving phospholipids do not move *with* the axon, but *in* the axon.

There are good reasons to believe that the axon is not a simple traffic line for the phospholipids, but that the phospholipids on the way exchange unlabelled and stationary phospholipids of the axon itself. Presumably because of different widths of channels as well as of different functions, the rate of exchange is much higher in the vagus than in the hypoglossus. There are at present no indications as to how this is performed and how many phospholipids are involved in the replacements.

The labelled phospholipids of the axon are as numerous as those of Schwann's sheath cells, but their proportion in the axon is very different from that of the myelin sheath. Further progress in this field may be obtained by fractional centrifugation of the vagal and hypoglossal nerves, a procedure which is now being used in our laboratory.

References p. 126

126

N. MIANI

REFERENCES

BRATTGÅRD, S.-O, EDSTRÖM, J.-E, AND HYDÉN, H., (1957); The chemical changes in regenerating neurons. *J. Neurochem.*, **1**, 316–325.
CLOUET, D. H., AND WAELSCH, H., (1961); Amino acid and protein metabolism of the brain. VII. The penetration of cholinesterase inhibitors into the nervous system of the frog. *J. Neurochem.*, **8**, 189–200.
DROZ, B., AND LEBLOND, C. P., (1962); Migration of protein along the axons of the sciatic nerve. *Science*, **137**, 1047–1048.
EVANS, D. H. L., AND MURRAY, J. G., (1954a); Histological and functional studies on the fibre composition of the vagus nerve of the rabbit. *J. Anat. (Lond.)*, **88**, 320–337.
EVANS, D. H. L., AND MURRAY, J. G., (1954b); Regeneration of non-medullated nerve fibres. *J. Anat. (Lond.)*, **88**, 465–480.
FOLCH, J., LEES, M., AND SLOANE-STANLEY, G. H., (1957); A simple method for the isolation and purification of total lipids from animal tissue. *J. biol. Chem.*, **226**, 497–509.
GUTMANN, E., GUTTMANN, L., MEDAWAR, P. B., AND YOUNG, J. Z., (1942); The rate of regeneration of nerve. *J. exp. Biol.*, **19**, 14–44.
HEBB, C. O., AND SILVER, A., (1961); Gradient of choline acetylase activity. *Nature (Lond.)*, **189**, 123–125.
HEBB, C. O., AND WAITES, G. M. H., (1956); Choline acetylase in antero- and retro-grade degeneration of a cholinergic nerve. *J. Physiol.*, **132**, 667–671.
KOENIG, E., AND KOELLE, G. B., (1961); Mode of regeneration of acetylcholinesterase in cholinergic neurons following irreversible inactivation. *J. Neurochem.*, **8**, 169–188.
KOENIG, H., (1958); An autoradiographic study of nucleic acid and protein turnover in the mammalian neuraxis. *J. biophys. biochem. Cytol.*, **4**, 785–792.
LAJTHA, A., (1961); Protein metabolism in nerve. *Chemical Pathology of the Nervous System*. J. Folch-Pi, Editor. Proceedings of the Third International Neurochemical Symposium. Strasbourg, Pergamon Press (p. 268).
LEVI, G., AND GODINA, G., (1959); La structure des neurones vivants. *C. R. Ass. Anat.* XLVI Réunion, Montpellier (p. 461–465).
LUBIŃSKA, L., NIEMIERKO, S., AND ODERFELD, B., (1961); Gradient of cholinesterase activity. *Nature (Lond.)*, **189**, 122–123.
LUBIŃSKA, L., (1963); Intra-axonal streaming and regeneration of nerve fibres. *Progress in Brain Research, Vol. 13, Mechanisms of Neural Regeneration*. Amsterdam, Elsevier (p. 1–71).
MIANI, N., (1960); Proximo-distal movement along the axon of protein synthesized in the perikaryon of regenerating neurons. *Nature (Lond.)*, **185**, 541.
MIANI, N., (1962a); Evidence of a proximo-distal movement along the axon of phospholipid synthesized in the nerve-cell body. *Nature (Lond.)*, **193**, 887–888.
MIANI, N., (1962b); The relationship between axon and Schwann cell. Phospholipid metabolism of degenerating and regenerating peroneal-tibial nerves of the rabbit *in vitro*. *J. Neurochem.* **9**, 525–536.
MIANI, N., (1963); Analysis of the somato-axonal movement of phospholipids in the vagus and hypoglossal nerves. *J. Neurochem.*, **10**, 859–874.
OCHS, S., DALRYMPLE, D., AND RICHARDS, G., (1962); Axoplasmic flow in ventral root nerve fibers of the cat. *Exp. Neurol.*, **5**, 349–363.
SAMUELS, A. J., BOYARSKY, L. L., GERARD, R. W., LIBET, B., AND BRUST, B., (1951); Distribution, exchange and migration of phosphate compounds in the nervous system. *J. Physiol.*, **164**, 1–12.
SAWYER, C. H., (1946); Cholinesterases in degenerating and regenerating peripheral nerves. *Am. J. Physiol.*, **146**, 246–253.
WAELSCH, H., (1958); Some aspects of amino acid and protein metabolism of the nervous system. *J. nerv. ment. Dis.*, **126**, 33–39.
WEISS, P., (1961); The concept of perpetual neuronal growth and proximo-distal substance convection. *Regional Neurochemistry*. S. S. Kety and J. Elkes, Editors. Proceedings of the Fourth International Neurochemical Symposium. Pergamon Press (p. 220).
WEISS, P., AND HISCOE, H. B., (1948); Experiments on the mechanism of nerve growth. *J. exp. Zool.*, **107**, 315–395.
WEISS, P., TAYLOR, A. C., AND PILLAI P. A., (1962); The nerve fiber as a system in continuous flow: microcinematographic and electronmicroscopic demonstration. *Science*, **136**, 330.

Factors Promoting Regeneration of Spinal Neurons: Positive Influence of Nerve Growth Factor

D. SCOTT, Jr. AND C. N. LIU

Departments of Physiology and Anatomy, School of Medicine, University of Pennsylvania, Philadelphia, Pa. (U.S.A.)

INTRODUCTION

I would like to express my appreciation for the kindness of the Central Institute for Brain Research in providing an opportunity to share with you the results of our recent experiments on regeneration of spinal neurons in kittens. This symposium will enable me to benefit by the comments and suggestions of fellow members as well as to meet and discuss my problems with many old friends.

At the outset I would like to draw to your attention the paradox we find when we examine the properties of the primary sensory neuron. Here, the cell body in the dorsal root ganglion gives forth two processes: one described as peripheral nerve and passing outwards to some sensory ending while the other enters the spinal cord via the dorsal root and becomes part of the dorsal funiculus. It is well known that regeneration will follow injury in the peripheral branch but there is so little evidence of regeneration of the spinal axon that this is generally considered impossible. Despite the fact that these two processes are both part of a single neuron, there is a dramatic difference in their capacity for regrowth following injury. Since Sperry (1951) has shown close similarity between growth and regeneration, I consider our problem basically one of nerve growth although it is important at all times to remember the possible effects of the environment of the regenerating axon and especially the trophic action of the products of degeneration. To make the present state of our knowledge of spinal regeneration as clear as possible I will proceed step by step with the observations which seem most pertinent to the situation with which we are confronted.

It is logical to start by seeing what can be learned from the extensive experiences of many investigators in the field of peripheral nerve regeneration. Fortunately the whole problem of regeneration has been extensively reviewed by several workers in the field (Windle, 1955; McCouch, 1963; Clemente, 1963). Earlier Gutmann and Sanders (1942) showed that physical impediments in the normal growth path of the regenerating axon will tend to block regeneration and Young has stated (1942, p. 368) '. . . it is clear that the most important factor determining the time and degree of recovery is the condition at the site of the lesion'. Numerous workers have suggested a multitude of techniques for providing guidance and encouragement to the growing tip of a regenerating axon. Campbell *et al.* (1957) have suggested that a sleeve of molecular membrane filter sheet will provide both guidance and favorable cellular environment at the site of the lesion.

Apart from providing a guidance path at the point of injury, numerous workers have offered evidence of axon growth promotion by systemic injection of substances extracted from neural and other tissue. Von Koechlin and Von Muralt (1947) described an extract of brain which they called 'NR' and which markedly reduced the time after nerve section for re-establishment of the corneal reflex as compared to that of the untreated control. Among numerous workers reporting regenerative enhancement after injection of non-neural extracts, Bazan (1954) administered vitamin T (Goetsch) with strongly positive results. Both the foregoing studies employed return of function as their criterion of regeneration but Hoffman (1951) demonstrated histologic evidence of sprouting of the terminal processes of motor fibers after partial section of the pre-junctional endings. The regeneration of these endings was greatly encouraged by an extract of degenerating neural tissue, suggesting that the products of degeneration have a profound effect on the process of regeneration. In our own studies of the dorsal spino-cerebellar tract, Liu and Scott (1958) have come to look on regeneration and sprouting as two inherently different forms of response to injury of these fibers as will be described shortly. A further requirement for regeneration in the sympathetic system is the formation of appropriate synaptic connections. This has been demonstrated by Gibson (1940) who measured synaptic delay following regeneration and found that it closely approximated control values.

Much more could be said concerning peripheral regeneration but from the evidence cited it would appear that we must bear in mind: (1) physical impediments in the path of the regenerating axons; (2) cellular environment at the point of injury; (3) the possible growth promotion of some special extract whose mode of action may not be known.

The failure of axons within the spinal cord to regenerate after either section or crushing of the cord has been reported by many investigators (Brown and McCouch, 1947; Davidoff and Ransohoff, 1948). Such axons, however, do show limited terminal growth which is frequently recurrent due to failure to penetrate the site of injury. Exception to this general finding has been reported by Sugar and Gerard (1940) and Freeman (1952). In both of these latter series of experiments, return of function, to a greater or lesser extent, was observed after operative interruption of spinal neurons, but in neither case did the experimental procedure suggest the mechanism of regeneration or the factors critical for its accomplishment.

Recent progress directed toward an understanding of the major impediment tending to prevent effective regeneration in the vertebrate spinal cord has focused on two principal aspects of the problem and may be summarized as follows.

1. *Blockade.* Operative interruption of neurons within the spinal cord is followed by an extensive cellular invasion of the site of the lesion starting within 12 h postoperatively. Of the cell types involved, glial and collagenous elements are especially effective in forming a scar blockade which is impenetrable by the limited growth of regenerating tips of interrupted axons. Such a cellular barrier may be made much

more porous, and thus allow penetration by probing regenerating axon tips, through the administration of bacterial polysaccharide to the animal post-operatively (Windle and Chambers, 1951; Scott and Clemente, 1955). Examination of the spinal cord by the evoked potential method in an animal so treated after a post-operative period of several months has shown the presence of axons capable of conducting impulses for a short distance beyond the site of the lesion (Fig. 1). Histologic sections from such an animal show axons penetrating the blockade at the site of the lesion (Fig. 2a and b).

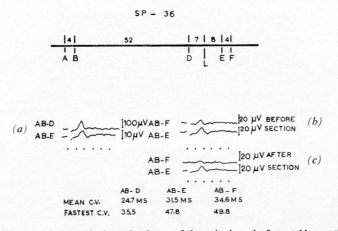

Fig. 1. Electrical response from the lateral column of the spinal cord of a cat 11 months after transection. Diagram shows position of electrodes relative to site of lesion L (A and B). Stimulating electrodes (D, E, F). Recording electrodes. (a) Responses recorded at D and E to stimulus applied at A and B. (b) Responses at E and F to stimulus applied at A and B. (c) Same as (b) after cord has been sectioned between E and F. Time is in msec.

In a separate series of experiments Scott and Liu (1963) sectioned only one dorsal spino-cerebellar tract (DSC) in cats some of which were subsequently treated with bacterial polysaccharide. Those treated with this agent showed limited regenerative growth in 4–6 months but those not treated showed the formation of collateral sprouts from the intact contralateral tract. Potentials were recorded from the DSC rostral to the lesion in response to stimulation of the uninterrupted contralateral tract caudal to the level of the lesion. No sprouting was found in animals treated with bacterial polysaccharide. It thus appeared after extensive experimentation with this agent that, despite the removal of the blocking effect of the cellular barrier, the axons did not have adequate growth potential to regenerate a significant distance beyond the site of the transection.

Much the same result appears to have been obtained when the spinal cord is wrapped in the vicinity of the lesion with a molecular membrane filter sheet (Millipore) which is said to provide physical discrimination between cellular elements and solutes invading the site of the lesion (Campbell *et al.*, 1957; Thulin, 1960). However, recent electron micrographic studies reported by Harkin (1963) showed no significant decrease in cell population at the site of a peripheral nerve lesion surrounded by a Millipore sleeve as compared to one in which this material was not used.

Fig. 2a. Longitudinal histological section of cat spinal cord, after transection taken midway ventro-dorsally through the site of the lesion. Silver pyridine stain, × 75. Control cat 3 months after operation.

2. *Regenerative growth.* The factors governing growth potential of the regenerating axons tips are more difficult to identify. Brown and McCouch (1947) have presented histologic evidence of the regeneration of the severed nerve tips subsequent to transection of the spinal cord of the cat. Such regenerating tips were found either embedded in the scar formed at the site of the lesion or deflected by the scar to take a recurrent course. Some advancing regenerative growth of the proximal tip would thus be expected when the blockade imposed by the scar had been rendered more penetrable by the therapeutic agent, but, for some unknown reason, this appears to be of very limited extent. In fact, it has not been shown whether regenerative growth is determined by environmental factors in the milieu surrounding the tip itself, or whether such growth is an expression of the rate of physiological activity in the cell body which is transmitted to the tip by axoplasmic streaming as has been suggested by Weiss and Cavanaugh (1959). A third possibility includes the influence of both factors.

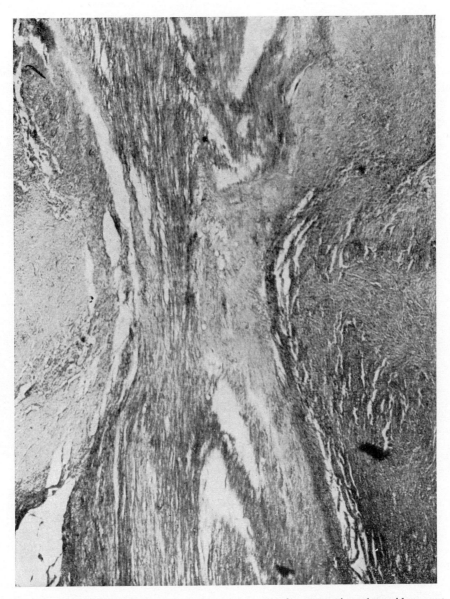

Fig. 2b. Longitudinal histological sections of cat spinal cord, after transection taken midway ventro-laterally through the site of the lesion. Silver pyridine stain, × 75. Experimental cat 11 months after operation having received a total of 6222 γ/kg bacterial polysaccharide Piromen.

Stimulation of regenerative growth through the administration of substances known to increase the metabolism of the animal (such as triiodothyronine) has been attempted without success (Scott, 1964). Likewise, vitamin T (Goetsch) which has been reported to give strong encouragement to the growth of regenerating peripheral nerves, has been employed in an effort to increase growth of spinal axons in the cat. No significant difference was seen between the treated and untreated animals.

Isolation of a powerful growth promoting substance from mouse submaxillary gland has been reported by Levi-Montalcini and Brooker (1960) and Bueker *et al.* (1960). This material has been shown to be a protein of molecular weight 20,000–22,000 which can be fractionated into three principal components, two of which are essential for stimulation of the nerve growth (Cohen, 1959; Schenkein and Bueker, 1962).

Explants of mouse sympathetic and sensory ganglia in tissue culture were found to respond to administration of 10^{-9} g of this material by the growth of a dense halo of nerve fibers surrounding the explant within 12 h (Fig. 3). Injection of this nerve

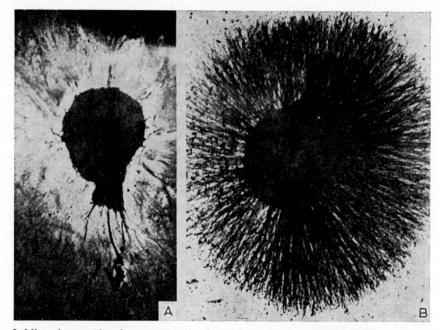

Fig. 3. Microphotographs of sensory ganglia after 24 h *in vitro*. Silver impregnation. (A). Ganglion of a $2\frac{1}{2}$ months human fetus in the standard control medium. (B). Ganglia of a 7 day chick embryo in a medium containing the purified salivary protein at a concentration of 1 : 18,000. (Permission received from Dr. R. Levi-Montalcini to reproduce this figure).

growth factor (NGF) into intact animals was also shown to produce hyperplasia and hypertrophy of neurons, especially in the sympathetic system and, to a limited extent, in sensory pathways within the spinal cord as well (Levi-Montalcini and Brooker, 1960). The present experiments examined the influence of NGF on regenerative growth of axons within the spinal cord.

Complete transection of the spinal cord involves interruption of fibers in the many separate pathways containing ascending, descending, and intrinsic neurons. This limits the possibility of discriminative analysis between the characteristics of the neurons in any one pathway as well as increasing the technical difficulties of animal maintenance during the post-operative period. In view of the demonstrated specific growth enhancement of neurons of the sensory pathway by the action of NGF the observations in the following experiments were restricted to the dorsal funiculus.

MATERIALS AND METHOD

Seven normal healthy kittens were selected for operative interruption of the dorsal funiculus by means of a crush lesion. All animals were fully weaned and inoculated against feline distemper. The pre-operative weight was between 700–800 g to allow administration at the selected daily dose level (B.U./g/day) without exceeding the limitations of our supply of growth factor. Systemic administration by subcutaneous injection had the advantage of providing slow sustained release of this material and also providing that it be available to both cell body and growing axon tips, as its site of action remains uncertain.

After anesthesia with sodium pentobarbital (0.36 mg/kg), the dura was exposed by laminectomy at the level of T 12. The exposed area was confined to 3 mm in diameter and great care was taken to avoid injury or impairment to the small arteries and veins found subdurally. The lesion was created by inserting the tips of fine watchmakers forceps through the dura on either side of the dorsal funiculus and sustaining the crush for 10 sec. To confirm the complete interruption of the dorsal funiculus, the gap between the ends of the pathway was observed to fill with pinkish fluid after removal of the forceps. The operative field was free from hemorrhage at closure and a small piece of Gelfoam was applied. The muscles, fascia and skin were sutured with interrupted stitches. No unfavorable post-operative sequelae were observed.

All animals were fed a high protein diet with 20–25% by wet weight fat and in addition vitamins A, B_1, B_6, D, and E and minerals. Daily exercise was provided and periodic neurologic examination evaluated coordination of movement, placing of feet during walking as well as presence of tactile placing reflex. All animals increased in weight by about 200 g during the interval between the operation and the time of sacrifice.

Purified nerve growth factor (NGF) was obtained through the courtesy of Abbott Laboratories (North Chicago, Ill.) in lyophylized form to prevent deterioration and loss of potency. This material was dissolved as needed in distilled water at an approximate concentration of 1 mg/ml depending on the potency of the sample and the magnitude of the intended dose. The potency of each sample in biological units (B.U.) was determined at the source by the tissue culture method and by injection into intact animals followed by histologic evaluation of the response. Dosage was evaluated in terms of units of biological activity per gram of kitten body weight per day (B.U./g/day). One unit of biological activity is defined as 'that amount (of NGF) per ml of tissue culture explant required to elicit a 3 + response corresponding to a dense halo of nerve fibers emerging from the explant within 12 h' (Levi-Montalcini and Booker, 1960, p. 374). Dosage levels of 280, 860 and 2200 B.U./g body weight/day respectively were administered 7 days per week to the three kittens receiving treatment (Table I).

Immediately following the initial operation each animal was given 10 γ of bacterial polysaccharide in the form of Piromen (Baxter) intraperitoneally and 0.5 ml Combiotic (Pfizer) containing 100,000 units penicillin G procaine and 0.125 mg dihydrostreptomycin intramuscularly. Identical therapy was administered after 24 h, following which the administration of NGF was started. The schedule of administration of

TABLE I

EFFECT OF NGF ADMINISTRATION ON DORSAL COLUMN NEURONS

	612 Control	613	624	625 Control	626 Control	628 Control	629
Initial weight (g)	900	800	880	880	860	800	750
Piromen dosage	10 γ 2 days	10 γ 2 days	10 γ 2 days	10–100 γ 7 days	0	10 γ 2 days	10 γ 2 days
NGF daily dose/g body weight	0	2200 B.U.	860 B.U.	0	0	0	280 B.U.
Days NGF administered	—	14	28	—	—	—	22
Total NGF administered	0	26.6×10⁶ B.U.	22.5×10⁶ B.U.	0	0	0	10.6×10⁶ B.U.
Interval in days between administration and examination	—	35	14	—	—	—	7
Response to dorsal root stimulation	—	Not attempted	Definite response dromic and antidromic	—	Small questionable response 1 mm rostral	Small response to 1 mm caudal	Small response to 5 mm rostral
Response to dorsal funiculus stimulation	No response at or above lesion	Response recorded up to 8 mm rostral	Response recorded up to 19 mm rostral	Trace of response at lesion	No response at lesion	Small response to 2 mm caudal	Small response to 4 mm rostral
Conduction velocity (m/sec)	—	60–90	69	—	—	—	43
Histologic: density of growing axon processes above lesion	0	+++	+	0	0	0	±
Maximum distance of growing tips seen above lesion	—	6.3 mm	In excess of 5.2 mm (limit of section)	—	—	—	—
Plane of sections	Dorsoventral	Dorsoventral	Sagittal	Sagittal	Sagittal	Dorsoventral	Dorsoventral

NGF was varied in each experiment to explore the effect of alteration of the following variables as shown in Table I: (*a*) daily dosage in terms of B.U./g body weight, (*b*) number of days during which NGF was administered, and (*c*) number of days between the end of NGF administration and the final neurophysiologic and histologic evaluation of the animal.

Final evaluation of the effect of the treatment consisted of electrophysiological studies by the evoked potential method followed by fixation and staining for histological examination. Electrical stimulation was with brief square wave pulses (0.1 msec) at a rate of 3/sec provided by a Grass S4B stimulator. The evoked potentials were led to an A.C. coupled pre-amplifier with a time constant of 0.5 sec and displayed beside a time calibration on a double beam oscilloscope. Both stimulating and recording electrodes were made of 0.005 in. platinum-iridium wire which was bent in the form of a fish hook for stimulating the dorsal roots and was ground to a point for stimulating and recording from the surface of the cord.

Stimulation was first applied to one dorsal root at the level of L7 after cutting the corresponding ventral root. Subsequently, stimuli were applied directly to the surface of the dorsal funiculus at a point caudal to the level of the lesion. The response to each type of stimulation was recorded from the surface of the dorsal funiculus by electrodes which were incrementally moved from an initial position 20 mm caudal to the lesion, then to the level of the lesion, and finally as far rostral as a response could be recorded. Similar observations were made on the dorsal spino-cerebellar tract for comparison.

Immediately following electrophysiological study, the spinal cords of these animals were fixed by perfusion (Koenig *et al.*, 1945). Serial sections, 10 μ thick, were made longitudinally from a segment of spinal cord 20 mm long including the lesion. The plane of the section in some animals was dorsoventral while in others it was sagittal (Table I). Additional transverse sections were made immediately adjacent to each end of this segment. Sections were stained on the slide by a modification of the Bodian protargol method.

A. Neurological and electrophysiological

1. Control kittens. These four animals received no NGF subsequent to operation but in three cases were given the usual post-operative dose of Piromen for the first 2 days (Table I). No evidence of functional recovery was seen in these animals such as might suggest restoration of conduction along the interrupted pathways.

When electrical stimuli were applied either to the dorsal root L7 or to the dorsal funiculus caudal to the lesion, no responses were evoked at the level of the lesion or rostral to it. For example, stimulation of the dorsal funiculus with 0.7 V just caudal to the lesion failed to evoke any response at a point 1 mm above the lesion in the control kitten No. 612. Retrograde degeneration of the sensory axons caudal to the lesion modified the rostral limit at which evoked responses were seen. On the other hand the electrotonic spread of the responses from the extreme point of conduction resulted in a detectable potential for 2–5 mm further rostral. A normal evoked response was obtained when the recording electrodes were placed 5–10 mm caudal to the lesion and a roughly linear decrease in amplitude in this response was observed as the recording electrodes were moved closer to the lesion. Conduction in adjacent intact pathways remained entirely normal.

2. *Experimental kitten No. 629* received NGF daily in a dose calculated on the basis of 280 B.U./g body weight for 22 days. A period of 7 days elapsed between the end of treatment and the evaluation. Several neurologic signs were present in this kitten suggesting involvement of pathways external to the dorsal funiculus at the time of making the experimental lesion. It was necessary to employ manual expression to empty the bladder for the first few days post-operatively. Weakness was observed in the hind legs subsequent to operation but recovery of walking and running occurred during the first 10 days after operation and by the time of the evaluation very little deficit remained. No evidence of tactile placing response was observed at any time and even at the end of the period of treatment the hind legs occasionally tripped over each other.

This animal showed a small but consistent evoked potential from the fibers of the dorsal funiculus when recording electrodes were placed as far rostral as 2 mm from the level of the lesion in response to stimulation applied to the dorsal root L7. Stimulation was also applied directly to the dorsal funiculus at a point 5 mm caudal to the level of the lesion and this evoked an identifiable response at the level of the lesion and up to a point 4 mm rostral to it, but little, if any, response was recorded beyond this point.

3. *Experimental kitten No. 624* received NGF daily in a dose calculated on the basis of 860 B.U./g body weight for 28 days. A period of 14 days elapsed between the end of treatment and the evaluation. This kitten was exceptionally healthy and active during the entire post-operative period. No walking or running deficit was observed except for a slight weakness on the first day after operation. At the time of evaluation a slow tactile placing response of questionable significance was observed.

Stimulation of the dorsal root L6 evoked a prominent spike with a single peak which could be recorded 6 mm rostral to the level of the lesion with a delay of 1.3 msec. No effort was made to record this response to dorsal root stimulation at any point further rostral. It was possible, however, to exchange stimulating and recording electrodes and in this way evoke an antidromic response from the dorsal root L6 by stimulation of the dorsal funiculus at a point 6 mm rostral to the lesion (Fig. 4c and d).

Direct stimulation was applied to the surface of the dorsal funiculus at a point 5 mm caudal to the lesion and this evoked a large unimodal spike when recording electrodes were placed 14 and 19 mm rostral to the lesion. Conduction velocity determined from these records gave an average value of 65 m/sec. No effort was made to record this potential from points further rostral, as the laminectomy only extended 20 mm beyond the lesion, in order to avoid any hazard to the subsequent fixation and sectioning for histologic study.

4. Experimental kitten No. 613 received NGF daily in a dose calculated on the basis of 2200 B.U./g body weight for 14 days. A period of 35 days elapsed between the end of treatment and the final evaluation. This kitten was healthy and active during the entire post-operative period but a slight weakness was initially present in the hind legs which gradually cleared up. When standing it tended to sway from an erect posture. No tactile placing response was observed in the hind legs at any time subsequent to operation.

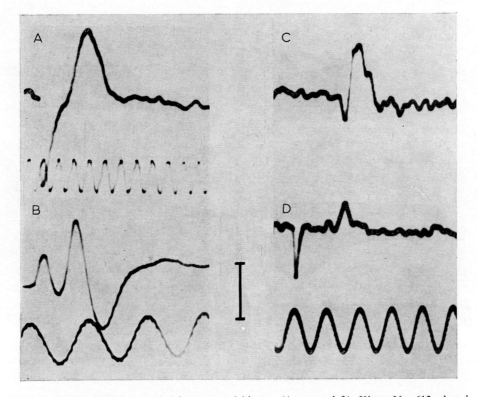

Fig. 4. Evoked potentials recorded from treated kittens. (A, upper left). Kitten No. 613: dorsal funiculus stimulated 30 mm caudal to lesion; recorded from dorsal funiculus 5 mm rostral to lesion; calibration 50 μV; 5000 c/sec. (B, lower left). Kitten No. 624: dorsal funiculus stimulated 5 mm caudal to lesion; recorded from dorsal funiculus 14 mm rostral to lesion; 2000 c/sec. (C, upper right). Kitten No. 624: dorsal root L6 stimulated; recorded from dorsal funiculus 6 mm rostral to lesion; 1000 c/sec. (D, lower right). Kitten No. 624: dorsal funiculus stimulated 6 mm rostral to lesion; recorded from dorsal root L6 (reverse arrangement of electrodes in C); 1000 c/sec.

Stimuli were applied directly to the dorsal funiculus in this kitten at a point 30 mm caudal to the level of the lesion. A large unimodal spike was evoked at a position 5 mm rostral to the lesion in response to stimulation with 0.7 V. The conduction velocity of this spike was 63.5 m/sec. A similar but smaller potential was observed from a point 8 mm rostral to the lesion. Stimulation of a dorsal root was not attempted (Fig. 4A).

B. Histology of spinal cord in vicinity of the lesion

Control kittens Nos. 612, 625, 626, 628

General. In all cases the level of the lesion is marked by a large vacuole or cyst which is usually separated by a thin layer of tissue from the dorsal surface of the spinal cord. A marked increase in glial cells can be seen both rostral and caudal to the level of the lesion.

Caudal to the lesion. Fibers of the dorsal funiculus appear normal when more than 3 mm caudal to the lesion. A progressive depopulation of the tract is observed at distances less than this until all but 5% of the number of fibers have disappeared at a point 1 mm from the lesion (Fig. 5B). In this 'area of disappearance' some neurons

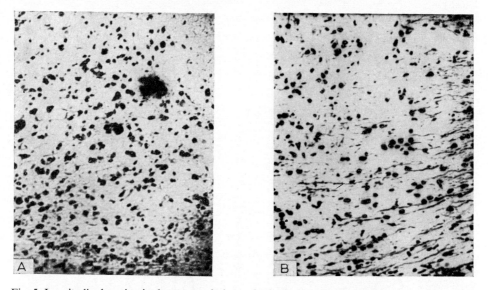

Fig. 5. Longitudinal section in dorsoventral plane of spinal cord of control kitten No. 612 showing dorsal funiculus (A) rostral and (B) caudal to lesion 49 days after crushing. Bodian protargol stain, × 250.

taper abruptly and the resulting filament then fragments. Other neurons terminate in a small Y-shaped enlargement or occasionally exhibit a more extensive enlargement resembling a growth cone. Branching of normal diameter neurons can occasionally be seen but more frequently fine collateral processes are given off. Thus, as the lesion is approached, fewer and fewer fibers of normal diameter are seen while fine filamentous processes (often fragmented) are seen to within 0.5 mm of the lesion. Throughout this area numerous glial cells are interspersed among the remaining fibers. The fibers become involuted and intertwined just caudal to the perimeter of the vacuole, changing direction at random and thus forming a small plexus in the path of the dorsal funiculus.

In the 'area of disappearance' glial cells are frequently seen in intimate relationship with axons looking much like 'snails on a piece of grass' (Fig. 6). In a few instances the glial cells can be seen in the process of extending a 'foot' to contact the axon,

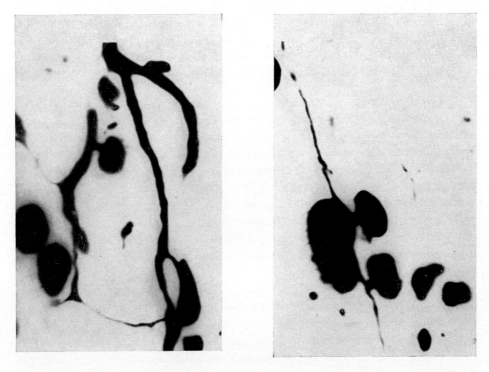

Fig. 6. Details from dorsal funiculus of control kitten No. 612, 2 mm caudal to lesion (see Fig. 5) showing axons tapering, branching and forming collateral sprouts; in both views oligodendroglia can be seen attached to axons and also in process of extending 'foot' on to an axon. Bodian protargol stain, × 2100.

but in most cases the glial cell lies closely adherent to the neuron. While glial cells in their normally unattached condition have a roughly circular outline, they assume an elongated outline once they have come to lie against the fibers.

Lesion area. The normal path of the dorsal funiculus and adjacent tracts is obliterated by the large vacuole usually seen at the level where the neurons were crushed in the initial operation. The diameter of this vacuole is between 0.5–1.0 mm. A closely packed invasion of collagenous fibers is seen immediately caudal to it, forming a complete blockade to the fibers of the dorsal funiculus. Among the collagenous fibers, an occasional neuron can be seen which in no case succeeded in penetrating the blockade.

In those sections cut in the dorsoventral plane, small fascicles of neurons can be seen sweeping around either side of the vacuole. These fibers, when carefully traced, are seen to have migrated towards the axis of the spinal cord from their origin in the lateral funiculus or the dorsal roots.

Rostral to the lesion. A high density of glial cells with an occasional axon borders the rostral perimeter of the vacuole (Fig. 5A). These axons appear to belong to one of three groups: (1) descending axons which probably represent descending branches of dorsal root fibers; (2) degenerating fibers which are clearly fragmented; (3) occasional very small fibers probably originating in the proprio-spinal tract. With increasing distance from the vacuole, an increasing number of axons sweep into the path of the dorsal funiculus from adjacent tracts until the true identity of this pathway is lost 4–5 mm rostral to the lesion. No growth cones are seen rostral to the lesion with the exception of a very occasional one on a descending axon.

NGF treated kittens

Gross examination of specimens. All three treated kittens showed increased vascularization of the lesion area. The vacuole or cyst at the site of the lesion caused either swelling or local depression of the substance of the cord, depending on whether it was fluid-filled or not. Due to the difference in dosage and length of treatment of the three kittens the observations on each animal will be described separately.

Kitten No. 629. Dosage 280 B.U./g/day (least). The depression of the substance of the cord at the level of the lesion resulted in an apparent disappearance of axons and cells in the more superificial sections. The mid-level of the lesion was marked by an invasion of deeply stained collagen fibers on a line almost completely across the cord.

Caudal to the lesion. A normal population of fibers ascends in the dorsal funiculus to a level about 1.3 mm caudal to the lesion at which point the number of fibers decreases and they start to intertwine tortuously. Closer to the lesion small vacuoles and increasing numbers of glial cells are seen (Fig. 7B). The collagenous invasion at the lesion is itself invaded by fascicles of fibers which never seem to penetrate but

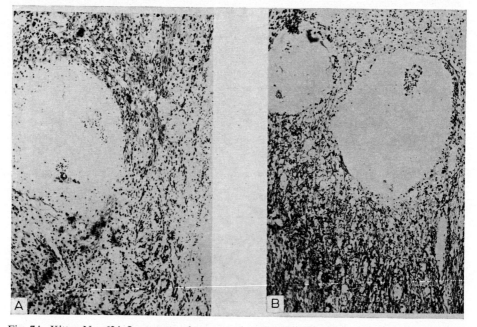

Fig. 7A. Kitten No. 624. Low power dorsoventral section showing large vacuoles at site of lesion and occasional axons passing around it. Rostral direction top. Bodian protargol stain, × 125. Fig. 7B. Kitten No. 629. Low power sagittal section of dorsal funiculus showing small fascicles of fibers passing ventral to the vacuole. Occasional small fascicles can be seen rostral to the vacuole but are better seen in Fig. 8 (detail). Rostral direction top. Bodian protargol stain, × 125.

often show growth cones at their tips. Between the collagenous blockade and the axons below, numerous small fragmented fibers can be seen.

Rostral to the lesion. Immediately rostral to the lesion, glial cells and degenerated debris are seen between the vacuoles with only a few single fibers appearing, and these are seen only in short lengths. Further rostral, an occasional growth cone is seen but no more than one or two of these appear in each section. Starting about 0.2 mm further rostral, fibers start appearing in the central avenue of the dorsal funiculus until the population of fibers is close to half that of the normal number caudal to the lesion. These fascicles of fibers can be seen entering from the lateral funiculi, dorsal roots, or the central gray matter. Such fibers entering from adjacent tracts occasionally show growth cones but these are easily distinguished by their position from the few fibers which appear to have regenerated past the lesion from the caudal segment of the dorsal funiculus.

Kitten No. 624. Dosage 860 B.U./g/day (median). At the level of the lesion a vacuole approximately 0.6 mm in diameter can be observed, centered 0.8 mm deep to the dorsal surface of the cord. This results in only a slight depression of the dorsal surface and consequent continuity of sections above and below the lesion (Fig. 7A).

Caudal to the lesion. The normal population of healthy fibers of the dorsal funiculus is seen caudal to a point 1.7 mm from the mid-level of the lesion. For a distance of about 1 mm rostral to this level a decrease in the number of fibers is found. Instead of the straight and parallel arrangement below this level, their direction becomes random and confused with an increase in glial cells. In this vicinity occasional growth cones can be observed as well as some branching and the formation of collateral sprouts. Significant groups of fibers are observed, however, which continue through this area, passing somewhat irregularly among the glial cells. As a result of this irregularity, no single fiber can be followed for any great distance, although short lengths of smooth healthy fibers travel from the region of the plexus to a level slightly rostral to the mid-level of the lesion.

Rostral to the lesion. Fascicles of large and small diameter fibers appear rostral to the lesion and continue for a considerable distance. In general, such fibers tend first to pass around the vacuole and then to continue rostrally in a normally straight path closer to the axis of the cord. Such fascicles pass in considerable number between the vacuole and the surface of the cord, but few of these occupy a path within 50 μ of the dorsal surface of the cord after passing the level of the lesion.

The rostral termination of some fibers is accompanied by the appearance of growth cones in the region starting 3 mm from the level of the lesion and extending to the limit of the section (Fig. 8B). However, the population of growth cones does not reach as sharp a concentration at any level as in the case of the kitten No. 613 which received the highest rate of administration of NGF. At all levels rostral to the lesion, smooth fibers are seen suggesting that the limit of growth of such fibers extends beyond the end of the section. In several instances a small blood vessel is seen to be closely accompanied by several axons for a considerable distance (Fig. 8A).

Between 1–3 mm rostral to the lesion, fibers originating from the gray matter enter the path of the dorsal funiculus. They can be seen passing horizontally, singly

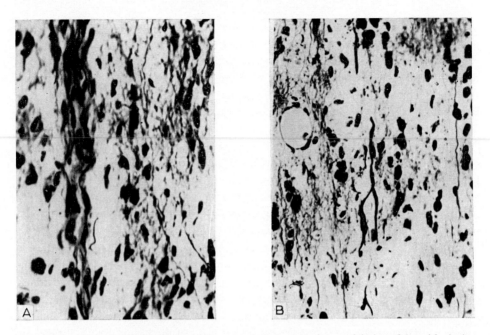

Fig. 8. Kitten No. 624. Details of regenerating axons 3–5 mm rostral to crush lesion of dorsal funiculus. (A). Small blood vessel accompanied by several regenerating axons; Bodian stain, × 700. (B). Rostral end of regenerating axon showing growth cone; Bodian stain, × 550.

and in groups, and when they reach the dorsal funiculus they turn and ascend in that portion nearest to the central gray. Some of these fibers are seen to terminate in growth cones and beyond 5 mm from the level of the lesion it becomes difficult to distinguish fibers which have passed up from the caudal segment of the dorsal funiculus from those which are extrinsic. For this reason no positive estimate can be made of the maximal distance which fibers passing the lesion have extended in a rostral direction in this kitten.

Kitten No. 613. Dosage 2200 B.U./g/day (highest). At the time of exposure for evaluation the gross appearance of the spinal cord in the area of the lesion was not gray-white, as in the control kittens, but was creamy-white in color, similar to the rest of the spinal cord. It was extensively vascularized and at the level of the lesion the dura was somewhat swollen. Upon reflexion of the dura, bundles of silver-whitish appearing tissue resembling fiber bundles were seen running along both dorsolateral aspects of the cord in this region. No place on the cord looked injured and no sharp limit to the area of the lesion was seen.

Formol fixation of the spinal cord resulted in the same local depression of tissue at the site of the lesion as observed in the other treated animals. For this reason, regenerating fibers can be seen growing vigorously just caudal to the lesion but disappearing from the plane of the section at the level of the crush only to reappear at a slightly more rostral level.

Caudal to the lesion (Fig. 9B). A reduction in the number of fibers in the dorsal funiculus is seen beginning 2 mm from the level of the lesion but this only results in

Fig. 9. Longitudinal section in dorsoventral plane of spinal cord of kitten No. 613 showing high density of normal axons on both sides of site of lesion. (A). Dorsal funiculus 2–3 mm rostral from level of crush lesion. (B). Same section 2–3 mm caudal to level of lesion. Compare these sections with similarly located sections from control kitten in Fig. 5. Bodian protargol stain, × 250.

the disappearance of approximately half of the normal population. The numerous remaining fibers are subject to curvature but, in marked contrast to all other kittens, their outline is smooth and of normal diameter. No tapering nor formation of collateral sprouts can be seen and the overall appearance is strongly suggestive of healthy vigorous growth. The collagenous barrier is present but is entered and penetrated by a considerable number of fibers which then pass rostrally in marked contrast to the situation obtained in the control animals and in those receiving a lower dosage of NGF.

Rostral to the lesion. As a result of the depression of the cord substance at the lesion site, the perimeter of the stained sections represents tissue at the surface of the cord and shows only glial cells and degenerative debris. However, commencing 1–2 mm from the lesion, increasing numbers of fibers are seen to emerge into the plane of the section and continue along a path parallel to the axis in a rostral direction. In those sections, deep to the surface, where the vacuole is seen, similar fibers sweep around and past it on either side. While the numerous large diameter fibers all present a smooth outline and follow a straight course, a few of the smallest fibers appear fragmented and their course is undulating (Fig. 9A).

These large fibers appear most numerous between 2–5 mm from the level of the crush, especially in the central third of the width of the cord. Glial cells are less numerous than observed caudal to the lesion and only occasional branching of fibers is observed. Near the rostral limit of this region numerous growth cones can be seen, most frequently associated with the termination of large diameter fibers (Fig. 10). All fibers in this pathway terminate between 5 and 6 mm rostral to the lesion, creating a

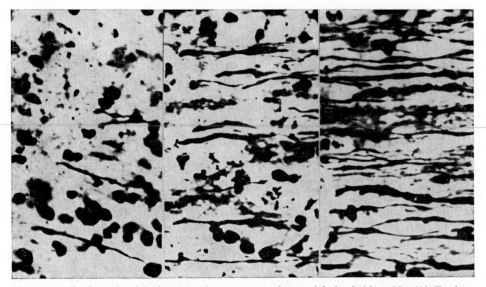

Fig. 10. Details of growing tips of regenerating axons rostral to crush lesion in kitten No. 613. Furthest advance of axons, 6.3 mm beyond lesion, represented at top of three serial views in longitudinal section of dorsal funiculus. Bodian protargol stain, × 850.

uniform limit of development beyond which only glial cells and degenerative debris can be seen. The greatest distance rostral to the lesion that growth cones have been identified is 6.3 mm.

In some stained sections where fine blood vessels can be seen to run in the plane of the section for a short distance, these are frequently accompanied in close relationship by two to four axons. Not all such vessels are accompanied by a group of fibers but where this does occur the association is continued for a considerable distance.

DISCUSSION

The response of axons in specific pathways in the spinal cord to an experimental lesion has been shown by previous investigators to vary with the form of treatment administered. In cats where the entire spinal cord was transected and the animal subsequently treated with the bacterial polysaccharide Piromen, Scott and Clemente (1955) found far greater evidence of regenerative growth in the cortico-spinal pathway when compared to the dorsal funiculus. This finding is in agreement with the increase in hypertrophy and hyperplasia of glial cells in this tract subsequent to transection of the spinal cord in the untreated cat.

When the lesion was restricted to the intrinsic fibers of the dorsal spino-cerebellar tract it was found that regeneration was possible for a very short distance beyond the site of the experimental crush (Liu and Scott, 1958). In the present experiments, the lesion has been limited as closely as possible to the fibers of the dorsal funiculus in keeping with the known effects of NGF on sensory neurons in tissue culture (Levi-Montalcini, 1955). It seems clear from the present study that marked acceleration of regenerative growth of such fibers results from systemic treatment of the animal with an adequate level of this material. While incidental observations were made on fibers of tracts adjacent to the dorsal funiculus and evidence of growth enhancement was observed, the lesions in the present study were not placed so as to permit a critical evaluation of regenerative growth in any but the fibers of the dorsal funiculus.

The smooth outline of axons caudal to the lesion in the kitten receiving highest dosage resembled normal uninterrupted fibers in contrast to the tapering, branching and fragmentation seen in the controls. Rostral to the lesion a high population of regenerating axons was seen in this same high dosage animal while no regenerating fibers were seen in any of the controls.

Glial cells at the site of the lesion may act to remove degenerated debris. While no marked difference in the number of glial cells per unit area has been found between the control and treated animals, the attachment of these cells to the fibers was only seen in the untreated kittens. This suggests that degeneration was decreased in the treated animals caudal to the lesion.

The presence of specific types of terminal enlargements has been described as indicative of active growth (Cajal, 1928) but the interpretation of this histological evidence requires the correlation with evoked potential evidence in the spinal cord to assure the identity of the growing fiber. The close correspondence between the most rostral limit reached by regenerated fibers in the histological sections and the evoked potential records supports the attribution of origin of the growing fibers and validates the measurement of maximum growth. This applies especially to the kittens receiving the larger doses (kittens Nos. 624 and 613).

Regenerative growth during the period of treatment might represent merely a transient enlargement of the terminal pseudopodia, and if so it would be expected that these would be retracted during any appreciable period following the conclusion of administrative therapy. The fact that the histological sections from kitten No. 613 show healthy vigorous axons well above the crush level despite the 35 days which elapsed after treatment before evaluation suggests that such growth as has been observed is not of a temporary character. On the other hand, it had been hoped that once regenerative growth of fibers had been initiated it might continue beyond the period of treatment and this has not been substantiated.

The evaluation by evoked potential method showed that in the control kittens and in kitten No. 629 (low dosage) there was no significant response rostral to the lesion when stimuli were applied to the intact fibers of the dorsal funiculus. On the other hand, the two kittens treated with higher dosages showed that: (1) the maximum distance rostral to the lesion at which an evoked potential could be recorded was proportional to the length of the period of administration of NGF; (2) the magnitude of the evoked response correlated roughly with the daily dosage but quantitation of response under the circumstances of these experiments is not precise.

Summary of the histologic results showed a consistent differentiation related to either the daily dosage or the length of the administration of NGF as follows.

1. The extent of the 'region of disappearance' of fibers rostral to the lesion is approximately inversely proportional to the daily dosage of NGF.

2. The population of viable axons arriving at the collagenous blockade is positively related to the daily dosage of NGF.

3. The close association of glial cells with axons (which appears to be associated with their degeneration) is seen caudal to the lesion in the control kittens but not in the treated kittens.

4. The number of fibers penetrating the collagenous blockade correlates with the daily dose of NGF.

5. The population of healthy fibers seen rostral to the lesion which exhibit growth cones is directly related to the daily dosage of NGF.

6. The distance that healthy fibers with growth cones can be traced from the site of the lesion in a rostral direction is correlated with the number of days of administration of NGF.

7. The forefront of outgrowth of axons seen rostral to the lesion of the high dosage kitten (No. 613) implies an extremely vigorous regenerative growth during the period of administration which is not seen in any of the other kittens.

These results are consistent with the view that nerve growth factor produces a marked enhancement of the regenerative growth of axons of the dorsal funiculus of the spinal cord of kittens. There is a consistency among all the effects observed as a result of administration which indicates that the magnitude of the daily dosage determines the density of the regenerating axon population while the number of days of administration determines the distance rostral to the lesion to which the regenerating axons will grow. There is no evidence that any continued regenerative growth will persist after the end of the period of administration nor is there evidence that regression will take place after administration is concluded.

While there are small but consistent histologic changes in the kitten receiving low dosage (No. 629) as compared to the controls, no evidence of the effect of this treatment was found by the evoked potential method, and this level of dosage is considered inadequate. The kitten which was treated for the longest period with the median dose showed fascicles of fibers whose evoked potential could be recorded at least 19 mm rostral to the lesion. Finally, the 'high dose' kitten (No. 613) showed a massive regenerative growth by all tests but the distance of outgrowth was limited by the short period of administration. Thus, a dosage of 900 B.U. NGF/g body weight/day appears to be the minimum which will produce a significant enhancement of regeneration. This compares with the minimum dosage of 1000 B.U. NGF/g body weight/day found by Crain and Wiegand (1961) to be required to produce either hypertrophy or hyperplasia in intact mice.

The present experiments were undertaken on the hypothesis that growth enhancement was the major deficit to be overcome in the accomplishment of spinal regeneration and the results from the dorsal funiculus support this concept. It is not yet known whether such growth stimulus will result in regeneration without modification of the scar tissue matrix or whether both impediments must be overcome for successful growth as in the present experiments. The success of the present study has been to demonstrate a means by which many of the unsolved problems may be answered and a wide range of further experiments are currently under way.

SUMMARY

Spinal axons will develop a blockade to regenerative growth after interruption by a crush lesion. This may be rendered penetrable by axon tips through the administration of a bacterial polysaccharide or by envelopment of the lesion site with a molecular membrane filter sheet. Since this regenerative growth of spinal neurons subsequent to treatment has proven very limited in extent, the employment of a nerve growth stimulating factor (NGF) extracted from mouse salivary gland has been examined in the current experiments. This substance has previously been shown to enhance the growth of sympathetic and sensory neurons and, therefore, all experimental lesions were made on the dorsal funiculus of kittens.

Administration of NGF systemically to such animals produced a marked enhancement of regenerative growth when dosage exceeded a liminal value. The extent of such growth was in close agreement when determined by both evoked potential and histologic methods; the distance regenerated being proportional to the length of administration while the abundance of axons showing growth beyond the experimental lesion was related to the therapeutic dosage.

These results suggest that enhancement of regenerative growth by an appropriate agent plays a major role in the re-establishment of neural connections in the spinal cord following an experimental lesion.

ACKNOWLEDGEMENT

This investigation was supported in whole by Public Health Service Research Grant B 837 from the National Institute of Neurological Diseases and Blindness.

REFERENCES

BAZAN, C., (1954); The influence of the new factor of growth (Vitamin T-Goetsch) upon the regeneration of peripheral nerve. *Minerva chir. (Torino)*, **9**, 692–699.

BROWN, J. C., AND MCCOUCH, G. P., (1947); Abortive regeneration of the transected spinal cord. *J. comp. Neurol.*, **87**, 131–137.

BUEKER, E. D., SCHENKEIN, I., AND BANE, J. L., (1960); The problem of distribution of a nerve growth factor specific for spinal and sympathetic ganglia. *Cancer Res.*, **20**, 1220–1228.

CAJAL, S. RAMÓN Y, (1928); *Degeneration and Regeneration of the Nervous System*. London, Oxford University Press.

CAMPBELL, J. B., BASSETT, C. A. L., HUSBY, J., AND NOBAK, C. R., (1957); Regeneration of adult mammalian spinal cord. *Science*, **126**, 929.

CLEMENTE, C. D., (1963); Regeneration in the vertebrate central nervous system. *Int. Rev. Neurobiol.*, **6**, 257–301.

COHEN, S. J., (1959); Purification and metabolic effects of a nerve growth promoting protein from snake venom. *J. biol. Chem.*, **234**, 1129–1137.

CRAIN, S., AND WIEGAND, R., (1961); Catecholamine levels of mouse sympathetic ganglia following hypertrophy by salivary nerve growth factor. *Proc. Soc. exp. Biol. Med.*, **107**, 663–665.

DAVIDOFF, L. M., AND RANSOHOFF, J., (1948); Absence of spinal cord regeneration in the cat. *J. Neurophysiol.*, **11**, 9–11.

FREEMAN, L. W., (1952); Experimental observations on axonal regeneration in transected spinal cord of mammals. *Clin. Neurosurg.*, **8**, 294–319.

GIBSON, W. C., (1940); Degeneration and regeneration of sympathetic synapses. *J. Neurophysiol.*, **3**, 237–247.

GUTMANN, E., AND SANDERS, F. K., (1942); Functional recovery following nerve grafts and other types of nerve bridge. *Brain*, **65**, 373–408.

HARKIN, J. C., (1963); Nerve regeneration: variations in ultrastructure. *Fed. Proc.*, **22**, 316.

HOFFMAN, H., (1951); Fate of interrupted nerve fibres regenerating into partially denervated muscles. *J. exp. Biol.*, **29**, 211–219.

KOENIG, H., GROAT, R., AND WINDLE, W. F., (1945); A physiological approach to perfusion fixation of tissues with formalin. *Stain Technol.*, **20**, 13–22.

LEVI-MONTALCINI, R., (1955); Neuronal regeneration *in vitro*. *Regeneration in the Central Nervous System*. W. F. Windle, Editor. Springfield, Ill., Thomas.

LEVI-MONTALCINI, R., AND BROOKER, B., (1960); Excessive growth of the sympathetic ganglia evoked by a protein isolated from the mouse salivary gland. *Proc. nat. Acad. Sci., (Wash.)*, **46**, 373–384.

LIU, C. N., AND SCOTT, D., JR., (1958); Regeneration in the dorsal spino-cerebellar tract of the cat. *J. comp. Neurol.*, **109**, 153–167.

McCOUCH, G. P., (1963); Degeneration and regeneration in the central nervous system. *Neuropathology*. J. Minkler and K. T. Neubuerger, Editors. New York, McGraw-Hill.

SCHENKEIN, I., AND BUEKER, E. D., (1962); Dialyzable cofactor in nerve growth promoting protein from mouse salivary gland. *Science*, **137**, 433–434.

SCOTT, D., JR., (1964); in the press.

SCOTT, D., JR., AND CLEMENTE, C. D., (1955); Regeneration of spinal cord fibers in the cat. *J. comp. Neurol.*, **102**, 633–670.

SCOTT, D., JR., AND LIU, C. N., (1963); The effect of nerve growth factor on regeneration of spinal neurons in the cat. *Exp. Neurol.*, **8**, 279–289.

SPERRY, R. W., (1951); Mechanisms of neural maturation. *Handbook of Experimental Psychology*. S. S. Stevens, Editor, New York, Wiley (Ch. 7).

SUGAR, O., AND GERARD, R. W., (1940); Spinal cord regeneration in the rat. *J. Neurophysiol.*, **3**, 1–19.

THULIN, C. A., (1960); Bioelectrical characteristics of regenerated fibers in the feline spinal cord. *Exp. Neurol.*, **2**, 533–545.

VON KOECHLIN, B., UND VON MURALT, A., (1947); Der neuro-regenerative Wuchsstoff 'N. R.' *Helv. chim. Acta*, **30**, 519–524.

WEISS, P., AND CAVANAUGH, M., (1959); Further evidence of perpetual growth of nerve fibers. *J exp. Zool.*, **142**, 461–473.

WINDLE, W. F., (1955), Editor; *Regeneration in the central nervous system*. Springfield, Ill., Thomas.

WINDLE, W. F., AND CHAMBERS, W. W., (1951); Regeneration in the spinal cord of the cat and the dog. *J. comp. Neurol.*, **93**, 241–257.

YOUNG, J. Z., (1942); The functional repair of nervous tissue. *Physiol. Rev.*, **22**, 318–374.

DISCUSSION

TREVOR HUGHES: In the examination of spinal cords of human diseases one occasionally encounters bundles of nerve fibers of peripheral nerve type 1 very rarely. A spinal cord is totally invaded by such fibers. It is my experience that these fibers arise either: (1) from damaged posterior nerve roots; (2) from damaged axons from anterior horn motoneurons.

The factors that permit this unusual type of nerve growth appear to be: (1) damage to axons; (2) *absence* of neuroglia, either normal central nervous system or an astrocytic glial scar; (3) long survival (years) after the axonal damage.

Could Dr. Scott or other members present comment on these findings?

SCOTT: Since I am a neurophysiologist I have an advantage on you, because we can stimulate our fibers. I would like to know where these came from, I am wondering whether they might be there somewhat incidentally as a conceivable invagination into the spinal cord, of even a peripheral nerve that might run as you suggest over some vascular defect and then simply remain there.

GLEES: From Dr. Scott's work I would say it is not surprising that posterior root fibers and posterior column fibers will regenerate. The cell body lies outside and developmentally the posterior columns are posterior roots, attaching themselves to the spinal cord to ascend. They might just as well have run outside as this happens evolutionary. So here we have a different problem. I don't think it is intraspinal regeneration in the very true sense of the word. If you could show this for the pyramidal tract it would be a different matter.

TREVOR HUGHES: Some of the serial sections showed clearly that they come from the posterior nerve roots. This of course is in line with Cajal's work, showing that there is regeneration in rhizotomy. What is different in the cases I showed is that the altered conditions in the spinal cord permit the invasions. What these altered conditions are I do not know precisely, but it seems to me that the absence of glials is very important. I do not think connective tissue is any barrier to the growth of these nerves, in fact it may be an advantage.

GUTMANN: I wonder if you have any picture of glial cells in these experiments. Evidently the effect could be due either to the neuron or to the satellite cells. The experiments of Levi-Montalcini all indicate that the factor is a diffusable agent acting on the neuron. It would be interesting to see whether the orientation of the glial cells would change after the treatment and whether this orientation is important for the regeneration.

The second point I would like to make is the following: We did some experiments in peripheral nerve regeneration, trying to get action potentials in the first days after crushing. The threshold is extremely high and in the first few days we never succeeded to stimulate it above the lesion.

SCOTT: To answer the first question most clearly we should have tissue culture studies with particular emphasis on glial development subsequent to administration of NGF. Since such studies are not available I can only compare the appearance of glial cells in our treated and our control kittens.

The principal cell type was oligodendroglia which were very numerous in the vicinity of the lesion in the control kitten. These cells frequently adhered to or were closely associated with the degenerating axons. In the treated kittens the glial cells were somewhat less numerous but by no means absent. However, they were only rarely seen associated with axons and almost entirely appeared with round or oval outlines distributed through the substance of the cord independent of the regenerating axons.

In reply to your second question we have never examined our regenerating neurons earlier than 1 month after crushing. In the kitten which was treated for 28 days we evoked a potential in regenerating fibers 7 mm rostral to the lesion by stimulating the dorsal root L7. We then showed that stimulation could be applied at the same point on the regenerating axons and evoke a potential response in dorsal root L7 using about the same strength of stimulus. However, our time interval after crushing is much longer than yours so we cannot comment on your observation.

GUTMANN: May I ask the question why you did not test the growth factor on peripheral regeneration? Because it should effect at least the rate of regeneration in peripheral nerve.

SCOTT: I quite agree that the effect of growth factor should be tested on peripheral regeneration but we have not done this in the kittens we have studied.

GUILLERY: Have any effects been noted on the normal cells of your material? For example, on the anterior horn cells, in terms of Nissl substance, nerve fibrils, or even of boutons ending up on the cells?

SCOTT: We have not yet employed the special stain required for adequate staining of Nissl substance, nerve fibrils or boutons.

Some Ultrastructural Features of Segmental Demyelination and Myelin Regeneration in Peripheral Nerve

H. DE F. WEBSTER

Massachusetts General Hospital, Boston, Mass. (U.S.A.)

Segmental demyelination, first described by Gombault in peripheral nerves of guinea pigs with chronic lead intoxication (Gombault, 1880), is characterized by focal breakdown of myelin sheaths with relative sparing of axons, and has been identified as the main histopathological lesion in a number of important human and experimental diseases of the nervous system, including multiple sclerosis (Adams and Kubik, 1952), acute idiopathic polyneuritis (Haymaker and Kernohan, 1949), experimental allergic neuritis (Waksman and Adams, 1956) and diphtheritic neuritis (Waksman *et al.*, 1957; Fisher and Adams, 1956).

Recently, the submicroscopic features of the segmental demyelination and remyelination occurring in experimental diphtheritic neuritis were described (Webster *et al.*, 1961) and subsequently, the same process was studied in tissue culture (Peterson *et al.*, 1962). As expected, the lesions were different from those encountered in our studies of Wallerian degeneration (Webster, 1962) and nutritional deprivation (Collins *et al.*, 1964).

However, the cardinal features of segmental demyelination were identified in a detailed study of two peripheral nerve biopsies from a patient with metachromatic leucodystrophy (Webster, 1963), a familial, degenerative disease of unknown cause resulting in widespread demyelination in the central nervous system associated with sulfatide accumulation (Brain and Greenfield, 1950; Austin, 1960).

Hopefully, presentation of selected, ultrastructural features of normal peripheral nerve and these two pathological processes will clarify some aspects of myelin formation and breakdown in Schwann cells.

Several observations on the normal ultrastructure of Schwann cells seem pertinent before considering segmental demyelination. The perinuclear and paranodal concentration of Schwann cell cytoplasm and its reduction to a thin, cytoplasmic rim around the remaining, internodal myelin are well known, consistent, features of myelinated nerve fiber histology. Mitochondria, endoplasmic reticulum and Golgi membranes are present in Schwann cell cytoplasm along with occasional dense bodies and lamellar inclusions (Fig. 1)*, which may represent mitochondria with highly ordered cristae similar to those described in lizard glia (Gray, 1960). Unfortunately, limitations in preparative techniques have prevented uniform preservation of all these organelles along the entire internode of large, myelinated fibers so that it has not yet been possible to undertake a detailed, critical analysis of their possible submicroscopic relationship to myelin during its formation and maintenance.

The ultrastructure of myelin and Schwann cell membranes has been reviewed recently (Robertson, 1962). The myelin sheath is a compact spiral of membrane layers. The outer mesaxon links the Schwann cell surface membrane and the outer layer of compact myelin while the innermost layer of the spiral is continuous with the inner mesaxon and the axon–Schwann cell membrane, which is immediately adjacent to the axolemma. Schwann cell cytoplasm lies between myelin lamellae in Schmidt-Lantermann clefts and also is present in small pockets surrounded by terminal loops of myelin lamellae at nodes of Ranvier. Although the contour of the myelin sheath is usually smooth and relatively cylindrical, focal variations in contour, consisting of loops and folds indenting the axon or Schwann cell cytoplasm have been described in a serial section study of peripheral nerve (Webster and Spiro, 1960) and are illustrated in rat sciatic nerve during myelination (Fig. 2). An understanding of these variations in contour and their appearance in different planes of section readily explains the apparent presence of two myelinated axons within a single Schwann cell (Fig. 3), an observation that has not yet been documented by serial section study.

A single myelin sheath surrounding a group of closely packed, small axons has been observed occasionally in peripheral nerve (Geren, 1956; Robertson, 1960). Fig. 4, although superficially similar to the illustrations of these authors, shows two features that are unique in our experience and have not been described previously. The individual axons are surrounded by Schwann cell cytoplasm and are separated from the cytoplasm (also Schwann cell) containing the myelin sheath by collagen. Whether the cytoplasm shown in this section originates in the same or different Schwann cells remains to be established by further serial section observations.

Demyelination

In our study, clinically apparent diphtheritic neuritis began 5–8 days after toxin injection and the first ultrastructural lesions were apparent at the onset of clinical weakness. They included focal alterations in the lamellar pattern of myelin at nodes, incisures, and adjacent to the loops and folds that are normal variations in myelin sheath contour. The myelin sheath became discontinuous and segmented 2–7 days later, as severe weakness developed and progressed. Mitochondria and granular endoplasmic reticulum were prominent at the margins of these myelin segments and ovoids; frequently, membranes separated them from the Schwann cell cytoplasm

---

* *Key to figures.* All figures are electron micrographs of osmium tetroxide fixed nerves embedded in epon or araldite and stained with lead (except Fig. 12, which is from an unstained section). Guinea-pig sciatic nerves are shown in Figs. 1, 3–8, 13, and 14; human sural nerve is illustrated in Figs. 9–12 and 15, and fig. 2 is of rat sciatic nerve, 48 h after birth.

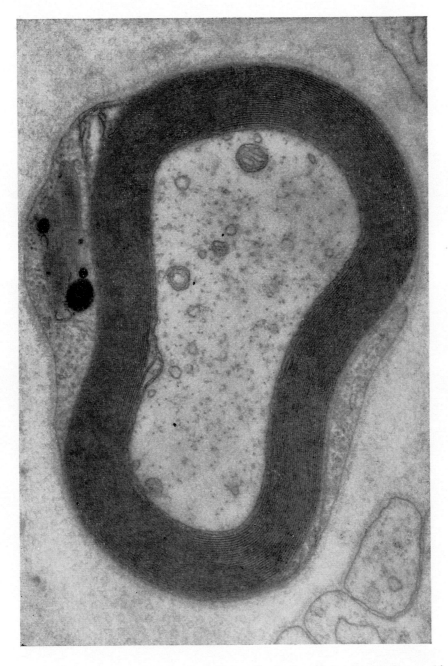

Fig. 1. Cross section, normal myelinated fiber. The myelin sheath, with its alternate dense and less dense lines arranged in a compact spiral, is continuous with the outer and inner mesaxons. To the left, the Schwann cell cytoplasm contains an irregular, partially membrane limited body made up of lamellae with the same period (approximately 125 Å) as the adjacent myelin. Dense bodies of varying size are also apparent, × 56,000.

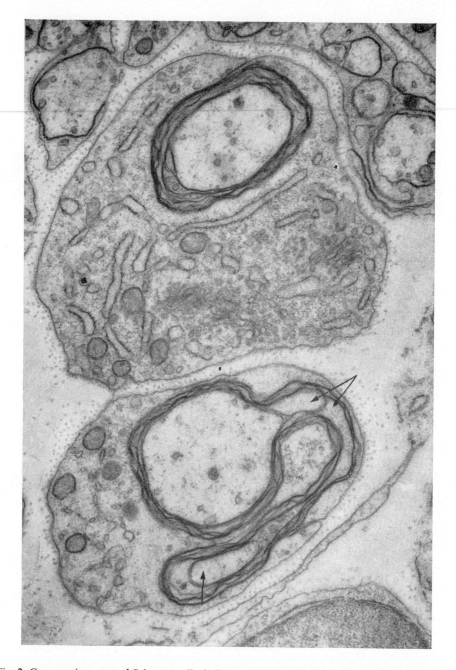

Fig. 2. Cross section, normal Schwann cells during myelination. A circular myelin sheath, granular endoplasmic reticulum, and Golgi membranes are present in the Schwann cell at the top of the figure. Lamellae of a long myelin loop in the lower Schwann cell surround axoplasm (lower arrow) and pockets of Schwann cell cytoplasm (upper arrow), × 32,000.

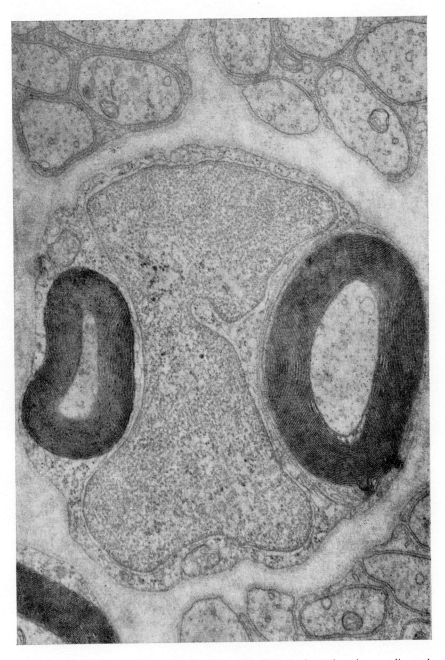

Fig. 3. Cross section, normal Schwann cell. To the left of the nucleus, there is a myelin oval containing axoplasm which is continuous on serial section with the main portion of the myelin sheath and axon shown on the right, × 43,500.

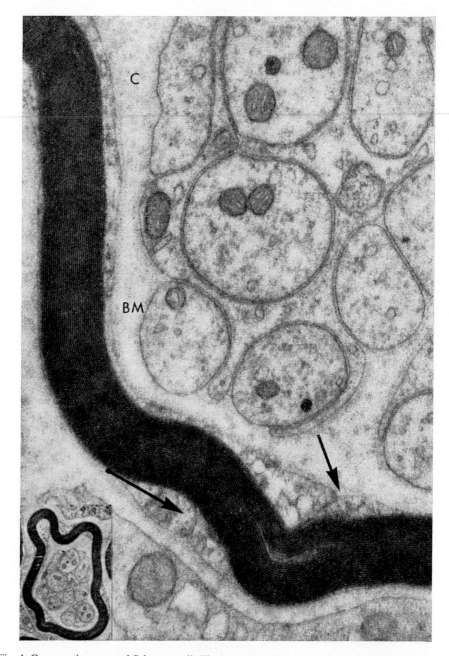

Fig. 4. Cross section, normal Schwann cell. The lower left portion of the Schwann cell shown in the insert is illustrated at higher magnification to demonstrate the external and internal mesaxons (arrows). The Schwann cell basement membranes (BM) adjacent to the Schwann cell and axon surface membranes as well as the collagen (C) separating the Schwann cell cytoplasm containing the myelin sheath and that surrounding the unmyelinated axons, although faintly stained, can be identified, × 48,000; insert, × 6,600.

adjacent to the axon (Fig. 5). As demyelination proceeded, the irregular, osmiophilic ovoids were segregated in one portion of the Schwann cell cytoplasm; the axon indented the opposite surface membrane. Histiocytes appeared 4–8 days after the onset of weakness, and were readily identified by their processes and array of cytoplasmic organelles. At this time, the Schwann cell cytoplasm containing myelin remnants and that which surrounded the axon were often discontinuous in a single plane of section (Figs. 6,7). Subsequently, the ovoids, with their rim of Schwann cell cytoplasm, were phagocytosed and the axons were remyelinated. In regions with extensive myelin breakdown and numerous macrophages, irregular lipid bodies of varying density were frequently encountered in endothelial cells (Fig. 8).

In an infant or child with metachromatic leucodystrophy, normal initial development is followed by progressive dementia, loss of motor function, and death within a few years. A sural nerve biopsy from a $2\frac{1}{2}$ year old girl with a mild ataxia showed characteristic metachromasia on frozen section stained with cresyl violet–acetic acid. Phase and electron microscopic study of osmium tetroxide fixed samples of this nerve revealed the cardinal features of segmental demyelination. Focal breakdown of myelin was apparent in almost every Schwann cell while axons, with their filaments, mitochondria, and tubules of agranular endoplasmic reticulum remained normal. Two other important alterations were also apparent. Numerous inclusions, similar in size and distribution to those showing metachromasia on frozen sections, were present in Schwann cells containing both myelinated (Fig. 9) and unmyelinated (Fig. 10) axons. These Schwann cell inclusions were also present in foci of myelin breakdown and similar inclusions were observed in macrophages, along with ovoids showing a lamellar pattern similar to that of normal myelin (Fig. 11). The ultrastructure of many myelin sheaths was normal in a single plane of section. In occasional fibers, scattered randomly within a fascicle, a band within the myelin sheath showed a striking alteration of its lamellar pattern characterized by an overall increase in density and a decrease in the distance between dense lines (Fig. 12). This focal, band-like change in the lamellar pattern occupied the entire circumference of the sheath; its width in cross section and its location within the sheath (*i.e.* adjacent to the axon, center of the compact myelin, or adjoining Schwann cell cytoplasm) varied.

The opposite sural nerve was biopsied 6 months later when the child was stuporous and quadriparetic. Schwann cell inclusions, foci of demyelination, and macrophages were more numerous in sections from this nerve; the lamellar pattern of most myelin sheaths was characterized by disappearance of the intermediate line and irregular separation as well as discontinuities of the major dense lines.

Remyelination

After 10–14 days of clinically progressive diphtheritic neuritis, early remyelination was identified in many Schwann cells while other myelin sheaths in the same fascicle either were normal or showed evidence of fragmentation and breakdown. The Schwann cell cytoplasm often surrounded the axon completely and contained numerous mitochondria, profiles of granular endoplasmic reticulum, as well as a long mesaxon, which

References p. 171/172

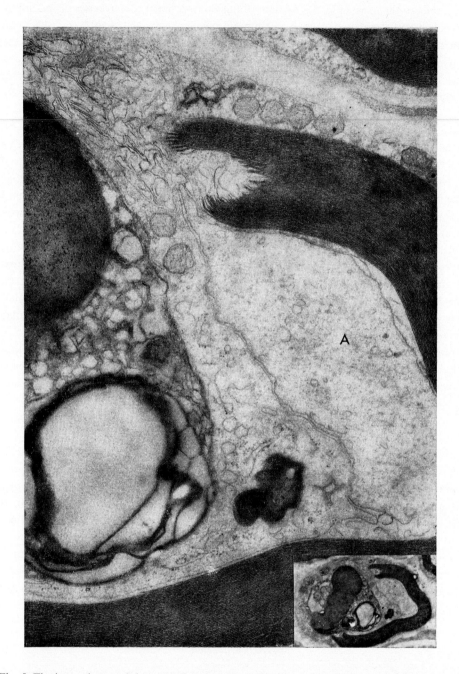

Fig. 5. The insert shows a Schwann cell during diphtheritic neuritis; the periaxonal region of this cell is also shown at higher magnification. Mitochondria and profiles of granular endoplasmic reticulum are prominent in the cytoplasm separating membrane limited, irregular, myelin remnants and the axon (A), × 32,000; insert, × 4900.

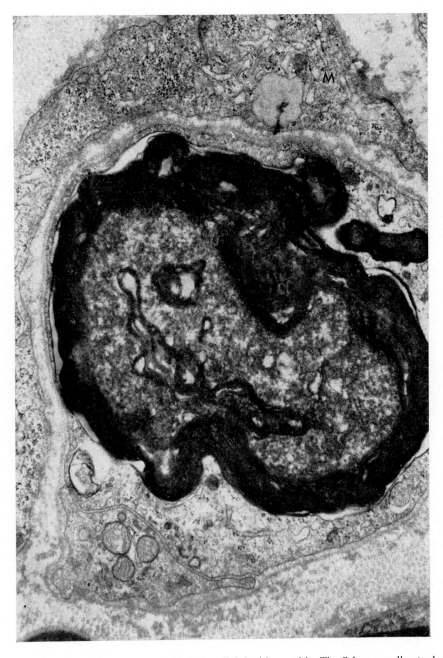

Fig. 6. Cross section of a Schwann cell during diphtheritic neuritis. The Schwann cell cytoplasm containing a large, osmiophilic ovoid is partially encircled by a macrophage process (M) and is continuous on serial section with that surrounding the axon in Fig. 7, × 26,000.

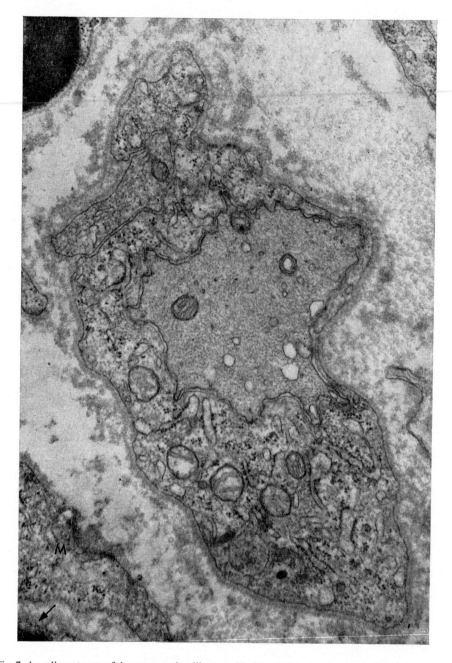

Fig. 7. An adjacent area of the same section illustrated in Fig. 6, showing the macrophage process (M) between the Schwann cell cytoplasm containing the osmiophilic ovoid (arrow) and that which surrounds the axon, × 34,000.

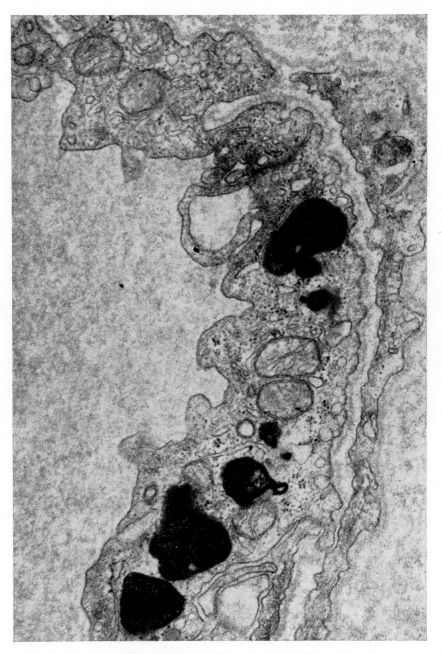

Fig. 8. Cross section, endothelial cell during diphtheritic neuritis. Several irregular, dense, ovoids are present in the cytoplasm, × 41, 000.

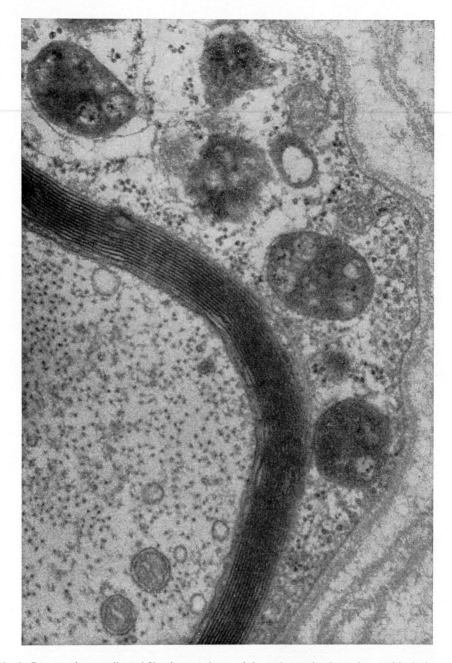

Fig. 9. Cross section, myelinated fiber in metachromatic leucodystrophy. Irregular, oval inclusions of varying density are adjacent to mitochondria and dispersed, granular endoplasmic reticulum in Schwann cell cytoplasm. The myelin sheath and axon appear normal, × 58,000.

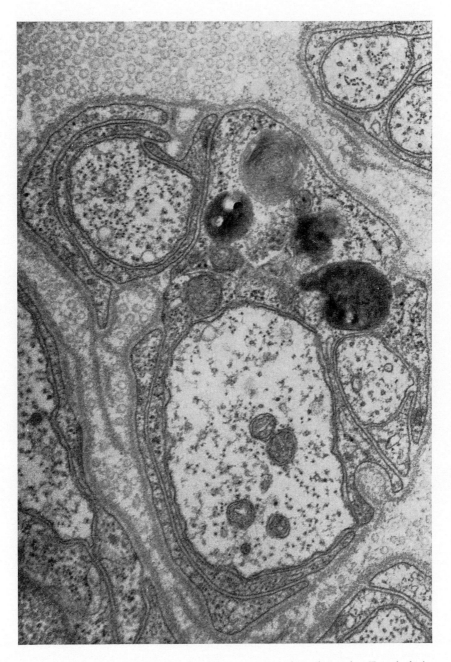

Fig. 10. Cross section, unmyelinated axons in metachromatic leucodystrophy. Four inclusions of varying size and density in this plane of section are present in Schwann cell cytoplasm surrounding unmyelinated axons, × 38,000.

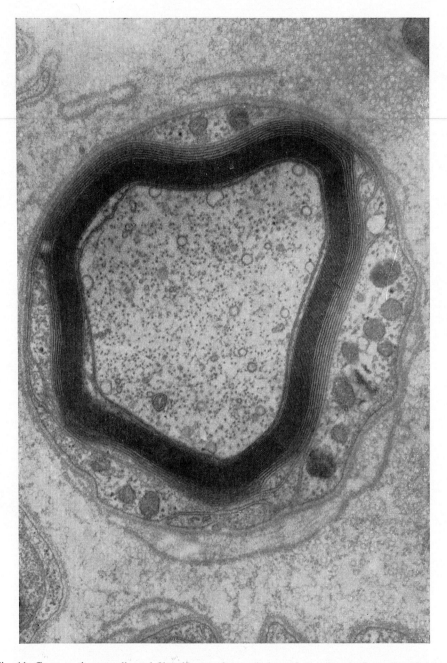

Fig. 11. Cross section, myelinated fiber in metachromatic leucodystrophy. A circumferential band of compact myelin lamellae adjacent to the axon shows an increase in overall density and a decrease in the period between dense lines to approximately 100 Å. The spacing of lamellae external to this band is slightly increased (130–140 Å) and two small inclusions are present in the Schwann cell cytoplasm, × 29,000.

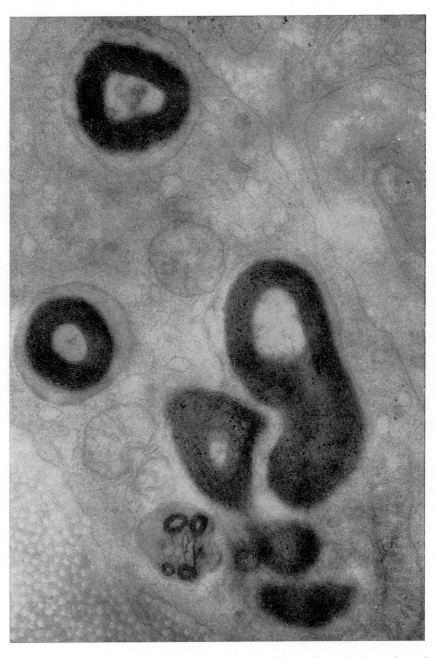

Fig. 12. Cross section, macrophage process in metachromatic leucodystrophy. Several membrane limited ovoids with the lamellar pattern and period similar to that encountered in normal myelin are present in macrophage cytoplasm, × 34,000.

frequently formed a simple spiral separating layers of Schwann cell cytoplasm. The Schwann cells with several lamellae of compact myelin still showed a rather broad band of cytoplasm between the axon–Schwann cell membrane and the inner layer of the sheath; small cytoplasmic pockets were also present between each layer of the sheath immediately adjacent to the junction of the mesaxons with the outer and inner margins of the compact myelin. These features, as well as the variations in contour of the newly formed myelin sheath have been well illustrated in serial sections (Webster et al., 1961).

At this same, early stage of remyelination, the configuration of many Schwann cell surface membranes was extremely complex; interdigitating cytoplasmic processes (Fig. 13) and the intimate relationship of their membranes to the Golgi complex and granular endoplasmic reticulum (Fig. 14) were observed frequently. The size and shape of these processes varied in serial sections.

In the initial peripheral nerve biopsy from the child with metachromatic leucodystrophy, some Schwann cells adjacent to macrophages filled with ovoids showed a long mesaxon arranged in a loose spiral (Fig. 15). Others contained a few lamellae of electron microscopically normal, compact myelin with small pockets of Schwann cell cytoplasm between each layer at the mesaxon–myelin junction. This appearance, thought to be consistent with myelin regeneration following segmental demyelination, was not observed in the second biopsy when neuropathy was pronounced clinically, and the demyelination much more severe histologically.

DISCUSSION

In analyzing these observations, it is quite apparent that their interpretation and significance depend on the limitations of current, preparative techniques and the statistical restrictions inherent in electron microscopic study.

The lack of critically uniform preservation of Schwann cells, their organelles, and the myelin sheaths surrounding large axons has precluded a high resolution study of mitochondria, endoplasmic reticulum, and the Golgi complex and their individual roles in myelin formation, maintenance or destruction during segmental demyelination; it has not interfered with the topographic study of the normal myelin sheath, the identification of some of its lesions, or the general pattern of remyelination. The relationship of preparative artifact and variations in myelin sheath contour was discussed in our original study (Webster and Spiro, 1960). This has been re-evaluated and their existence confirmed following the use of perfusion fixation in which all peripheral nerves of the lower extremities were rapidly fixed in situ while a natural limb posture was maintained (Webster and Collins, 1964). This technique greatly improved the quality of our peripheral nerve preservation and enabled us to study, in a single 2 μ longitudinal section, entire myelin internodes (500–800 μ) which were free of pleating and other signs of distortion. Also, even though exact contour is more difficult to determine during examination of unfixed, whole nerve fibers and their myelin sheaths, Speidel (1932) observed occasional, focal thickening of the paranodal myelin in living, tadpole nerves; furthermore, in tissue cultures of dorsal root ganglia,

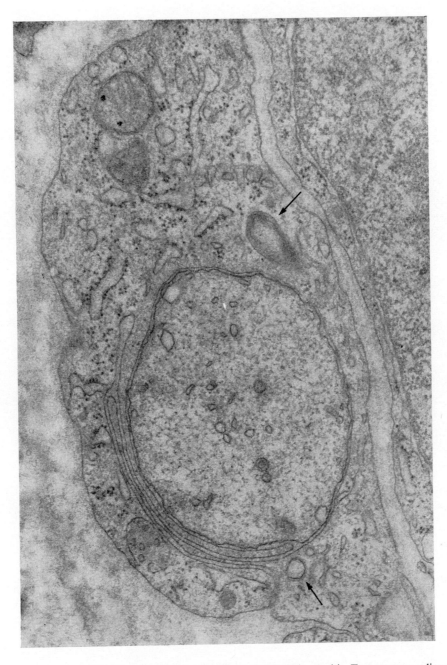

Fig. 13. Cross section, Schwann cell and axon during diphtheritic neuritis. Two, narrow, adjacent, tongues of Schwann cell cytoplasm are bounded by surface membranes forming a complex mesaxon. A circular profile (lower arrow) may represent a cross section of a similar tongue. An inclusion with an internal layered structure (upper arrow) is also present in Schwann cell cytoplasm, × 23,000.

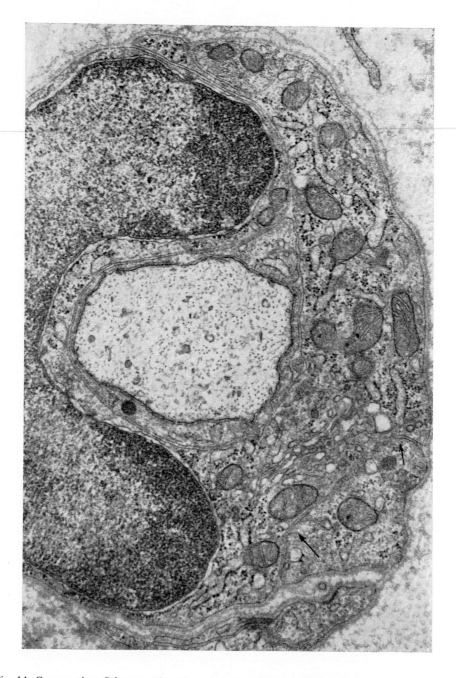

Fig. 14. Cross section, Schwann cell and axon during diphtheritic neuritis. A separate tongue of Schwann cell cytoplasm surrounds the axon. Two extensions of Schwann cell surface membrane (arrows) can be traced into the cytoplasm where Golgi membranes, cisternae of granular endoplasmic reticulum and mitochondria are numerous. Another, small, separate process containing Schwann cell cytoplasm is present at the top of the figure, × 32,000.

Peterson *et al.* (1962) noted that the initially smooth myelin sheaths developed rippling, herniations, and nodal overgrowths during subsequent development and maintenance. These observations also indicate that not all myelin sheaths are smooth and cylindrical

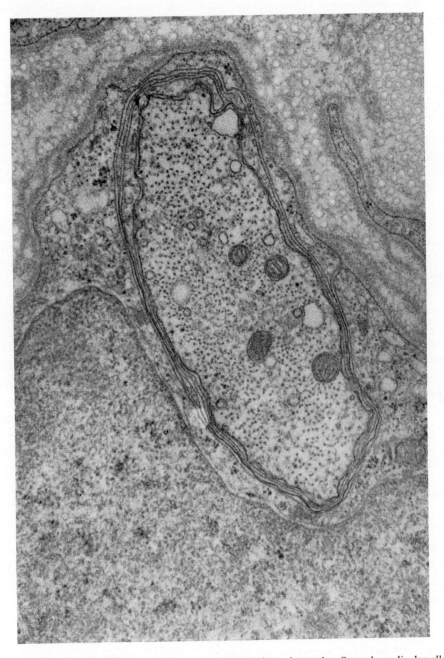

Fig. 15. Cross section, Schwann cell in metachromatic leucodystrophy. Several myelin lamellae, occasionally separated by narrow zones of Schwann cell cytoplasm, are continuous with the external and internal mesaxons and form a simple spiral around the axon, × 38,000.

References p. 171/172

throughout their internodal length even though Finean (1962) has recently suggested that these variations in contour were gross contortions of myelin related to preparative artifact and could be minimized by maintaining nerve under tension during fixation; he did not mention any of the well known artifacts resulting from surgical exposure and removal of nerve prior to fixation.

As mentioned previously, our ultrastructural study of diphtheritic neuritis delineated the sequential pattern of myelin breakdown in Schwann cells. Although the description of a dynamic process by a selection of fixed images may have many disadvantages, the same sequence and topographical pattern of myelin breakdown in Schwann cells were observed in dorsal root ganglia cultures treated with diphtheria toxin (Peterson et al., 1962). Perhaps the most interesting ultrastructural features of this demyelinative process were the persistence of the axon and Schwann cell surface membrane contact and the possibility that substantial membrane synthesis might have taken place in Schwann cells during myelin breakdown as well as during regeneration. Unfortunately, our observations did not define any consistent, significant alteration prior to the onset of weakness that could be correlated with the immediate decrease observed in the incorporation of inorganic phosphate into ATP of cultured normal, human, kidney cells, an effect that could be reversed by the addition of antitoxin (Kato and Pappenheimer, 1960). The variation in the severity and distribution of the observed demyelination also remained unexplained.

The segmental demyelination, distribution of inclusions, and the alterations in the lamellar pattern of myelin observed in the two nerves from a patient with metachromatic leucodystrophy were also found in sections of sural nerve from a second child, severely ill with this disease. Regeneration of myelin was found only in the initial biopsy of the first patient, whose clinical symptoms were relatively mild. If the Schwann cell inclusions corresponding to those showing metachromasia prove to be deposits of sulfatide by chemical analysis, then our electron microscopic study of these nerves will have demonstrated that sulfatide deposition in Schwann cells does not depend on myelin formation, maintenance, or breakdown since it also occurs in Schwann cell cytoplasm surrounding unmyelinated axons. Also, its presence in Schwann cells probably does not result from its accumulation in brain and subsequent transport to peripheral nerve. Finally, if our criteria for the identification of remyelination are correct, myelin breakdown in this disease may be followed, for some time at least, by the formation of electron microscopically normal myelin.

Although our study of the remyelination that follows diphtheritic neuritis was limited to the early stages, several observations differ from those previously described in normal myelination (reviewed by Robertson, 1962) and deserve brief, cautious interpretation. Although a mesaxon (Fig. 24 of Webster et al., 1961) or a simple spiral similar to that shown in Fig. 15 are occasionally seen, a complex array of surface membranes and cytoplasmic organelles (Figs. 13, 14) is more frequently encountered. If such appearances are representative of the *in vivo* situation along a substantial length of remyelinating axon, they might account for the reversal of mesaxons and the subsequent development of variations in contour of compact myelin (see Figs. 24–26, Webster et al., 1961). Also they might imply that membrane synthesis in this process of remyelination takes place at multiple foci and variable rates; the Schwann cell cytoplasm that persists adjacent to the axon and between lamellae at mesaxon–myelin junctions may be important in adjusting the size and form of the myelin sheath to that of the axon as recovery of function occurs. Since changes in the position of Schwann cell nuclei and Ranvier nodes were frequently observed in living, peripheral nerve fibers by Speidel (1932), the possibility that the myelin sheath may change its contour and dimensions during normal development and maintenance, as well as during recovery from segmental demyelination, deserves consideration.

SUMMARY

The myelin breakdown with relative sparing of axons (segmental demyelination) which occurs in experimental diphtheritic neuritis has been studied electron microscopically in order to help clarify the mechanism of myelin destruction and formation in Schwann cells. Focal alterations in the lamellar pattern of myelin were present at the onset of clinical symptoms. Then, the myelin sheath became discontinuous. Intracytoplasmic membranes frequently separated myelin fragments from the axon. Later, the axon and myelin remnants occupied opposite margins of the Schwann cell. Finally, the myelin breakdown products appeared in isolated islands of Schwann cell cytoplasm adjacent to macrophages.

During remyelination of the surviving axon by the Schwann cell, the arrangement of mesaxons and cytoplasmic organelles were frequently complex. The variations in contour of newly formed myelin were similar to those observed in normal nerve fibers during myelinogenesis.

In three nerve biopsies from two patients with metachromatic leucodystrophy, cytoplasmic inclusions corresponding to metachromatic material on frozen section were present in Schwann cells with unmyelinated as well as myelinated axons. In addition to the ultrastructural features of segmental demyelination and remyelination described above, a few fibers contained a circumferential alteration in the lamellar pattern of myelin.

ACKNOWLEDGEMENT

This study was supported by a Research Grant (NB-03789-02) from the National Institute of Neurological Diseases and Blindness, Bethesda, Md.

Participation in this Symposium was made possible by a Travel Grant (GB-871) from the National Science Foundation, Washington, D.C.

REFERENCES

ADAMS, R. D., AND KUBIK, C. S., (1952); The morbid anatomy of demyelinative diseases. *Amer. J. Med.*, **12**, 510–546.

AUSTIN, J. H., (1960); Metachromatic form of diffuse sclerosis III. Significance of sulfatide and other lipid abnormalities in white matter and kidney. *Neurology (Minneap.)*, **10**, 470–483.

BRAIN, W. R., AND GREENFIELD, J. G., (1950); Late infantile metachromatic leukoencephalopathy with primary degeneration of the interfascicular oligodendroglia. *Brain*, **73**, 291–317.

COLLINS, G. H., WEBSTER, H. DE F., AND VICTOR, M., (1964); The ultrastructure of myelin and axonal alterations in sciatic nerves of thiamine deficient and chronically starved rats. *Acta neuropath.*, in the press.

FINEAN, J. B., (1962); Correlation of electron microscope and X-ray diffraction data in ultrastructure studies of lipoprotein membrane systems. *The Interpretation of Ultrastructure*. R. J. C. Harris, Editor. *Symp. int. Soc. Cell Biol.*, **1**, 89–100.

FISHER, C. M., AND ADAMS, R. D., (1956); Diphtheritic polyneuritis. A pathological study. *J. Neuropath. exp. Neurol.*, **15**, 243–268.

GEREN, B. B., (1956); Structural studies of the formation of the myelin sheath in peripheral nerve fibers. *Cellular Mechanisms in Differentiation and Growth*. D. Rudnick, Editor. Princeton, N. J., Princeton University Press (p. 213–220).

GOMBAULT, M., (1880/81); Contribution à l'étude anatomique de la néurite parenchymateuse subaiguë et chronique — Névrite segmentaire péri-axile. *Arch. Neurol. (Paris)*, **1**, 12–38 and 178–190.

GRAY, E. G., (1960); Regular organization of material in certain mitochondria of neuroglia of lizard brain. *J. biophys. biochem. Cytol.*, **8**, 282–285.

HAYMAKER, W., AND KERNOHAN, J. W., (1949); Landry–Guillain–Barré syndrome; clinico-pathologic report of 50 fatal cases and critique of literature. *Medicine (Baltimore)*, **28**, 59–141.

KATO, I., AND PAPPENHEIMER, A. M., (1960); An early effect of diphtheria toxin on the metabolism of mammalian cells grown in culture. *J. exp. Med.*, **112**, 329–349.

PETERSON, E. R., YONEZAWA, T., AND MURRAY, M. R., (1962); Experimental demyelination with diphtheria toxin in cultures of dorsal root ganglia. *Proc. IVth Int. Congr. Neuropath.*, **2**. H. Jacob, Editor. Stuttgart, Georg Thieme (p. 274–278).

ROBERTSON, J. D., (1960); The molecular structure and contact relationships of cell membranes. *Progress in Biophysics*, **10**. Oxford, Pergamon Press (p. 343–418).

ROBERTSON, J. D., (1962); The unit membranes of cells and mechanisms of myelin formation. *Ultrastructure and Metabolism of the Nervous System*. S. R. Korey, A. Pope, and E. Robins, Editors. *Res. Publ. Ass. nerv. ment. Dis.*, **40**, 94–158.

SPEIDEL, C. C., (1932); Studies of living nerves. I. The movements of individual sheath cells and nerve sprouts correlated with the process of myelin sheath formation in amphibian larvae. *J. exp. Zool.*, **61**, 279–332.

WAKSMAN, B. H., AND ADAMS, R. D., (1956); A comparative study of experimental allergic neuritis in the rabbit, guinea pig, and mouse. *J. Neuropath. exp. Neurol.*, **15**, 293–333.

WAKSMAN, B. H., ADAMS, R. D., AND MANSMANN, H. C., (1957); Experimental study of diphtheritic polyneuritis in the rabbit and guinea pig. I. Immunologic and histopathologic observations. *J. exp. Med.*, **105**, 591–614.

WEBSTER, H. DE F., (1962); Experimental diphtheritic neuritis and Wallerian degeneration: a comparative study of demyelination utilizing phase and electron microscopy. *Proc. IVth int. Congr. Neuropath.*, **2**. Stuttgart, Thieme (p. 6–7).

WEBSTER, H. DE F., (1963); Schwann cell alterations in metachromatic leukodystrophy: Preliminary phase and electron microscopic observations. *J. Neuropath. exp. Neurol.*, **21**, 534–554.

WEBSTER, H. DE F., AND COLLINS, G. H., (1964); A comparison of osmium tetroxide and glutaraldehyde perfusion fixation for the electron microscopic study of the normal rat peripheral nervous system. *J. Neuropath. exp. Neurol.*, in the press.

WEBSTER, H. DE F., AND SPIRO, D., (1960); Phase and electron microscopic studies of experimental demyelination I. Variations in myelin sheath contour in normal guinea pig sciatic nerve. *J. Neuropath. exp. Neurol.*, **19**, 42–69.

WEBSTER, H. DE F., SPIRO, D., WAKSMAN, B. H., AND ADAMS, R. D., (1961); Phase and electron microscopic studies of experimental demyelination II. Schwann cell changes in guinea-pig sciatic nerves during experimental diphtheritic neuritis. *J. Neuropath. exp. Neurol.*, **20**, 5–34.

DISCUSSION

SZENTÁGOTHAI: Your beautiful pictures have very convincingly shown that the undoubtedly ingenious theory of myelin formation by rotation does not fully explain the facts. I only want to direct attention to the strange loose myelin formations seen in the satellite cells surrounding sympathetic ganglion cells in mammals, birds and reptiles. Below the surface of these cells immediately adjacent to the ganglion cells one finds up to 5–10 double layers with irregular spacing, which only very occasionally admit presynaptic terminals to get close to the surface of the nerve cell. As some part of the many dendrites of the ganglion cells is similarly surrounded by such double layers of loose myelin it is difficult to imagine how they could be formed by simple rotation either of the ganglion cell or the satellites.

Have you any idea how these double layers can be produced: for example by infolding and invagination and finally interstitial growth and division of the invaginated membrane systems as we could very crudely visualize on a piece of tissue (*e.g.* a handkerchief)?

WEBSTER: The means by which membranes are synthesized in satellite cells surrounding neurons has not yet been clearly established. The complex arrangements you describe as well as those described by Rosenbluth and Palay (*J. biophys. biochem. Cytol.*, **9** (1961) 853) could not be formed by simple rotation. Presumably, the pattern and extent of satellite cell membrane growth is determined quite specifically by the adjacent neuronal surface membrane. This growth may occur by reduplication of membrane molecular constituents or by the addition of components synthesized in the satellite cell cytoplasm.

GUTMANN: Could you comment on the changes in number of the mitochondria during degeneration and regeneration of the axon?

WEBSTER: The paranodal accumulations of axonal mitochondria during the early phase of Wallerian degeneration may represent either migration of pre-existing mitochondria to nodal regions or formation of new mitochondria. (*J. Cell Biol.*, **12** (1962) 361). Neither the biochemical function of these morphologically normal mitochondria nor their role in the early phase of axonal degeneration are known.

The appearance and number of mitochondria during axonal regeneration has not been investigated in our laboratory. However, as pointed out in the above publication, the number of mitochondria observed electron microscopically in a single section is not a reliable, quantitative estimate; interpretations derived from such observations are frequently misleading.

GLEES: I was very much impressed by the excellent quality of your pictures. Could you say something more about the fixation and embedding techniques?

WEBSTER: The preparative techniques utilized are described in detail in the references cited.

LUBIŃSKA: Is there any information regarding the number of mitochondria in the node of Ranvier in normal and regenerating nerve?

WEBSTER: As far as I know, no quantitative data based on serial section study of nodes with the resolving power necessary to identify and count axonal mitochondria have been published.

ECCLES: These very beautiful pictures of the complex folding of myelin lamellae should be converted into three dimensional models so that we can visualize their actual relationship along an appreciable length of the axon. Could this technically be possible, as seems likely, because Dr. Webster has shown us serial sections with electron microscopy?

In reply to Dr. Szentágothai's question Dr. Webster has already in part formulated a modification of the Geren rotational hypothesis that would help at least in part to account for his remarkable findings. I hope he will continue in this important theoretical development.

WEBSTER: Your comments are appreciated and hopefully; when enough serial sections have been examined to establish a consistent pattern, construction of three dimensional models can be utilized to show these complex arrangements.

GLEES: I wonder whether some of the larger cisterna in the cytoplasm of Schwann cells could also have been used to build up membranes when they join up with the surfaces. It this a reasonable assumption?

WEBSTER: The quality of preservation achieved in published electron-microscopic studies of peripheral nerve has been inadequate to define accurately the relationships between Schwann cell organelles, the mesaxon and the myelin sheath. The answer to your question awaits further refinements in preparative technique.

LEHMANN: I would like to ask a few questions regarding the neuritis induced by diphtheria toxin. Did you find naked axons in the time interval between demyelination and remyelination? Do you have any information regarding the time interval between the onset of demyelination and the onset of remyelination in your cases?

WEBSTER: No 'naked' axons were observed; although demyelinated, they were always at least partially enclosed by Schwann cell cytoplasm.

In our study of guinea-pig sciatic nerves, remyelination was first identified approximately 10 days after the onset of myelin breakdown.

SINGER: I would like to ask a question regarding the dark bodies which I saw in the micrographs of your axons. Is this a common feature, or is it mainly due to your staining technique and treatment of the material?

WEBSTER: The dark bodies are found in degenerating axons and probably represent mitochondrial remnants. Their appearance is not the result of staining or tissue preparation.

Development, Degeneration and Regeneration
of Receptor Organs

J. ZELENÁ

Institute of Physiology, Czechoslovak Academy of Sciences, Prague

The problem of differentiation and maintenance of receptor organs is more or less a problem of their dependence upon the nervous system. The question was raised a century ago, when Ranvier (1875) found that taste buds disintegrate after the section of gustatory nerves. Thus a receptor organ consisting of a group of specialized cells of non-nervous character was found to depend for the maintenance of its structural integrity on the nervous system. Another example was thus added to the cumulating evidence on the trophic effect of innervation on the maintenance of the peripheral tissues.

The trophic influence of nerve fibres on the periphery has many modalities (for nervous effect on regeneration see Singer, 1952, 1963, and this Volume; for neuro-muscular relations see Gutmann, 1962, 1963; Gutmann and Hník, 1962; Gutmann, this Volume; Eccles, 1963a, b). From these, the effect of sensory nerve fibres on their receptor organs represents a special case of the trophic effect exerted in the reverse direction to the conduction of impulses. In some receptors the nervous effect on differentiation probably precedes the onset of function. For these reasons, receptor organs appear to be a suitable model for studying the trophic and inductive effects of nerve fibres and their relation to function. However, main problems have not yet been subjected to experimental analysis, and the nature of the trophic factor hitherto remains unknown.

As far as receptor organs are concerned, their dependence on innervation was studied on different types of receptors after peripheral nerve degeneration and regeneration with varying results and conclusions. The present evidence is reviewed in four chapters: 1. taste organs (p. 175); 2. lateral-line organs (p. 182); 3. skin receptors (p. 186); and 4. muscle receptors (p. 190). General implications are discussed in chapter 5 (p. 202).

1. TASTE ORGANS

The investigation of taste buds yielded consistently clear-cut evidence of the trophic influence of nerve fibres upon receptor organs, until the controversial results of the transplantation experiments in urodeles have shown that the conclusions cannot yet be generalized and that the problem still requires further analysis.

References p. 206–211

A. Development

Taste organs begin to differentiate at a time when the tongue — or barbel — epithelium becomes invaded by gustatory nerve fibres. This time coincidence was observed both in mammals (Marchand, 1902), in human foetuses (Kubota and Kubota, 1960), in mouse and cat embryos (Cajal, 1929), in rats shortly after birth (Torrey, 1940), and in fish (Landacre, 1907, in *Ameiurus*). It has been explained as a manifestation of the organizing influence of gustatory nerve fibres upon epithelial cells. When in-growing nerve fibres arrive at the basal membrane of the papillae, adjacent groups of epithelial cells undergo a gradual change in shape. The cells become elongated and penetrate from the basal layer, where they originate, to the outer surface where their sensory hairs protrude to the gustatory porus (Fig. 1). An intimate

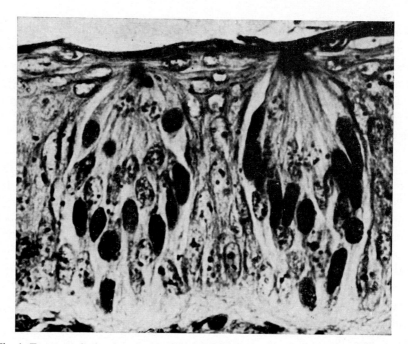

Fig. 1. Two taste buds of a circumvallate papilla of the rat, × 922. (From Guth, 1963).

relationship exists between gustatory nerve endings and taste cells. Button-shaped nerve endings are embedded in deep infoldings of the plasmal membrane of taste cells (Engström and Rytzner, 1956; De Lorenzo, 1957, 1963; Murray and Murray, 1960; Trujillo-Cenóz, 1961). According to electron-micrographic studies, the classification into gustatory and sustentacular cells seems to be incorrect. A rapid turnover of cells into taste buds, their degeneration and differentiation take place even under normal conditions (Beidler *et al.*, 1960; Beidler, 1963). The two cell types probably represent different stages in the life cycle of the taste cell. For information on their function see '*Olfaction and Taste*' (Zotterman, 1963).

In salamanders an increase in the number of organs during growth can be brought about by budding and migration (Stone, 1933a,b,c) but this mechanism has not been demonstrated in mammals.

No attempt has been made to reveal the assumed mechanism of nervous induction of taste buds by denervation experiments at early developmental stages. Another approach was used to test the hypothesis, namely transplantation to a nerve-free environment. Prior to the appearance of taste buds, the tongues of 7-day-old rats were excised and transferred into the anterior eye chamber; taste buds, however, developed in spite of the absence of nerve fibres (Torrey, 1940). The author argued that the nervous influence had possibly been exerted before transplantation was performed, because the tongue epithelium was already innervated several days before grafting. Morphological criteria, however, were insufficient to detect more subtle distinctions of future taste cells at initial stages of differentiation.

In similar experiments on salamander larvae (Stone, 1933a, b, c, 1940) transplantation was carried out at much earlier stages of development. Tongue primordia were removed from the donor before the formation of cranial nerves and transplanted to the body-wall of the host of the same age. Taste buds developed in the grafts at a normal rate. Similarly as in the control tongues *in situ*, they appeared at stage 40 according to Harrison, were increased in number as the grafted tongue grew in size, and persisted up to and through metamorphoses. Older grafts, transplanted just before and during the beginning of taste organ formation, also continued to develop normally. In adult salamanders, taste buds can survive in transplanted tongues for long time-intervals (see page 180). The experiments of Stone (1933a, b, c, 1940) prove beyond doubt that in salamander larvae gustatory fibres are not necessary for the formation of taste organs; they do not, however, exclude the interference of foreign sensory fibres from the new environment.

The problem whether a nervous factor is involved in the initial formation of taste buds thus remains to be answered by further experiments, in which development could be traced from early stages onwards under conditions of a total, controlled denervation.

B. Degeneration

In adult animals, both mammals and fishes, taste organs degenerate in a relatively short time after denervation. Degeneration of taste cells is a physiological event (Beidler, 1963). When innervation is intact, degenerated cells are replaced by newly differentiated ones. In case the mitotic activity is arrested, *e.g.* with colchicin, old taste cells degenerate, but new ones cannot be formed, and consequently taste buds disappear from the tongue epithelium of the rat within 10–20 h (Beidler *et al.*, 1960). Denervation of taste buds probably results in a similar arrest of cell differentiation. The first observation on denervated taste buds dates from 1875 when Ranvier described their degeneration after nerve section in the rabbit (Ranvier, 1875). Since then, the result has been corroborated by numerous additional experiments in different mammals (Vintschgau and Hönigschmied, 1876; Vintschgau, 1880; Drasc, 1887, in rabbits; Baginsky, 1893, 1894; Sandmayer, 1895; Meyer, 1896; Boeke, 1917, in the hedgehog; Olmstead, 1921, 1922, in the dog; Whiteside, 1927; Hayes and Elliot, 1942; Guth,

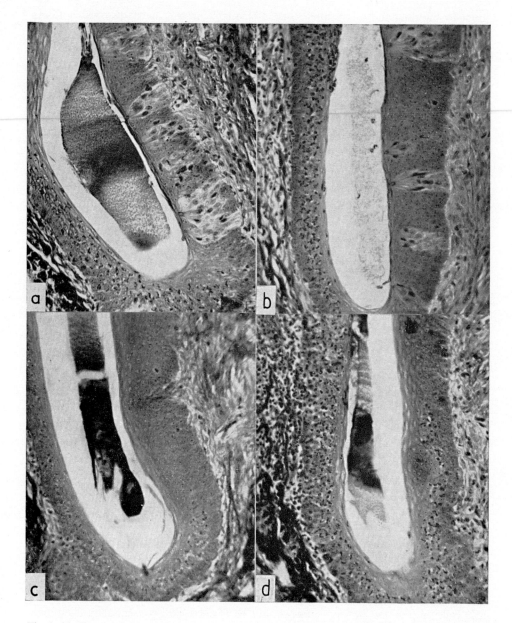

Fig. 2. (a) Circumvallate papilla of a rat 19 weeks after anastomosis of proximal and distal ends of the glossopharyngeal nerve (G-G). Numerous taste buds are on inner trench wall. (b) Circumvallate papilla of a rat 19 weeks after end-to-end anastomosis of proximal vagal and distal glossopharyngeal nerve segments (V-G). Numerous taste buds are on inner trench wall. (c) Circumvallate papilla of a rat 19 weeks after end-to-end anastomosis of proximal hypoglossal and distal glossopharyngeal nerve segments (H-G). Taste buds are absent. (d) Circumvallate papilla of a rat 19 weeks after transection of the glossopharyngeal nerve and evulsion of the proximal segment (G-evulsion). Taste buds are absent. In all parts of the figure the inner trench wall of the circumvallate papilla is to the right. Heidenhain's iron hematoxylin, × 340. (From Guth, 1958).

1958, in the cat; Guth, 1957, in the rat, see Fig. 2). Similarly, degeneration of taste buds was observed after nerve section in the barbel of fish (Olmstead, 1920; May, 1925; Torrey, 1934, 1940; Wagner, 1953). Degeneration of taste organs and their disappearance from the epithelium (Fig. 3) was found to occur with in 7–13 days (Meyer,

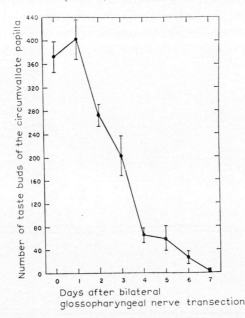

Fig. 3. Decrease of the number of taste buds of the circumvallate papilla of the rat after bilateral transection of the glossopharyngeal nerve. (From Guth, 1957.)

1896; Olmstead, 1920, 1922; May, 1925; Torrey, 1934; Guth, 1957). The process can be slowed down by decreased temperature (May, 1925). Degenerated cells are discarded from the epithelium by phagocytosis (Olmstead, 1920) or by desquamation (Guth, 1957, 1958). However, a gradual dedifferentiation of the taste cells and their persistence at the basal layer were also described (Meyer, 1896; Wagner, 1953). A more detailed study of the degeneration of taste buds in different species is, therefore, necessary either to clarify the mechanisms of their final disintegration or to prove their survival in a dedifferentiated form.

Some of the taste buds in mammals were found to persist for long periods after nerve section, although the majority of organs succumbed to degeneration (Vintschgau, 1880; Baginsky, 1893). According to a semi-quantitative estimation one taste bud was present in every tenth section through the trench-wall of the circumvallate papilla 5 months after unilateral evulsion of the glossopharyngeus nerve (Guth, 1958).

The findings of surviving organs (Vintschgau, 1880; Baginsky, 1893) were occasionally cited as evidence against the validity of the hypothesis that there is a trophic influence of gustatory nerves. However, the innervation areas of the gustatory nerves overlap and many taste buds have a double innervation (Whiteside, 1927; Hayes and Elliot, 1942; Guth, 1963), so that the seemingly denervated taste organs can maintain their structure due to the sensory supply received from contralateral or adjacent nerves which were left uninjured.

An independence of taste organs in relation to gustatory nerve fibres is, on the other hand, clearly demonstrated in the transplantation experiments on urodeles, not only during development (see page 177), but also in adult animals (Mintz and Stone, 1934; Wright, 1951a, b, 1955). In the tongues which were grafted to the orbit, intact taste organs were found 1–12 months after the operation. The number of organs per surface area did not decrease during this time (Fig. 4) (Wright, 1955). It was, however, not

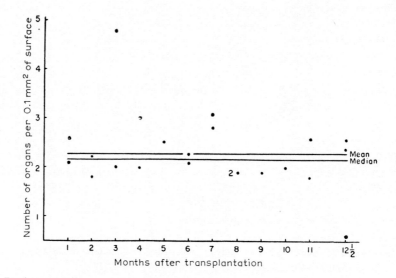

Fig. 4. Persistence of the average number of taste organs per unit surface area in tongue-to-orbit grafts in adult newt. (From Wright, 1955.)

clear whether non-gustatory nerve fibres, which invaded the transplant, could act as a substitute for the gustatory fibres in respect to their end organs (Wright, 1951b, 1955). At the initial period up to 3 weeks after transplantation a short interval was noted when no taste organs could be detected in the grafts (Mintz and Stone, 1934; Wright, 1951b). This phenomenon has been ascribed to the reorganization of the grafted tissue (Wright, 1951b, 1955). It was, however, of interest to learn whether it could be related to the degeneration of the original nerve supply, and whether the appearance of the taste buds was not induced by sensory fibres growing in the tongue from the orbit. This problem was investigated by Poritsky and Singer (1963). In their experiments on the tongue-to-orbit transplants in the urodele *Triturus*, the number of taste buds per unit surface area gradually declined from the first day after transplantation onward. From the 15th to the 25th day, after the original nerve supply had degenerated, taste buds completely disappeared from most of the grafts. They gradually reappeared again, as new nerve fibres grew in the graft and reached the epithelium. After 25 days taste buds were regularly found in all the grafts together with new nerve supply.

To avoid the possibility of a massive invasion of foreign nerve fibres, tongue tips of adult newts were transplanted into the liver (Wright, 1958). Nevertheless, well-preserved taste buds were observed even in these grafts as late as 4 months after transplantation. The occurrence of taste buds depended on the extent to which the tongue epithelium maintained its normal structure. In grafts with normal epithelium taste buds were abundant, whereas in those covered entirely or partly with a membranous thin epithelium taste buds were reduced in number or absent (Wright, 1958) as was the case with the tongue which remained free in the body cavity. It was assumed that the epithelium and taste buds were well preserved in those grafts which become attached early to the liver and become vascularized.

However, an effect of foreign nerve fibres on the maintenance and new formation of taste buds cannot be entirely excluded even in the tongue-to-liver transplants. Sensory nerve fibres are present in the mammalian liver where they form receptor endings in perivascular spaces (Merkulova, 1948). If the innervation pattern is analogous in the newt, sensory nerve fibres might enter the graft with blood vessels and eventually exert a trophic influence on taste buds. Just as with development, complementary experiments are essential for the elucidation of this problem.

C. Regeneration

Following reinnervation, taste buds differentiate anew in the epithelium. The regeneration takes place in a relatively short time, approximately about 11–40 days after crushing the nerve (Olmstead, 1920; May, 1925). Decreased temperature slows down not only degeneration (May, 1925; Parker, 1932), but also regeneration of taste organs (May, 1925) by changing the rate of degeneration and regeneration of nerve fibres.

Can the non-gustatory nerves also induce the formation of taste organs when they are guided to the denervated epithelium after cross-union of the nerves? The vagus nerve stimulates the differentiation of taste organs (Fig. 2) (De Castro, 1944; Guth, 1958), but the vagus contains sensory nerve fibres (Foley and Dubois, 1937), probably even gustatory in character. An experiment of this type thus cannot answer the question. On the other hand no regeneration of taste organs has been observed after reinnervation of the tongue epithelium by motor fibres of the hypoglossal nerve (Fig. 2) (Arey and Monzingo, 1942; Guth, 1958), although previous experiments had indicated such a possibility (Boeke, 1917; Olmstead and Pinger, 1936). It would, however, be of interest to know which types of sensory nerve fibres, besides the gustatory, are competent to initiate the special differentiation of taste organs, and this question still remains to be clarified.

What are, in short, the results?

The problem of the nervous influence on the development of taste buds is still unsolved. On the other hand, degeneration and regeneration of taste buds in relation to degeneration and regeneration of the gustatory nerve fibres is a well-established fact; only in anurans it still requires additional analysis. Furthermore, there are indications that non-gustatory nerve fibres may also exert a morphogenetic and trophic influence on taste organs, and further analysis of this question appears to be very important.

References p. 206–211

2. LATERAL-LINE ORGANS

Lateral-line organs are receptors in the epidermis of amphibians and fish which react to vibration and pressure and thus record stream movements and their changes. They are found in all aquatic lower vertebrates — in larval stages of amphibians and in some adult amphibians, and as canal organs in most fishes. The organs are distributed in lines on the head of the animals, and on both sides of the body along the longitudinal axis. For detailed information on their structure and function see review articles of Wright (1951a) and Dijkgraaf (1963).

The relation of these sense organs to nerve fibres has been subjected to intense investigation both during development and in adult animals. The ampullary lateral-line organs which are apparently electroreceptors (Dijkgraaf, 1963) have not been investigated in this connection and are therefore not referred to in the following chapter.

A. Development

The lateral-line organs develop from an epidermal placode which differentiates in close vicinity to the vagal ganglion forming an alternating thickening of the surface (Harrison, 1903; Stone, 1933c). The primordial cells, after they have reached a certain degree of differentiation, migrate in strands beneath the surface layer of the epidermis. They form groups dispersed in the epidermis above the underlying nerves which supply them. The primordial cells then differentiate into the sense cells with sensory hairs on which the nerve endings terminate and into supporting cells which form a layer around the sense cells (Fig. 5). In most species the organs are submerged under the epidermis and open into a small porus on the surface, so that the hair-like processes of the sensory cells containing a kinocilium and many short stereocilia are set free. Lateral-line organs multiply by budding and migration of the placodal material or of the supporting cells, some of which progressively differentiate into sense cells in the centre of new organs (Stone, 1922, 1933a, b). These accessory organs may either remain attached to the primary ones, thus forming clusters, or, during longitudinal growth, the supporting cells migrate and give rise to new organs in continuation of the lateral-line system (Stone, 1933b, 1935), so that finally the lateral-line system is represented by groups of organs distributed along the nerves. In fish, the organs are localized in canals and the sensory maculae are connected by an undifferentiated cord of mesenchymal cells (Van Bergelik and Alexander, 1962). The lateral-line nerves terminate on the hair cells with rounded endings which contain a large number of synaptic vesicles. The adjacent plasma membrane of the hair cells forms an intricate network of interdigitating folds and tubules (Fig. 6), so that the surface area at the synaptic region is highly increased (Flock and Wersäll, 1962).

Nerve fibres establish contact with the primordial cells very early, before the migration stage. In experimental studies an attempt was made to analyze whether nerve terminals induce the differentiation of lateral-line nerves or not.

In the fish (*Salmo fario*) the lateral-line primordia cannot develop independently of innervation at the early developmental stage before the 10th day after birth (Devil-

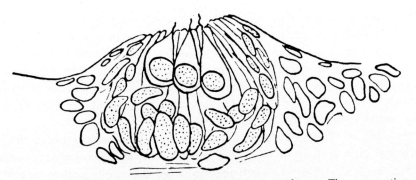

Fig. 5. Schematic drawing of a lateral-line organ of *Triturus viridescens*. The cross-section shows central position of sense cells, surrounded by sustentacular cells. (From Wright, 1951a.)

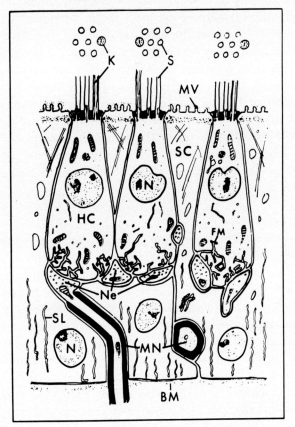

Fig. 6. Schematic drawing of a lateral-line canal organ in the fish, according to electron micrographs. HC, hair cell; SC, supporting cell; MN, myelinated nerve fibre; Ne, nerve ending; K, kinocilia; S, stereocilia; MV, microvilli; N, nucleus; FM, folding membrane system; SL, supporting lamellae; BM, basal membrane. (From Flock and Wersäll, 1962.)

lers, 1948). They need the influence of the nerves to complete differentiation success-fully. If the undifferentiated sensory epithelium is transplanted into the infraorbital space or into the vitellin sac and thus deprived of innervation, only a mass of amorphous tissue is formed and no special organs develop. However, if the grafts are transplanted to the supraorbital canal where they receive adequate innervation, the sense organs differentiate readily even from the immature primordia. In the grafts of fish older than 10 days lateral-line organs differentiate further independently of innervation.

On the other hand, lateral-line organs in amphibians can differentiate without innervation from early developmental stages. Harrison (1903) first rendered clear proof that primordial cells are able to migrate and form lateral-line organs independently, in the absence of lateral-line nerves. Migration of the placodal material and differentiation of the sense organs took place both after extirpation of the vagal ganglia and after grafting of migrating primordia to hosts deprived of lateral-line nerves. Stone (1931, 1936, 1937) corroborated these findings by further variations of the transplantation experiments, proving that the primordium, after it has attained the ability to migrate may be isolated from nervous connections and grafted to any place on the body where it will give rise to the organ. Migration and differentiation continued undisturbed even after the vagal ganglion had been destroyed (Harrison, 1903; Stone, 1937). It has therefore been concluded that the development of lateral-line organs in amphibians is entirely independent of the nervous influence (Harrison, 1903; Stone, 1937).

However, considering the close contact between the vagal ganglion and the placode, an early nervous induction exerted by the vagus cannot be excluded. The cells partly differentiated at this early stage under the nervous influence would then develop independently. Only long deprivation of the nerve supply unmasks their relative independence and reveals the indispensability of the trophic action of the nerves for their maintenance and growth.

B. Degeneration

Lateral-line organs react to denervation by dedifferentiation and degeneration, but species differences evidently exist in the time when these changes begin to appear. In fish, lateral-line organs seem to disappear within a short time after denervation (Brockelbank, 1925; Parker and Paine, 1934; Bailey, 1937). A dependence on the rate of degeneration of the lateral-line nerves was observed (Parker, 1932; Parker and Paine, 1934). Structural integrity of the end organs was maintained as long as degeneration and fragmentation of severed axons were not advanced. Accordingly, when the rate of degeneration was changed by lowering or raising the temperature, disintegration of the end organs was changed correspondingly.

In urodeles and anurans, on the other hand, lateral-line organs may persist without conspicuous changes for long periods even after repeated nerve section (Stone, 1937; Bedell, 1939). Although Williams (1930) believed to have found the proof of the trophic influence of lateral-line nerves on their end organs in a rapid change of the affinity of the sense cells to the methylene blue stain, this criterion for degenerative changes does not seem fully reliable (Wright, 1951a).

However, when studying end organs continuously deprived of their nerve supply for long time intervals, qualitative and quantitative changes may be revealed, so giving a demonstration of the lack of the trophic influence exerted normally by the supplying nerve (Speidel, 1944b, 1946a, 1948, 1949, 1950; Wright, 1946, 1947, 1951a).

The first visible effect of denervation is atrophy. This usually is not conspicuous during the first 2 months after denervation. Thereafter — following a certain period of latency — dedifferentiation sets in. Sensory cells lose their hairs, the radial arrangement of cells is lost. A rapid degeneration and removal of remnants by macrophages probably precedes the complete disappearance of the organs (Wright, 1951a).

These processes are reflected in qualitative changes, in the decrease in the number of sense organs after denervation (Wright, 1947; Speidel, 1948). First of all, the normal increase in the number of organs during growth is slowed down after denervation. The capacity to budding is reduced in denervated organs (Speidel, 1944a, 1947b; Wright, 1947). It decreases gradually with time. Finally regeneration is arrested after prolonged denervation. Exceptionally, budding has been observed as late as 10 months after nerve section (Speidel, 1949, 1948).

A progressive decrease in the number of organs occurs in comparison to the control lateral-line system of the opposite side. This is the result both of the decreased budding and an actual disintegration of some of the sense organs. The progress of disintegration is expressed in Fig. 7; after one year following denervation, only single organs survive (Speidel, 1948). Degeneration was also observed by Wright on hypophysectomized tadpoles (Wright, 1947) during the first 5 months.

C. Regeneration

After regeneration of the lateral-line nerves, the structure of the transiently denervated organs is restored, the sense cells differentiate again and their hair processes reappear (Speidel, 1946a, b, 1947a; Wright, 1951a). The regeneration progresses readily after a short denervation period (Speidel, 1947a, b). On the other hand, sense organs denervated for several months have less capacity for readjustment than freshly denervated receptors (Speidel, 1948).

Budding and regeneration of sense organs take place even after denervation (Speidel 1944a, 1947b; Wright, 1947, 1962). Regeneration is brought about by proliferation of the supporting cells forming a placodal material from which new organs are separated and new sense cells differentiate with a short delay (Wright, 1947; Speidel, 1948). Thus new organs always arise only from the pre-existing receptors, or from the partially dedifferentiated remnants of organs (Speidel, 1948).

Regenerating lateral-line nerves are not able to stimulate differentiation of normal apithelial cells into sense organs (Wright, 1947; Devillers, 1948). When the nerves ere deflected and forced to grow to regions devoid of receptors, no new organs appear at the regenerating nerve fibres (Wright, 1947). Bailey (1937) asserted that in the catfish, if the nerve was transposed into a new region, new lateral-line organs were formed from the normal epithelium. According to Speidel (1948), however, a transfer of special cells adhering to the nervous stump cannot be excluded in her experiments. Wright (1947) pointed out that those organs could possibly arise by budding from neighbouring sense organs.

When summarizing the present evidence, it can be stated that during development the morphogenetic influence of nerve fibres on the formation of lateral-line organs

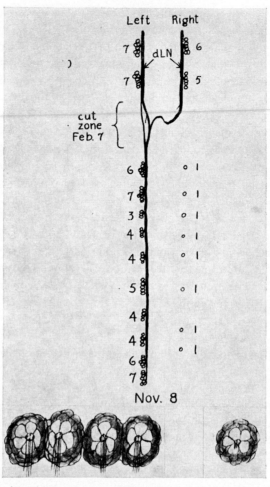

Fig. 7. Diagram of the lateral-line organs in the frog tadpole 9 months after cutting the nerve. Left side, after nerve regeneration; right side, denervated; below, schematic drawing of the respective sense organs as seen from above. (From Speidel, 1948.)

has been demonstrated only in the fish. An independent development of sense organs was found in amphibians, but a nervous influence might play a role in the determination of the placodal material.

It has been proved, however, that innervation is important for the maintenance of these organs. A long-lasting denervation results in their dedifferentiation and degeneration. Regeneration of organs may occur also in the absence of innervation. New organs arise only from the placodal material or persisting organs.

3. SKIN RECEPTORS

Although the receptor organs of the skin appear most suitable for the study of the dependence on the nervous system, because of their conspicuous and characteristic structure, the subject did not attract much attention and the results are scarce. The mosaic of experimental data does not yet allow the development of a coherent and clear-cut story of the nervous influence on their differentiation and regeneration.

A. Development

There are no experimental data on development of skin receptors that relate to the formative influence of their nerve supply. The findings on normal development (*e.g.* Szymonowicz, 1896; Cajal, 1929) indicate a close correlation between the onset of skin innervation and the beginning of the differentiation of receptor organs.

B. Degeneration

Following denervation, degenerative changes occur in the structure of skin receptors, but the onset and extent of the changes differ according to structural differences.

Epidermal receptors, such as 'touch spots' in the hairy skin of the cat (Iggo and Muir, 1962; Iggo, 1963a, b) dedifferentiate at a relatively rapid rate. 'Touch spots' are circular elevations of the skin surface, with thickened epidermis and special tactile cells at the stratum basale (Fig. 8a). They are slowly adapting mechanoreceptors (for further information on function see Iggo, 1963a, b). One thick myelinated axon supplies each 'touch spot' and branches profusely at its base. The nerve endings are invested by tactile cells so that they lie just beneath the polylobulated nucleus (Iggo and Muir, 1962). Degenerative changes appear by the 4th day after denervation; tactile cells in the thinned epidermis become small, with centrally placed nuclei and shrunken 'clear sacs'. Twenty to thirty days after nerve section tactile cells are reduced in number or absent (Fig. 8b). The touch spots are, however, still clearly recognizable by the arrangement of capillaries and the dermal papillae, which do not change by this time (Brown and Iggo, 1962).

The encapsulated receptors have been studied mainly with tactile Grandry and Herbst corpuscles of the duck's bill after denervation. Grandry corpuscles consist of one or two big special cells surrounded by a thin cellular capsule. The terminal nerve branches are located inbetween the two cells or on the surface of the single special cell, under the capsule. Tamura (1922) and Boeke (1913, 1940) found only a small atrophy in the Grandry corpuscles of the duck during the first weeks after nerve section. Dijkstra (1933) prolonged the denervation period by repetitive section of the nerve, and observed surviving end organs in the skin of the duck as long as 4 months after denervation. In the Grandry corpuscles the atrophy and shrinkage of the special cells was accompanied by proliferation of cells of the capsule (Boeke and Dijkstra, 1932; Dijkstra, 1933).

In Herbst corpuscles which correspond roughly to Vater-Pacini's receptors and consist of an inner core with the axon terminal surrounded by several fibrous lamellar layers of the capsule, only minor changes were noted after denervation (Dijkstra, 1933; Quilliam and Armstrong, 1961). Similarly, Sasybin (1930) found empty capsules of Vater-Pacini and Krause's corpuscles almost intact after 1 month of denervation in the cow.

It thus appears that denervation changes are more marked and conspicuous with the special tactile cells of the epidermis than with the dermal encapsulated receptors,

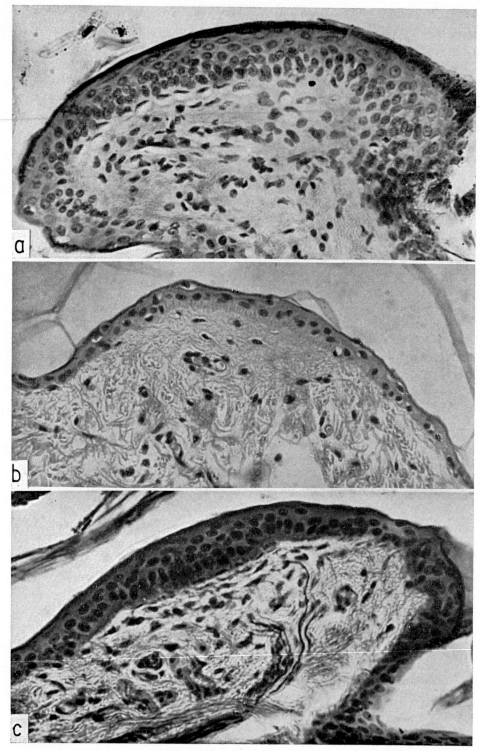

Fig. 8. For legend see p. 189.

where not only the capsules, but even the special cells are more resistant to denervation changes.

C. Regeneration

After crushing the nerve in the cat, regenerating nerve branches reappear at the touch spot after 16–20 days and tactile cells with large clear sacs are redifferentiated or regenerated after 25–30 days (Fig. 8c). Only after the reappearance of tactile cells the normal, slowly adapting response to pressure and the reaction to thermal changes are restored (Brown and Iggo, 1962).

When the special structures of the receptor organs persist throughout the denervation period, they may be reinnervated after nerve regeneration (Tamura, 1922; Boeke, 1917, 1940; Quilliam and Armstrong, 1961). Boeke (1917), however, observed young forms of Grandry corpuscles in the reinnervated area, and first suggested the possibility (as Dijkstra, 1933, also did), that a new formation of corpuscles was initiated by ingrowing fibres. Nasarow (1922), investigationg the scar tissue of the human skin, described a gradual development of simple encapsulated forms, probably of the Golgi–Mazzoni type, whereas more complicated receptors were absent. On the other hand, Cajal (1928) never found tactile corpuscles in the scar and doubted whether they could be formed anew after reinnervation. Similarly Sasybin (1930) denied the possibility of the formation of normal encapsulated end organs in the human scar, although he investigated scar tissue up to 10 years after the lesion. His pictures (Sasybin, 1930), however, suggest that atypical, probably encapsulated organs were present in the scar. Sergeev (1960) found only two atypical bulbous corpuscles in the scar tissue specimens 2 years after injury.

In the experimental material evidence was obtained for a new formation of end organs after complete removal of the skin. Grandry and Herbst corpuscles were differentiated in the regenerates of the beak of ducklings (Werber and Goldschmidt, 1909). Dijkstra (1933) described a very retarded differentiation of Grandry and Herbst organs in the regenerated skin of adult ducks. Grandry corpuscles emerged in the regenerate after 5 months, after 8–9 months they had a normal appearance. At this time Herbst corpuscles were also present, although the author had not observed any young forms suggesting their development before this date. His impression that end organs which are numerous in the regenerated skin after 6 months, disintegrate later on and are rarely to be found after 8 months (Dijkstra, 1933) might be the result of individual variations in the material and requires further support based on quantitative data.

In transplantation experiments the problem of the specific influence of the nerve supply was attacked, but the results, up to now, seem inconclusive. Kadanoff (1925) found no encapsulated receptors in plantar skin grafted onto the mouth in rabbits

Fig. 8. (a) Cutaneous 'touch corpuscle', normal skin of cat. Van Gieson stain, 4 μ thick section. (b) Denervated cutaneous 'touch corpuscle'. The epidermis is similar to the adjacent epidermis, bu the basement membrane is still folded. Van Gieson, 4 μ section. (c) Cutaneous 'touch corpuscle' afte nerve crush, and allowing time for regeneration. The axon can be seen entering from the left. Holm' silver stain, 15 μ section; × 800. (From Iggo, unpublished.)

and guinea-pigs up to one year, but he did not use appropriate staining in his experiments. Dijkstra (1933) took advantage of the big differences between the skin on the duck's beak and foot, and transplanted small pieces of the skin from the beak to the foot and *vice versa*. He found a rapid disintegration of old corpuscles 4–6 weeks after transplantation, which is in contrast to their survival in the denervated pieces of the skin. According to his observations reinnervation of the graft begins very late, after 3 months, which seems, however, improbable. He assumes that corpuscles, both Grandry and Herbst, which appear in the grafts 6–11 months after transplantation, are newly formed.

On the other hand, no corpuscles were found in the foot-to-beak skin transplants. This is due, according to the author, to the unsatisfactory reinnervation of the grafts. Dijkstra (1933) concluded on the basis of his experiments that new organs formed in the transplants are characteristic for the original skin, and that they are not influenced by the character of innervating sensory fibres. This would undermine the hypothesis of the specifity of sensory fibres, provided that Dijkstra's evidence (1933) was strengthened by reliable proof of the full disintegration of original end organs, by quantitative data on the appearance of the new receptors, and by functional tests.

After critical evaluation of the scattered data on skin receptors, it seems evident that their structure undergoes denervation changes, although there is not sufficient evidence for the complete disintegration of encapsulated receptors. Similarly, the problem of induction of receptor organs by regenerating nerve fibres and questions concerning their specificity require further analysis.

4. MUSCLE RECEPTORS

The effect of innervation on the development of muscle tissue entered very early into the forefront of experimental interest (Harrison, 1904). The investigation, however, led to a negative result, as far as differentiation of muscle fibres is concerned. It was conclusively proved that muscle differentiation takes place even in the absence of innervation, although the aneurogenic or denervated muscle tissue is atrophic and may finally degenerate (Harrison, 1904; Hooker, 1911; Hamburger, 1927, 1929; Hunt, 1932; Eastlick, 1943; Eastlick and Wortham, 1947; Zelená, 1957, 1959; Wortham and Eastlick, 1960).

Surprisingly enough, the problem of muscle spindle formation has not been mentioned in this connection, as if muscle were a homogenous tissue and muscle receptors non-existing. Yet muscle spindles and tendon organs were well-known as sensory end organs since the end of the last century.

Thus the trophic dependence of the spindles on innervation was not revealed until 1932 (Tower) and muscle spindle differentiation was only subjected to experimental analysis in the fifties (Zelená, 1957).

A. Development

The development of muscle receptors has mainly been investigated in mammals —

in pig, man, sheep, guinea-pig, and rat embryos (Sutton, 1915; Langworthy, 1924; Cuajunco, 1927a, b; Hewer, 1935; Dickson, 1940; Couteaux, 1941; Kalugina, 1956; Zelená, 1957), but the first fundamental study was done on the chicken embryo (Tello, 1922). The process of development, however, has common features in all these forms.

Muscle spindles begin to develop in the muscle tissue at the myotubal stage (Fig. 9). In the near vicinity of sensory nerve endings there is a different developmental process than in the majority of future extrafusal muscle fibres. Instead of a rapid multiplication of myofibrils, nuclei begin to proliferate, forming at first a disconnected, and later a continuous chain of nuclei stretched along the longitudinal axis of the fibre (Fig. 10). This first visible sign of spindle differentiation appears in the muscle during embryonic life, e.g. on the 11th day of development in the chicken, during the 4th month of intra-uterine life in human embryos, 7 days before birth in the rabbit and 3 days

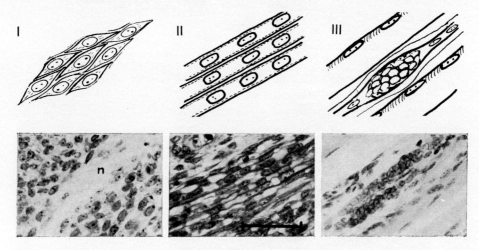

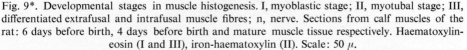

Fig. 9*. Developmental stages in muscle histogenesis. I, myoblastic stage; II, myotubal stage; III, differentiated extrafusal and intrafusal muscle fibres; n, nerve. Sections from calf muscles of the rat: 6 days before birth, 4 days before birth and mature muscle tissue respectively. Haematoxylin-eosin (I and III), iron-haematoxylin (II). Scale: 50 μ.

before birth in rat foetuses. The nuclear division further continues and the accumulating nuclei give rise to the nuclear bag, a formation of nuclei closely packed together and distending the lumen of the fibre. On both sides of the nuclear bag a myotubal structure with a row of nuclei is preserved, whereas at the poles fibres are gradually filled out with myofibrils and the nuclei become located at the circumference. In the polar regions these intrafusal fibres differ from the extrafusal ones only by their smaller diameter. During this differentiation a thin connective tissue capsule is formed at a distance around the group of intrafusal fibres, leaving free a periaxial space filled with an amorphous liquid substance. The initial number of two differentiating fibres per organ in the rat is approximately doubled later, and the thin nuclear chain fibres become clearly distinguished from nuclear bag fibres.

* Figs. 9, 11, 13, 14 and 16–19 are reprinted from Zelená and Hník, 1963d.

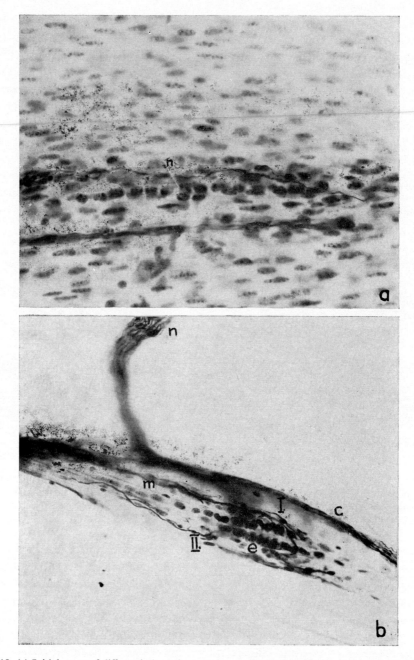

Fig. 10. (a) Initial stage of differentiation of a muscle spindle at the sensory nerve ending (n) in the rat 2 days before birth; × 500. (b) Muscle spindle of adult rat. e, equatorial zone; m, myotubal zone; c, capsule; n, nerve fibres. I, primary endings; II, secondary endings. Bielchowsky–Gros impregnation; × 300. (From Zelená, 1962.)

During the initial stage of differentiation, primary endings represent the only innervation of the spindle. They change gradually from a simple V-shaped branching to a complex network of annulospiral endings around the equatorial zone of the spindle. Secondary sensory nerve fibres and γ-fibres do not reach the spindle until after the equatorial sensory region at the primary ending has been transformed in the nuclear bag, which occurs in the rat, for example, after birth (Zelená, 1957, 1959).

The mature spindle consists of several intrafusal muscle fibres of the nuclear bag and nuclear chain type that are divided into three characteristic regions: the equatorial zone with the annulospiral endings of Group I A fibres, myotubal zones with the secondary, Group II sensory endings ('flower spray') and bipolar motor zones supplied with fusimotor γ_1 and γ_2 fibres. For further details on structure see Barker (1948, 1962) and Boyd (1962a, b); on ultrastructure see Katz (1963). As is well known, the spindle records change in stretch and tension (for information see, *e.g.*, Laporte, 1962).

Tendon organs differentiate at the musculotendinous junctions of a small group of muscle fibres usually beneath the superficial fascia or aponeurosis, or at the intramuscular septa (Tello, 1922, in the chicken; Zelená and Hník, 1963c, in the rat). In these regions sensory nerve fibres branch on the surface of the terminal parts of muscle fibres which still retain a myotubal character. At these sites the acetylcholinesterase is greatly increased (Zelená and Hník, 1963c) so that the organs can readily be recognized even before their non-nervous connective tissue components are differentiated (Fig. 11). Gradually small tendon fascicles are formed beneath the nerve endings. They

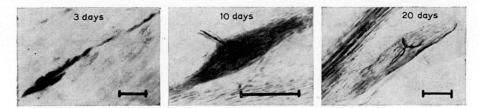
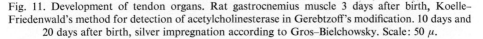

Fig. 11. Development of tendon organs. Rat gastrocnemius muscle 3 days after birth, Koelle–Friedenwald's method for detection of acetylcholinesterase in Gerebtzoff's modification. 10 days and 20 days after birth, silver impregnation according to Gros–Bielchowsky. Scale: 50 μ.

connect the ends of the muscle fibres with the aponeurosis or the tendon and protrude like small fibrous islets among the neighbouring muscle tissue. A fibrous capsule finally envelopes the whole organ, and the simple nerve branching changes into intricate end-loops among the fibrous fascicles. In the chicken, the differentiation is terminated before hatching (Tello, 1922). In the rat, the formation of the fibrous components begins after birth and is roughly terminated by the 10th day, although the organ continues to grow further. (For information on structure and function see Cooper, 1960; ultrastructure, Merrillees, 1962.)

How does innervation influence the complex process of the development of muscle receptors? It has been demonstrated that sensory innervation induces the formation of muscle receptors and ensures its progress during the early developmental stages (Zelená, 1957, 1959). If muscles are deprived of innervation at the myotubal stage,

no muscle spindles develop in the denervated muscle (Fig. 12). Only exceptionally abortive formation of a nuclear chain can be observed in muscles denervated by
section of the sciatic nerve before the onset of spindle differentiation, *i.e.* 3 days before
birth in rat foetuses and 7 days before birth in the rabbit.

Even when muscle nerves are sectioned in new-born rats, *i.e.* at a time when the

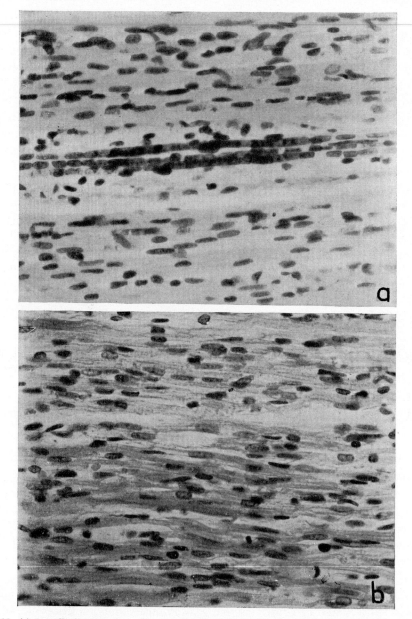

Fig. 12. (a) Longitudinal section of a muscle spindle in newborn rabbit. (b) Denervated muscle
without spindles in a new-born rabbit 7 days after intrauterine muscle nerve section. Haematoxylin-
eosin; × 500. (From Zelená, 1962.)

nuclear bag of spindles has just been formed, muscle spindles do not differentiate further and disintegrate within several days. Ten days after the operation (Fig. 13) only occasional spindle remnants can be found in the denervated muscles (Zelená, 1957; Hník and Zelená, 1961). Similarly the differentiation of tendon organs is completely arrested after this postnatal denervation (Zelená and Hník, 1963a).

Since future muscle spindles receive only sensory innervation when they begin to differentiate (Zelená, 1959), the arrest of their development is evidently the result of the loss of sensory innervation.

After birth, however, muscle spindles also become innervated by fusimotor nerve fibres. Do these fibres participate in ensuring further development of spindles? If sensory innervation is preserved and motor and fusimotor fibres eliminated from muscles by sectioning the anterior spinal roots in new-born rats, muscle spindles continue to differentiate. Ten days after de-efferentation they are not reduced in number and contain well-formed and distinguishable nuclear bag and nuclear chain fibres. They are, however, small in size, and intrafusal fibres are atrophic. On the other hand, when muscles undergo atrophy after tenotomy, both the sensory and motor innervation being maintained, spindles do not participate in the atrophy of the

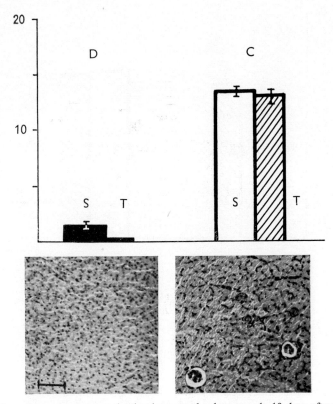

Fig. 13. Number of muscle receptors in the denervated soleus muscle 10 days after section of the sciatic nerve at birth (D), and control muscle (C). S, muscle spindles; T, tendon organs. Mean values of 5 animals. Below, cross-sections from a denervated and a control muscle stained with haematox-ylin–eosin. Scale: 50 μ.

surrounding muscle tissue (Fig. 14), although they are reduced in length (Zelená, 1960, 1963).

Motor innervation thus seems to support normal development of the spindle, but its particular role in the process of differentiation warrants further study.

B. Degeneration

It has generally been accepted that in contrast to extrafusal muscle fibres, muscle spindles remain practically unchanged for a long time after nerve section. This observation was already included in the fundamental paper of Sherrington on muscle spindles (1894) and was corroborated by subsequent findings (Batten, 1897; Willard and Graw, 1924; Sunderland and Ray, 1950; Adams et al., 1954).

Tower (1932) first proved conclusively that muscle spindles do change after denervation, although their changes are less conspicuous and appear later than the atrophy of extrafusal muscle fibres. She clearly demonstrated that muscle spindles which are supplied both by sensory and motor nerve fibres, are under a double trophic influence. Sensory nerve fibres control the structural maintenance of equatorial regions, whereas fusimotor fibres ensure the integrity of polar regions. If sensory nerve endings are

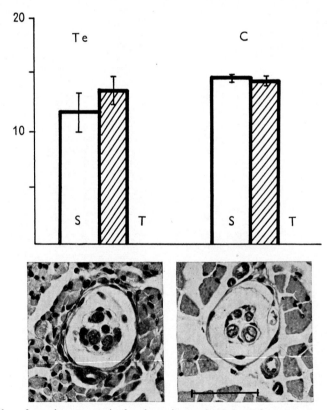

Fig. 14. Number of muscle receptors in the plantaris muscle 20 days after tenotomy at birth (Te) and in the control muscle (C). S = muscle spindles; T = tendon organs. Mean values of 8 animals. Below: cross-section of spindles from a tenotomized and control muscle stained with haematoxylin–eosin. Scale: 50 μ.

eliminated by extirpation of the spinal ganglia, the nuclear bag dedifferentiates and its nuclei become gradually reduced, whereas polar zones retain their structure. On the other hand, after ventral root section polar zones atrophy, but sensory regions remain unaltered. This was also confirmed by Boyd (1962a, b). Atrophy of intrafusal fibres seems to be less extensive than that of extrafusal muscle fibres (Sunderland and Ray, 1950; Adams et al., 1954; Boyd, 1962a, b; Gutmann and Zelená, 1962).

After total denervation, spindles shrink and atrophy and their periaxial space becomes narrower: the diameters of the spindles at the equatorial zone are reduced approximately by 40 % after a 15 months' to 2 years' denervation period (Gutmann and Zelená, 1962). Tower (1932) assumed that the degeneration and fibrotic changes observed in denervated spindles finally result in their complete disintegration. This has not been confirmed in the rat, where the average number of muscle spindles in the soleus and extensor digitorum longus was not substantially decreased (Fig. 15) even if denervation lasted for 2 years (Gutmann and Zelená, 1962).

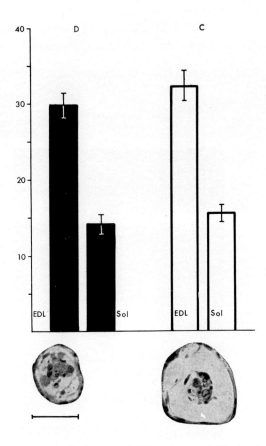

Fig. 15. Number of muscle spindles in denervated (D) and control (C) muscles 15–24 months after nerve section in adult rats. EDL, extensor digitorum longus; Sol, soleus muscle. Mean values of 5 animals. Below, cross-sections of representative spindles from the extensor digitorum longus. Scale: 50 μ.

198   J. ZELENÁ

C. Regeneration

Since in adult animals muscle receptors do not undergo degeneration and can be reinnervated again, the question about the possibility of their regeneration was neither raised nor studied for a long time. A new approach to the problem opened up, however, when it became feasible to eliminate receptors from muscles by denervation at early developmental stages (Zelená, 1957) and to study the results of reinnervation in these spindleless muscles.

The first experiments gave a negative answer (Zelená and Hník, 1960a, b, c; Hník and Zelená, 1961). Muscle spindles did not regenerate in the investigated muscles, the extensor digitorum longus, the tibialis anterior and the soleus muscle of the rat. After crushing the sciatic nerve at birth, the first regenerating nerve fibres arrive in these muscles on about the 10th day, when muscle differentiation, although slowed down by transient denervation (Zelená, 1962) is nearly completed. By that time, the investigated muscles consist mainly of atrophic extrafusal muscle fibres, and only occasional myotubes (Zelená, 1959, 1962) or remnants of disintegrating spindles can be found in the muscle tissue (Hník and Zelená, 1961). Following reinnervation, the extrafusal muscle fibres are considerably reduced in number (Hník and Zelená, 1962; Zelená and Hník, 1963d), but the remaining fibres fully recover from the denervation

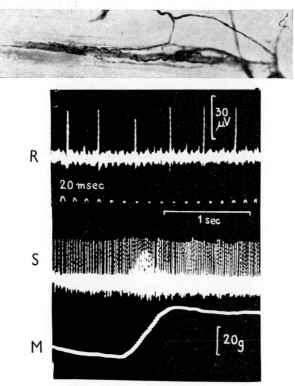

Fig. 16. Innervation and function of an atypical spindle after muscle reinnervation. Above, longitudinal section through atypical spindle; silver impregnation; scale: 50 μ. Below, resting discharge (retouched) from muscle nerve at zero tension (R) and response to maintained stretch (S). M, myographic record.

atrophy and, after 5 months' reinnervation, their diameter even somewhat exceeds the control values (Zelená and Hník, 1960a, b, 1963a). On the other hand, muscle spindles do not differentiate anew and the muscle remains practically devoid of receptors even after 10 months of reinnervation. Only occasional atypical spindles are found in some of the reinnervated muscles. Although they are extremely small, their function is not impaired (Fig. 16). Quite exceptionally, a tendon organ can be discovered beneath the aponeurosis (Zelená and Hník, 1963b). On the average, however, the number of receptors is very near to zero in these muscles (Fig. 18) in spite of the fact that the sensory nerve supply is reduced only by 25% in the deep peroneal nerve innervating the tibialis and the extensor digitorum muscles, and by 15% in the nerve to the soleus muscle (Fig. 17) (Zelená and Hník, 1960a, b, 1963b).

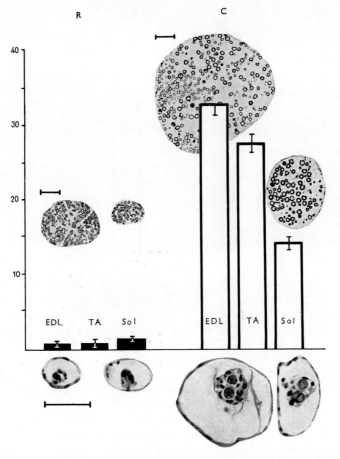

Fig. 17. Number of muscle spindles in the extensor digitorum longus (EDL), anterior tibial (TA) and soleus (Sol) muscles 5 months after crushing the sciatic nerve at birth (R) as compared with control muscles (C). Mean values of 20, 4 and 10 animals respectively. Above, cross-section of the deep peroneal nerves and nerve branches to the soleus 3 weeks after anterior rhizotomy on the reinnervated (R) and control (C) sides respectively, stained according to Fleming–Weigert. Below, cross-sections of muscle spindles from EDL and Sol muscles, stained with haemotoxylin–eosin and Van Gieson. Scale: 50 μ.

Although the diameters of the regenerated sensory fibres are extremely small and a substantial loss of group I A fibres cannot be excluded, it seems improbable that all these fibres could be selectively impaired. Probably the ability of the periphery to undergo the special differentiation process contributes more to the negative result.

Under more favourable conditions, however, regenerating nerve fibres do induce regeneration of muscle spindles as has been observed in the gastrocnemius muscle.

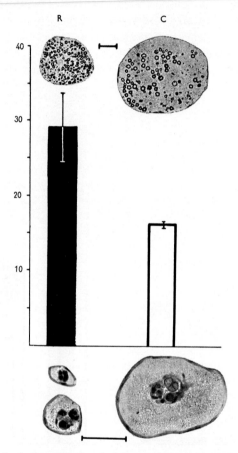

Fig. 18. Number of spindles in the medial head of the gastrocnemius muscles 5 months after crushing the sciatic nerve at birth (R = 6 animals), as compared with control muscles (C = 14 animals). Above: muscle nerves 3 weeks after anterior rhizotomy. Below: cross-sections of representative muscle spindles. Scale: 50 μ.

The medial head of the gastrocnemius muscle is reinnervated shortly (6 days) after crushing the nerve at birth because of the shorter distance from the nerve lesion. At the onset of reinnervation the muscle tissue still contains a certain number of myotubes,

---

* In adult animals an increase in the number of nerve fibres in the peripheral stump is an earmark of the immaturity of the regenerated nerve (Aitken et al., 1947). On the other hand, after nerve lesions in very young animals the deficient regeneration is characterized by a decrease in the number of nerve fibres (Romanes, 1946; Bueker and Myers, 1951; Zelená and Hník, 1963b).

besides some dedifferentiating muscle spindle remnants. It is invaded by an exceptionally high number of regenerating sensory nerve fibres which exceed the control values
by 60 % (Fig. 19). The origin of this increase has not yet been analyzed (See * p. 200).

These sensory nerve fibres are apparently able to simulate muscle spindle differentiation. Five months after crushing the nerve the medial head of the gastrocnemius
muscle contains 70 % more spindles than the contralateral control muscle (Fig. 19).
There is, however, a great scatter in the quantity of regenerated spindles in individual
muscles, ranging from a normal spindle content to a threefold increase. Although

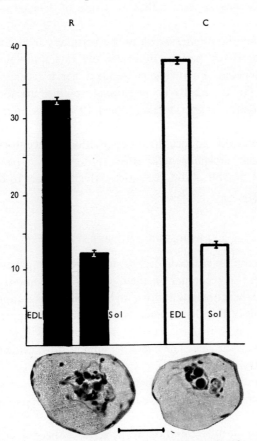

Fig. 19. Number of spindles in reinnervated (R) and control (C) muscles 10 months after crushing the
sciatic nerve in 14-day-old rats. EDL, extensor digitorum longus; Sol, soleus. Mean values of 3
animals. The two cross-sections of spindles are from the soleus muscle. Scale: 50 μ.

some of the spindles may originate from reinnervation and restoration of the spindle
remnants surviving the denervation period, it is obvious that a great number of
spindles is formed anew .The sensory outflow from the gastrocnemius muscle with
a high spindle content is correspondingly increased both at rest and after muscle
stretch (Zelená and Hník, 1963d).

When considering the difference between the reinnervated gastrocnemius muscle
rich in spindles and the experimental group of muscles deprived of receptors after

regeneration, the problem arose: Is the limiting factor for spindle regeneration a reduction in the nerve supply or changes in the muscle periphery? To test the possibilities, the reinnervation of the gastrocnemius muscle was studied following a prolonged denervation interval after repeated crushing of the nerve. Histogenesis is then completed before the onset of nerve regeneration. Although the regenerated nerves again contained an increased number of fibres, no spindles were found in the reinnervated muscle 5 months after crushing the nerve. Evidently spindles do not differentiate at later developmental stages. The formation of spindles in the gastrocnemius muscle after a single crush thus appears rather as a case of delayed development than of regeneration.

The conditions for the reinnervation of the periphery indeed change very rapidly during the early postnatal period. In 14-day-old rats spindles do not disintegrate after crushing the nerve. Following subsequent nerve regeneration, they become innervated again, but apparently no additional spindles are formed *de novo*, since the number of spindles is not increased even 10 months after crushing the nerve (Fig. 19).

Sensory nerve fibres thus induce the differentiation of receptors, both spindles and tendon organs. Their morphogenetic effect, however, can be exerted only when muscle tissue is still capable of differentiation, which appears to be restricted to early developmental stages.

5. PROBLEMS AND PERSPECTIVES

The available evidence on receptor organs, however incomplete at the present time, reveals a dependence of receptors on their sensory innervation, although there is a wide variability and there are limitations with the various tissues and species concerning the mode and extent of this dependence. Some of the facts appear to be contrary to this idea as a first approximation. Further investigation will prove whether they do or do not comply with the rule. The overwhelming positive evidence, however, merits a tentative generalization.

We may now briefly characterize typical features of the effect of sensory nerve fibres on receptor organs, on their development, on their maintenance, and, on their regeneration.

1. During ontogenesis differentiation of the cells localized in close proximity to the sensory nerve endings begins to diverge from that of the surrounding tissue under the influence of sensory nerve fibres. The structure, metabolism and reactivity of the affected cells become gradually adjusted to the special requirements of their future function by responding to the physical or chemical changes in their environment. This determination takes place at early developmental stages; the correlation of such a special structural differentiation with the onset of receptor function is not known. The morphogenetic influence of sensory nerve fibres on receptor development was, however, conclusively demonstrated only in case of muscle receptors. The evidence *e.g.* on lateral-line organs in amphibians speaks rather in favour of an independent development, with an establishment of a trophic dependence on inner-

vation in a later stage, probably after the onset of function. Nevertheless, further analysis might reveal an early formative influence of innervation even with these end-organs, and also with other types of receptors.

2. Once the structure of the receptors is fully developed and functioning, the nerve fibres evidently contribute further to their maintenance. It is not clear, however, whether the neural factor ensuring the structural integrity of receptors is identical with that inducing their development. The nervous influence on mature end organs seems to be less powerful and its existence can mostly be detected after its elimination by a long-lasting denervation period. In epithelial and epidermal tissues, where proliferation and desquamation of cells occur continuously, even receptor cells may, in some species, dedifferentiate and deteriorate at a rapid rate after denervation.

It remains to be elucidated whether the lack of function could play a role in initiating atrophy and degeneration of denervated end organs. Receptor cells continue to be exposed to changes of their environment. The only functional difference is that the local changes at the receptors are no longer transmitted through the nerve endings as they were in normally innervated organs. If the membrane of denervated sense cells is, however, denuded in the synaptic regions, the loss of contact with terminal nerve branches or leakage of ionic exchanges occurring normally during depolarization could initiate a chain of metabolic reactions resulting in the rearrangement or even breakdown of the cell. The possibility of such a backward effect on receptor cells cannot fully be excluded until more is known about the electrogenesis in receptor organs.

3. After reinnervation, receptors which have survived denervation with a more or less advanced dedifferentiation, are restored. The dedifferentiated cells reacquire their former characteristics. If the receptor organs suffer from a complete disintegration during the period of denervation, regeneration cannot take place unless the reinnervated tissue is responsive to the nervous effect and plastic enough to undergo special differentiation. This is evidently the case with taste organs, which regenerate from the epithelium in which the cells incessantly proliferate, mature and die during a relatively short life-cycle. On the other hand, in muscle, regeneration of muscle receptors can be brought about — although in an atypical form — only if the muscle tissue is still differentiating and thus responsive to the nervous induction.

Lateral-line organs, however, cannot be formed from indifferent epithelial cells, but readily regenerate by budding from old organs or by transformation of the placodal material. In amphibians, their regeneration may occur even in the absence of nerve fibres and this ability decreases only after long lasting denervation. In fish, however, it is closely correlated with the nerve regeneration.

Evidently, favourable conditions in the target organ, similar to those found in the course of development, are indispensable for an effective regenerative process.

No doubt, in the future many particular facets of the relation of nerve fibres to the receptor organs can be successfully studied on simple experimental models which have been used up to now. This applies *e.g.* to the question whether the different types of sensory fibres destined for different receptors can substitute for each other as far as their trophic role is concerned. Application of functional criteria and more quantitative observations could be of great help in this respect. Extending of the investigation to other kinds of receptors is most necessary for a better understanding of the problem.

The nature of the nervous factor involved in the morphogenetic and trophic action is unknown. A hypothesis was put forward more than forty years ago by Olmstead (1920). It was postulated that the trophic effect is carried out by a hormone-like substance secreted at the nerve endings. This interpretation found favour with many investigators and was also applied to explaining the induction of receptor differentiation during development (e.g., May, 1925; Brockelbank, 1925; Whiteside, 1927; Parker, 1932; Torrey, 1948; Devillers, 1940; Guth, 1957). Other authors, e.g., Stone (1937), Speidel (1948), Wright (1955), stressed the relative independence and the long survival of receptors deprived of their nerve supply and held that this hypothesis was improbable, at least for lateral-line and taste organs. However, as yet no alternative concept concerning the nature of the nervous factor has been proposed.

It is not an easy task to bring the investigation more up to date. The research has first to be carried out on the cellular and subcellular level. An analysis of the interactions taking place between nerve endings and the differentiating sense cells before and after the onset of function will be necessary. A deep insight into the metabolic processes connected with the function of the receptors presumably could lead to the reformulation of the hypothesis. Degeneration and dedifferentiation have to be traced back to the initial changes of metabolic patterns in sense cells after denervation. Only then can we hope to define more precisely the character of the chemical agents and physical factors that participate in the inductive and trophic action of sensory nerve endings.

However, it may be asked if there are methods available at the present time which could enable us to study the character and the mode of operation of the trophic factor. From the many kinds of trophic interrelations between nerve cells and the peripheral field, only once an attempt has been made to isolate and identify the trophic agent. This was done in the case of the growth promoting factor inducing hypertrophy and hyperplasia in the spinal and sympathetic ganglia (Levi-Montalcini and Hamburger, 1951, 1953; Cohen et al., 1954; Hamburger, 1954, 1956). However, a precise determination of the trophic agent was not then achieved (see Scott, this Volume). Even in the field of embryology, where the problem of induction is vigorously pursued not a single inductive substance has been identified biochemically from the active tissue extracts. It would be difficult, if not impossible, to prepare and test active nerve extracts specific for the receptor organs. Besides, it is doubtful whether such a trophic effect could be exerted by diffusion of the trophic substance without requiring special structural conditions. New approaches may open up, however, with further progress in experimental embryology, when much more becomes known about the basic mechanisms of induction.

Biochemical micromethods have been successfully introduced into brain research by Hydén and his school (c.f. Hydén, 1963). This has made possible the analysis of the chemical composition of the isolated nerve cells and their components. If we should succeed in the isolation of nerve endings and sense cells, their chemical analysis might be of utmost importance. It would be essential, however, to clarify our concepts first and to formulate the correct questions before trying to hit the target in this way.

The same applies for the potential histochemical and histoautoradiographical approach in electron microscopy.

The investigation of peripheral synapses is being very successfully pursued at the present time thanks to conjoint attack of electrophysiological, biochemical and electron microscopical methods. Let us hope that, as it gains more interest, the investigation of inductive and trophic functions of the nervous system by a common effort of physiological disciplines will soon lead to further progress.

SUMMARY

Experimental data on the development, degeneration and regeneration of receptor organs were reviewed in order to trace out the effect of sensory nerve terminals on the non-nervous components of various kinds of receptors. In most receptor organs sensory innervation appears to ensure structural integrity of their specialized cells.

1. In taste organs sense cells degenerate at a rapid rate when deprived of innervation and they are differentiated anew when regenerating gustatory nerve terminals reach the epithelium. Non-gustatory nerve fibres also appear to have a trophic effect on taste buds, but further analysis of this problem is necessary.

2. Lateral-line organs atrophy and disintegrate at a different rate in different species after denervation. After reinnervation the structure of sense cells is restored. Differentiation of lateral-line organs during development and regeneration can take place also in the absence of innervation, but nervous influence is essential for their development in the fish.

3. In some cutaneous receptors, such as touch spots in the hairy skin of mammals, special cells degenerate in a short time following denervation and regenerate after reinnervation. Encapsulated receptors, however, atrophy and dedifferentiate very slowly as a rule. The role of innervation during development and regeneration requires further study.

4. Development of muscle receptors, both muscle spindles and tendon organs, is induced by sensory nerve endings. During the initial period of development muscle spindles are highly dependent upon innervation and they degenerate within a few days after nerve section.

In adult animals denervation changes in muscle spindles are less conspicuous and they do not result in a complete disintegration of the receptors. After the degeneration of sensory endings, atrophy and dedifferentiation appear in the sensory region of muscle spindles; polar regions of intrafusal fibres atrophy after motor denervation.

The available evidence speaks in favour of a trophic effect of nerve endings exerted on the maintenance and eventually on the differentiation of receptor organs. The nature and character of this trophic action of sensory nerve terminals are unknown.

ACKNOWLEDGEMENTS

I wish to express my gratitude to Drs. Eccles, Gutmann, Guth, Stone and Margaret Wright for their critical comments and helpful suggestions. I also wish to thank Dr. Iggo for granting me the use of his unpublished illustrations, and to the other authors who kindly allowed me to reproduce their figures.

References p. 206–211

REFERENCES

ADAMS, R. D., DENNY-BROWN, D., AND PEARSON, C. M., (1954); *Diseases of Muscle; a Study in Pathology.* New York, Hoeber.

AITKEN, J. T., SHARMAN, M., AND YOUNG, J. Z., (1947); Maturation of regenerating nerve fibres with various peripheral connexions. *J. Anat. (Lond.)*, **81**, 1–22.

AREY, L. B., AND MONZINGO, F. L., (1942); Can hypoglossal nerve fibres induce the formation of taste buds? *Quart. Bull. Northw. Univ. med. Sch.*, **16**, 170–178.

BAGINSKY, B., (1893); Über das Verhalten von Nervenendorganen nach Durchschneidung der zugehörigen Nerven. *Arch. Anat. Physiol.*, 559–560.

BAGINSKY, B., (1894); Über das Verhalten von Nervenendorganen nach Durchschneidung der zugehörigen Nerven. *Virchows Arch. path. Anat.*, **137**, 389–404.

BAILEY, S. W., (1937); An experimental study of the origin of lateral-line structures in embryonic and adult teleosts. *J. exp. Zool.*, **76**, 187–233.

BARKER, D., (1948); The innervation of the muscle spindle. *Quart. J. micr. Sci.*, **89**, 153–186.

BARKER, D., (1962); The structure and distribution of muscle receptors. *Symposium on Muscle Receptors.* D. Barker, Editor. Hong Kong, Hong Kong University Press (p. 227–240).

BATTEN, F. E., (1897); Muscle spindles under pathological conditions. *Brain*, **20**, 138.

BEDELL, S. G., (1939); The lateral-line organs of living amphibian larvae with special reference to orange coloured granules of the sensory cells. *J. comp. Neurol.*, **70**, 231–247.

BEIDLER, L., (1963); Dynamics of taste cells. *Olfaction and Taste.* Y. Zotterman, Editor. New York, Pergamon Press (p. 133–144).

BEIDLER, L. M., NEJAD, M. S., SMALLMAN, R. L., AND TATEDA, H., (1960); Rat taste cell proliferation. *Fed. Proc.*, **19**, 302.

BOEKE, J., (1917); Studien zur Nervenregeneration. II. Die Regeneration nach Vereinigung ungleichartiger Nervenstücke (heterogene Regeneration), und die Funktion der Augenmuskel- und Zungennerven. Die allgemeinen Gesetze der Nervenregeneration. *Verh. kon. Akad. Wet. (Amst.)*, **19 (5)**, 1–71.

BOEKE, J., (1940); *Problems of Nervous Anatomy.* London, Oxford University Press.

BOEKE, J., AND DIJKSTRA, C., (1932); De- and regeneration of sensible corpuscles in the duck's bill (corpuscles of Grandry and Herbst) after cutting of the nerve, the removing of the entire skin or the transplantation of the skin in another region. *Verh. kon. Akad. Wet.*, *(Amst.)*, **35**, 3–8.

BOYD, I., (1962a); The nuclear-bag fibre and nuclear-chain fibre system in the muscle spindles of the cat. *Symposium on Muscle Receptors.* D. Barker, Editor. Hong Kong, Hong Kong University Press (p. 185–190).

BOYD, I., (1962b); The structure and innervation of the nuclear-bag muscle fibre system and the nuclear-chain muscle fibre system in mammalian muscle spindles. *Phil. Trans. B*, **245**, 81–136.

BROCKELBANK, M. C., (1925); Degeneration and regeneration of lateral-line organs in *Ameiurus nebulosus. J. exp. Zool.*, **42**, 293–305.

BROWN, A. G., AND IGGO, A., (1962); The structure and function of cutaneous "touch corpuscles" after nerve crush. *J. Physiol. (Lond.)*, **165**, 28–29P.

BUEKER, E. D., AND MEYERS, CH. E., (1951); The maturity of peripheral nerves at the time of injury as a factor in nerve regeneration. *Anat. Rec.*, **109**, 723–744.

CAJAL, S. R. Y, (1928); *Degeneration and Regeneration of the nervous System.* R. M. May, Editor. London, Oxford University Press.

CAJAL, S. R. Y, (1929); The mechanism of development of intraepithelial, sensory and special sense nerve terminations. *Studies on Vertebrate Neurogenesis.* Springfield, Ill., Thomas (p. 149–200).

COHEN, S., LEVI-MONTALCINI, R., AND HAMBURGER, V., (1954); Nerve growth promoting factor in sarcomas 37 and 180. *Proc.. Amer. Ass. Cancer Res.*, **1**, 3.

COOPER, S., (1960); Muscle spindles and other muscle receptors. *Structure and Function of Muscle.* G. H. Bourne, Editor. New York, London, Academic Press (Vol. I., p. 381–420).

COUTEAUX, R., (1941); Recherches sur l'histogenèse du muscle strié et de la formation des plaques motrices. *Bull. Biol.*, **75**, 101–239.

CUAJUNCO, F., (1927a); The embryology of the neuromuscular spindles. *Anat. Rec.*, **35**, 8–9.

CUAJUNCO, F., (1927b); Embryology of the neuromuscular spindles. *Contr. Embryol. Carneg. Instn.*, **19**, 45–72.

DE CASTRO, J., (1944); Sobre el mecanismo de excitación de los quimioceptores y baroceptores del glosofáringeo, utilizando un arco reflejo formado en tre los sistemos vago-aferente y simpático. *Trab. Lab. Invest. biol. Univ. Madrid*, **36**, 345–395.

DE LORENZO, A. J., (1957); Electron microscopic observation on the taste buds of the rabbit. *J. biophys. biochem. Cytol.*, **4**, 143–150.

DE LORENZO, A. J., (1963); Studies on the ultrastructure and histophysiology of cell membranes, nerve fibres, and synaptic junctions in chemoreceptors. *Olfaction and Taste*. Y. Zotterman, Editor. New York, Pergamon Press (p. 5–20).

DEVILLERS, CH., (1948); La genèse des organes sensoriels latéraux de la Truite (*Salmo fario — S. iridens*). *C. R. Acad. Sci. (Paris)*, **226**, 354–356.

DICKSON, L. M., (1940); The development of nerve-endings in the respiratory muscles of the sheep. *J. Anat. (Lond.)*, **74**, 268–276.

DRASCH, C., (1887); Untersuchungen über die papillae foliatae et circumvallatae des Kaninchens und des Feldhasen. *Abh. sächs. Ges. (Acad.) Wiss.*, **24**, 229–252.

DIJKGRAAF, S., (1963); The functioning and significance of the lateral-line organs. *Biol. Rev.*, **38 (1)**, 51–105.

DIJKSTRA, C., (1933); Die De- und Regeneration der sensiblen Endkörperchen des Entenschnabels (Grandry- und Herbst-Körperchen) nach Durchschneidung des Nerven, nach Fortnahme der ganzen Haut und nach Transplantation des Hautstückchens. *Z. mikr.-anat. Forsch.*, **34**, 75–158.

EASTLICK, H. L., (1943); Studies on transplanted embryonic limbs of the chick. I. The development of muscle in nerveless and in innervated grafts. *J. exp. Zool.*, **93**, 27–49.

EASTLICK, H. L., AND WORTHAM, R. A., (1947); Studies on transplanted embryonic limbs in nerveless and innervated grafts. *J. Morphol.*, **80**, 369–389.

ECCLES, J. C., (1963a); Interrelationship between nerve and muscle cell. *The Effect of Use and Disuse on neuromuscular Functions*. E. Gutmann and P. Hník, Editors. Proceedings of a symposium held at Liblice, Sept. 18–23, 1962. Prague, Publishing House of the Czechoslovak Academy of Sciences (p. 19–21).

ECCLES, J. C., (1963b); The trophic and plastic properties of synapses. *The Physiology of Synapses*. Berlin, Springer Verlag (p. 239–263).

ENGSTRÖM, H., AND RYTZNER, C., (1956); The fine structure of taste buds and taste fibres. *Ann. Otol. (St. Louis)*, **65**, 361–375.

FLOCK, A., AND WERSÄLL, J., (1962); Synaptic structures in the lateral line canal organ of the teleost fish *Lota vulgaris*. *J. Cell Biol.*, **13**, 337–343.

FOLEY, J. O., AND DUBOIS, F. S., (1937); Quantitative studies of the vagus nerve in the cat. I. The ratio of sensory to motor fibres. *J. comp. Neurol.*, **67**, 49–68.

GUTH, L., (1957); The effects of glossopharyngeal nerve transection on the circumvallate papilla of the rat. *Anat. Rec.*, **128**, 715–731.

GUTH, L., (1958); Taste buds on the cat's circumvallate papilla after reinnervation by glosso-pharyngeal, vagus and hypoglossal nerves. *Anat. Rec.*, **130**, 25–38.

GUTH, L., (1963); Histological changes following partial denervation of the circumvallate papilla of the rat. *Exp. Neurol.*, **8**, 336–349.

GUTMANN, E., (1962); Denervation and disuse atrophy in cross-striated muscle. *Rev. canad. Biol.*, **21**, 353–365.

GUTMANN, E., (1963); Evidence for the trophic function of the nerve cell in neuromuscular relations. *The Effect of Use and Disuse on neuromuscular Functions*. E. Gutmann and P. Hník, Editors. Proceedings of a symposium held at Liblice, Sept. 18–23, 1962. Prague, Publishing House of the Czechoslovak Academy of Sciences (p. 29–34).

GUTMANN, E., AND HNÍK, P., (1962); Denervation studies in research of neurotrophic relationships. *The denervated Muscle*. E. Gutmann, Editor. Prague, Publishing House of the Czechoslovak Academy of Sciences (p. 13–51).

GUTMANN, E., AND ZELENÁ., (1962); Morphological changes in the denervated muscle. *The denervated Muscle*. E. Gutmann, Editor. Prague, Publishing House of the Czechoslovak Academy of Sciences (p. 57–102).

HAMBURGER, V., (1927); Entwicklungsphysiologische Beziehungen zwischen den Extremitäten der Amphibien und ihrer Innervation. *Naturwissenschaften*, **15**, 657–661; 677–681.

HAMBURGER, V., (1929); Entwicklung experimentell erzeugter nervenloser und schwach innervierter Extremitäten von Anuren. *Wilhelm Roux'Arch. Entwickl.-Mech. Org.*, **114**, 272–363.

HAMBURGER, V., (1956); Developmental correlations in neurogenesis. *Cellular Mechanisms in Differentiation and Growth*. D. Rudnick, Editor. Princeton, N.J., Princeton University Press.

HARRISON, R. G., (1903); Experimentelle Untersuchungen über die Entwicklung der Sinnesorgane der Seitenlinie bei den Amphibien. *Arch. mikr. Anat.*, **63**, 35–149.

HARRISON, R. G., (1904); An experimental study of the relation of the nervous system to the developing musculature in the embryo of the frog. *Amer. J. Anat.*, **3**, 117–220.

HAYES, E. R., AND ELLIOTT, R., (1942); Distribution of the taste buds on the tongue of the kitten, with particular reference to those innervated by the chorda tympani branch of the facial nerve. *J. comp. Neurol.*, **76**, 227–238.

HEWER, E. E., (1935); The development of nerve endings in the human foetus. *J. Anat. (Lond.)*, **69**, 369–379.

HNÍK, P., AND ZELENÁ, J., (1961); Atypical spindles in reinnervated rat muscles. *J. Embryol. exp. Morph.*, **9**, 456–467.

HNÍK, P., AND ZELENÁ, J., (1962); Sensory and motor nerve regeneration in young animals. Proceedings XXII. International Congress of Physiological Sciences, Leiden. E. Duyff *et al.*, Editors. Amsterdam, *Excerpta Med.* (Vol. II, p. 1110).

HOOKER, D., (1911); The development and function of voluntary and cardiac muscle in embryos without nerves. *J. exp. Zool.*, **11**, 159–186.

HUNT, E. A., (1932); The differentiation of chick limb buds in chorioallantoic grafts, with special reference to the muscles. J. exp. Zool., **62**, 57–91.

HYDÉN, H., (1963); The metabolic and functional interaction between neuron and its glia. *The Effect of Use and Disuse on neuromuscular Functions*. E. Gutmann and P. Hník, Editors. Proceedings of a symposium held at Liblice, Sept. 18–23, 1962. Prague, Publishing House of the Czechoslovak Academy of Sciences.

IGGO, A., (1963a); New specific sensory structures in hairy skin. *Acta neuroveg. (Wien)*, **24**, 175–180.

IGGO, A., (1963b); An electrophysiological analysis of afferent fibres in primate skin. *Acta neuroveg. (Wien)*, **24**, 225–240.

IGGO, A., AND MUIR, A. R., (1962); A cutaneous sense organ in hairy skin. Proceedings XXII. International Congress of physiological Sciences, Leiden. E. Duyff *et al.*, Editors. *Excerpta med. (Amst.)*, *Int. Congr. Ser.*, **48** (vol. II, p. 1024).

KADANOFF, D., (1925); Untersuchungen über die Regeneration der sensiblen Nervenendigungen nach Vertauschung verschieden innervierter Hautstücke. *Wilhelm Roux'Arch. Entwickl.-Mech. Org.*, **106**, 249–278.

KALUGINA, M. A., (1956); Development of receptors in skeletal muscles of mammals. (In Russian.) *Arh. Anat. Gistol. Embriol.*, **33**, 59–63.

KATZ, B., (1961); The determinations of the afferent nerve fibre in the muscle spindle of the frog. *Phil. Trans. B*, **243**, 221–240.

KUBOTA, K., AND KUBOTA, J., (1960); Contribution to nerve development of so-called gustatory papillae in human tongue. *Bull. Tokyo med. dent. Univ.*, **7**, 475–505.

LANDACRE, F. L., (1907); On the place of origin and method of distribution of taste buds in *Ameiurus melas*. *J. comp. Neurol.*, **17**, 1–66.

LANGWORTHY, O. R., (1924); A study of the innervation of the tongue musculature with particular reference to the proprioceptive mechanism. *J. comp. Neurol.*, **36**, 273–297.

LAPORTE, Y., (1962); Fuseaux neuro-musculaires. Proceedings XXII. International Congress of Physiological Sciences, Leiden. E. Duyff *et al.*, Editors. *Excerpta med. (Amst.)*, *Int. Congr. Ser.*, **47** (Vol. I, p. 70–78).

LEVI-MONTALCINI, R., AND HAMBURGER, V., (1951); Selective growth-stimulating effects of mouse sarcoma on the sensory and sympathetic nervous system of the chick embryo. *J. exp. Zool.*, **116**, 321–362.

LEVI-MONTALCINI, R., AND HAMBURGER, V., (1953); A diffusible agent of mouse sarcoma, producing hyperplasia of symphathetic ganglia and hyperneurotization of viscera in the chick embryo. *J. exp. Zool.*, **123**, 233–288.

MARCHAND, L., (1902); Développement des papilles gustatives chez le foetus humain. *C. R. Soc. Biol. (Paris)*, **54**, 910–912.

MAY, R. M., (1925); The relation of nerves to degenerating and regenerating taste buds. *J. exp. Zool.*, **42**, 371–410.

MERKULOVA, O. C., (1948); On receptors in the liver. (In Russian) *Bull. Akad. Sci. U.S.S.R.*, **4**, 493–504.

MERRILLEES, C. R., (1962); Some observations on the fine structure of a Golgi tendon organ of a rat. *Symposium on Muscle Receptors*. D. Barker, Editor. Hong Kong, Hong Kong University Press (p. 199–206).

MEYER, S., (1896); Durchschneidungs-Versuche am Nervus glossopharyngeus. *Arch. mikr. Anat.*, **48**, 143–145.

MINTZ, B., AND STONE, L. S., (1934); Transplantation of taste organs in adult *Triturus viridescens*. *Proc. Soc. exp. Biol. (N.Y.)*, **31**, 1080–1082.

MURRAY, R. G., AND MURRAY, A., (1960); The fine structure of taste buds of *Rhesus* and *Cynomolgus* monkeys. *Anat. Rec.*, **138**, 211–233.

NASAROW, W., (1922); Über die Regeneration der Endnervenapparate in den Narben der menschlichen Haut. *Dissertation*. Quoted by N. Sasybin, (1930); *Z. mikr.-anat. Forsch.*, **22**, 1–72.

OLMSTEAD, J. M. D., (1920); The results of cutting the seventh cranial nerve in *Ameiurus nebulosus*. *J. exp. Zool.*, **31**, 369–401.

OLMSTEAD, J. M. D., (1921); Effect of cutting the lingual nerve of the dog. *J. comp. Neurol.*, **33**, 149–154.

OLMSTEAD, J. M. D., (1922); Taste fibres and the chorda tympani nerve. *J. comp. Neurol.*, **34**, 337–341.

OLMSTEAD, J. M. D., AND PINGER, R. R., (1936); Regeneration of taste buds after suture of the lingual and hypoglossal nerves. *Amer. J. Physiol.*, **116**, 225–227.

PARKER, G. H., (1932); On the trophic impulse, so-called, its rate and nature. *Amer. Natural.*, **66**, 147–158.

PARKER, G. H., AND PAINE, V. L., (1934); Progressive nerve degeneration and its rate in the lateral-line nerve of the catfish. *Amer. J. Anat.*, **54**, 1–19.

PORITSKY, R. L., AND SINGER, M., (1963); The fate of taste buds in tongue transplants to the orbit in the urodele, *Triturus*. *J. exp. Zool.*, **153**, 211–218.

QUILLIAM, T. A., AND ARMSTRONG, J., (1961); Structural and denervation studies of the Herbst corpuscle. *Cytology of nervous Tissue*. Proceedings of the Anatomical Society of Great Britain and Ireland. London, Taylor and Francis (p. 33–38).

RANVIER, L., (1875); *Traité Technique d'Histologie*. Paris, Sary (Footnote, p. 948–949).

ROMANES, G. J., (1946); Motor localization and the effects of nerve injury on the ventral horn cells of the spinal cord. *J. Anat. (Lond.)*, **80**, 117–131.

SANDMAYER, W., (1895); Über das Verhalten der Geschmackknospen nach Durchschneidung des N. glossopharyngeus. *Arch. Anat. Physiol.*, 269–270.

SASYBIN, N., (1930); Über die Regeneration der Nervenfasern in mehrschichtigem Plattenepithel. *Z. mikr.-anat. Forsch.*, **22**, 1–72.

SERGEEV, K. K., (1960); On morphologic and physiologic correlation of cutaneous receptors. (In Russian.) *Arh. Anat. Gistol. Embriol.*, **39**, 70–77.

SHERRINGTON, C. S., (1894); On the anatomical constitution of nerves of skeletal muscles; with remarks on recurrent fibres in the ventral spinal nerve root. *J. Physiol. (Lond.)*, **17**, 211–258.

SINGER, M., (1952); The influence of the nerve in regeneration of the amphibian extremity. *Quart. Rev. Biol.*, **27**, 169–200.

SINGER, M., (1963); Nervous control of the regrowth of body parts in vertebrates. *The Effect of Use and Disuse on neuromuscular Functions*. E. Gutmann and P. Hník, Editors. Proceedings of a symposium held at Liblice, Sept. 18–23, 1962. Prague, Publishing House of the Czechoslovak Academy of Sciences (p. 83–94).

SPEIDEL, C. C., (1944a); The regeneration of denervated lateral-line organs. *Anat. Rec.*, **68**, 456.

SPEIDEL, C. C., (1944b); The trophic influence of specific nerve supply on special sensory organs, as revealed by prolonged survival of denervated lateral-line organs. *Anat. Rec.*, **88**, 459.

SPEIDEL, C. C., (1946a); Ciné-photomicrographs of tadpole cells *in vivo*, with special reference to experiments on nerves and special sense organs of the lateral-line. *Anat. Rec.*, **94**, 551.

SPEIDEL, C. C., (1946b); Correlated histories of individual sense organs and their nerves, as seen in living frog tadpoles. *Biol. Bull.*, **91**, 224–225.

SPEIDEL, C. C., (1947a); Reinnervation phenomena as revealed by prolonged observation of vagus nerve stumps and associated sense organs. *Anat. Rec.*, **97**, 371–372.

SPEIDEL, C. C., (1947b); Correlated studies of sense organs and nerves of the lateral-line in living frog tadpoles, I. Regeneration of denervated organs. *J. comp. Neurol.*, **87**, 29–55.

SPEIDEL, C. C., (1948); Correlated studies of sense organs and nerves of the lateral-line in living frog tadpoles, II. The trophic influence of specific nerve supply as revealed by prolonged observations of denervated and reinnervated organs. *Amer. J. Anat.*, **82**, 277–320.

SPEIDEL, C. C., (1949); Correlated studies of sense organs and nerves of the lateral-line in living frog tadpoles, III. Experiments on the orange granules and sense hairs of denervated and innervated organs. *J. Morph.*, **85**, 113–139.

SPEIDEL, C. C., (1950); Adjustments of peripheral nerve fibers. *Genetic Neurology*. P. Weiss, Editors. Chicago, University of Chicago Press (p. 66–77).

STONE, L. S., (1922); Experiments on the development of the cranial ganglia and the lateral-line sense organs in *Amblystoma punctatum*. *J. exp. Zool.*, **35**, 421–496.

Stone, L. S., (1931); Studies on the migratory lateral-line primordia in *Amblystoma*. *Anat. Rec.*, **48**, 64.

Stone, L. S., (1933a); Independence of taste organs with respect to their nerve fibres demonstrated in living salamanders. *Proc. Soc. exp. Biol. (N.Y.)*, **30**, 1256–1257.

Stone, L. S., (1933b); Developmental changes in primary lateral-line organs studied in living larvae of Anurans and Urodeles. *Proc. Soc. exp. Biol. (N.Y.)*, **30**, 1258–1259.

Stone, L. S., (1933c); The development of the lateral-line sense organs in amphibians observed in vital-stained preparations. *J. comp. Neurol.*, **57**, 507–540.

Stone, L. S., (1935); Expirimental formation of accessory organs in midbody lateral-line of amphibians. *Proc. Soc. exp. Biol. (N.Y.)*, **33**, 80–82.

Stone, L. S., (1936); Experimental studies of various developmental stages in the lateral-line system of amphibians. *Anat. Rec.*, **64**, 48.

Stone, L. S., (1937); Further experimental studies of the development of lateral-line organs in amphibians observed in living preparations. *J. comp. Neurol.*, **68**, 83–115.

Stone, L. S., (1940); The origin and development of taste organs in salamander observed in the living condition. *J. exp. Zool.*, **83**, 481–506.

Sunderland, S., and Ray, L. J., (1950); Denervation changes in mammalian striated muscle. *J. Neurol. Neurosurg. Psychiat.*, **13**, 159–172.

Sutton, A. C., (1915); On the development of the neuromuscular spindle in the extrinsic eye muscles of the pig. *Amer. J. Anat.*, **18**, 117–144.

Szymonowicz, L., (1896); Über den Bau und die Entwicklung der Nervenendigungen im Entenschnabel. *Arch. mikr. Anat.*, **48**, 329–358.

Tamura, A., (1922); Die Folgen der Nervendurchschneidung am Entenschnabel. *Wilhelm Roux' Arch. Entwickl.-Mech. Org.*, **51**, 552–574.

Tello, F., (1922); Die Entstehung der motorischen und sensiblen Nervenendigungen. I. In dem lokomotorischen System der höheren Wirbeltiere. Muskuläre Histogenese. *Z. Anat. Entwickl.-Gesch.*, **64**, 348–440.

Torrey, T. W., (1934); The relation of taste buds to their nerve fibres. *J. comp. Neurol.*, **59**, 203–220.

Torrey, T. W., (1940); The influence of nerve fibers upon taste buds during embryonic development. *Proc. nat. Acad. Sci. (Wash.)*, **26**, 627–634.

Tower, S., (1932); Atrophy and degeneration in the muscle spindle. *Brain*, **55**, 77–89.

Trujillo-Cenóz, O., (1961); Electron microscope observation on chemo- and mechanoreceptor cells of fishes. *Z. Zellforsch.*, **54**, 654–676.

Van Bergelik, W. A., and Alexander, S., (1962); Lateral-line canal organs on the head of *Fundulus heteroclitus*. *J. Morph.*, **110**, 333–346.

Vintschgau, M., (1880); Beobachtung über die Veränderungen der Schmeckbecher nach Durchschneidung des N. glossopharyngeus. *Pflüg. Arch. ges. Physiol.*, **23**, 1–13.

Vintschgau, M., and Hönigschmied, J., (1876); Nervus glossopharyngeus and Schmeckbecher. *Pflüg. Arch. ges. Physiol.*, **14**, 443–448.

Wagner, E. C., (1953); Dedifferentiation of taste bud cells following transection of their nerve supply. *Anat. Rec.*, **115**, 442.

Werber, E. I., and Goldschmidt, W., (1909); Regeneration des Schnabels bei der Hausgans (*Anser cinerinus*) und bei der Hausente (*Anas boschas*). *Wilhelm Roux' Arch. Entwickl.-Mech. Org.*, **28**, 661–677.

Whiteside, B., (1927); Nerve overlap in the gustatory apparatus of the rat. *J. comp. Neurol.*, **44**, 363–377.

Willard, W. A., and Graw, E. C., (1924); Some histological changes in striated skeletal muscle following nerve section. Anat. Rec., **27**, 192.

Williams, S. C., (1930); Regeneration of peripheral nerves in Amphibia studied with the acid of a vital stain. *J. exp. Zool.*, **57**, 145–181.

Wortham, R. A., and Eastlick, H. L., (1960); Studies on transplanted embryonic limbs of the chick. IV. The development of muscles and tendons in nerveless and weakly innervated chick limb grafts. *J. Morph.*, **106 (2)**, 131–141.

Wright, M. R., (1946); Experiments on the lateral line system of anurans. *Proc. Soc. exp. Biol. (N.Y.)*, **62**, 242–243.

Wright, M. R., (1947); Regeneration and degeneration experiments on lateral-line nerves and sense organs in anurans. *J. exp. Zool.*, **105**, 221–257.

Wright, M. R., (1951a); The lateral line system of sense organs. *Quart. Rev. Biol.*, **26**, 264–280.

Wright, M. R., (1951b); Maintenance of denervated taste organs in adult *Triturus* v. *viridescens*. *Proc. Soc. exp. Biol. (N.Y.)*, **76**, 462–463.

WRIGHT, M. R., (1955); Persistence of taste organs in tongue transplants of *Triturus* v. *viridescens*. *J. exp. Zool.*, **129**, 357–373.

WRIGHT, M. R., (1958); Persistence of taste organs in tongue grafted to liver. *Proc. Soc. exp. Biol. (N.Y.)*, **97**, 367–368.

WRIGHT, M. R., (1962); Repeated regeneration from nerveless lateral-line organs. *Amer. Zool.*, **2**, 62.

ZELENÁ, J., (1957); Morphogenetic influence of innervation on the ontogenetic development of muscle spindles. *J. Embryol. exp. Morph.*, **5**, 283–292.

ZELENÁ, J., (1959); *Effect of Innervation on the Development of skeletal Muscle*. (In Czech.) Prague, Statní Zdravotnické Nakladatelství.

ZELENÁ, J., (1960); Development of muscle receptors in tenotomized muscles. (In Czech.) *Čsl. Fysiol.*, **9**, 485.

ZELENÁ, J., (1962); The effect of denervation on muscle development. *The denervated Muscle*. E. Gutmann, Editor. Prague, Publishing House of the Czechoslovak Academy of Sciences (p. 103–126).

ZELENÁ, J., (1963); Development of muscle receptors after tenotomy. *Physiol. bohemoslov.*, **12**, 30–36.

ZELENA, J., AND HNÍK, P., (1960a); Absence of muscle spindles in muscles reinnervated during development. *J. Anat. (Lond.)*, **94**, 294.

ZELENÁ, J., AND HNÍK, P., (1960b); Muscles without spindles. (In Czech.) *Čsl. Fysiol.*, **9**, 279.

ZELENÁ, J., AND HNÍK, P., (1960c); Irreversible elimination of muscle receptors. *Nature (Lond.)*, **188**, 946–947.

ZELENÁ, J., AND HNÍK, P., (1963a); A new approach to muscle deafferentation. *Central and peripheral Mechanisms of neuromuscular Functions*. Prague, Publishing House of the Czechoslovak Academy of Sciences.

ZELENÁ, J., AND HNÍK, P., (1963b); Motor and receptor units in the soleus muscle after nerve regeneration in young rats. *Physiol. bohemoslov.*, **12**, 277–290.

ZELENÁ, J., AND HNÍK, P., (1963c); The development and incidence of muscle receptors in relation to their innervation. A. M. Dalcq *et al.*, Editors. *Excerpta med. (Amst.)*, *Int. Congr. Ser.*, **70**, 221–222.

ZELENÁ, J., AND HNÍK, P., (1963d); Effect of innervation on the development of muscle receptors. *The Effect of Use and Disuse on neuromuscular Functions*. E. Gutmann and P. Hník, Editors. Proceedings of a symposium held at Liblice, Sept. 18–23, 1962. Prague, Publishing House of the Czechoslovak Academy of Sciences (p. 95–105).

ZOTTERMAN, Y., (1963); *Olfaction and Taste*. Y. Zotterman, Editor. New York, Pergamon Press.

DISCUSSION

ARIËNS KAPPERS: If I understood you correctly, Miss Zelená, you found a difference between the degeneration and regeneration of two kinds of striated muscle: the gastrocnemius and the extensor digitorum. I wonder whether you are considering the possibility that this difference is due to the difference in structure or to some other factor.

ZELENÁ: We only found a difference in regeneration of muscle spindles. This was abundant in the gastrocnemius muscle in case that nerve fibers reached the muscle early, *i.e.* when it still contained myotubes capable of special differentiation. This early reinnervation was found to be important, since no formation of muscle spindles occurred when nerve regeneration was experimentally delayed.

SCOTT: I would like to say that I had a little packet of growth factor in my pocket to give you, but unfortunately this is not the case. However, I am very sympathetic to your concept that a modification of protein synthesis would be one of the first places I would look for in studying the possibility of modifying the end organs under the influence of the afferent supply.

ZELENÁ: It would certainly be of interest to look at the effect of growth promoting factor on regeneration of sensory nerve fibers and receptor organs in very young animals, and I hope that your precious substance will be available for such an experiment some time in the future.

ECCLES: In this important field I have the impression that very significant questions arise in regard to the specificity of afferent fibers in their trophic function of differentiation and maintenance. It seems that with taste buds and lateral line organs the evidence is that the trophic influence is non-specific, and is effected by reinnervation from nerves of different modality. I wonder if there has been any attempt at comparable investigations with muscle spindles. For example with the gastrocnemius in young rats it should be possible to cross-unite cutaneous nerve, sural or superficial peroneal, with the peripheral gastrocnemius nerve stump. Of course the cutaneous fibers can make no functional contact with the motor endplates, but the question under examination is whether the regenerating cutaneous fibers can cause differentiation and maintenance of muscle spindles. If it should happen that several modalities of afferent fiber are effective, it will be a much more attractive problem to prepare neural extracts in the hope of defining the chemical substance or substances that are responsible for the trophic influence. It is of fundamental importance to advance further in our understanding of these trophic neural influences on receptor organs.

ZELENÁ: I agree with you that the question of specificity of sensory nerve fibers in respect to their receptor organs is of great importance, and certainly it can be successfully pursued in cross-union experiments. Up to now, the evidence that sensory fibers of different modalities can substitute each other in their trophic influence was obtained only for taste buds. No such experiments were made on muscle spindles. The experimental approach you suggest is very promising, but it might meet with considerable difficulties. For studying the possible effect of cutaneous fibers on spindle differentiation, it would be necessary to cross-unite the nerves at a very early developmental stage — in rats probably *in utero* — so that the crossed fibers could reach the periphery when muscles are still differentiating. Such an operation would not be easy and it would probably cause an extensive retrograde degeneration in spinal ganglion cells. With a postnatal cross-union, on the other hand, one would run the risk that regenerating fibers would reach the muscles too late, when histogenesis had been completed. Under such conditions no spindle differentiation can be evoked, not even with primary afferents. In adult animals, a study of trophic influence of alien sensory fibers on the maintenance of muscle spindles would require a very careful quantitative evaluation of the results, since mature muscle spindles change very slowly even after complete denervation and some of them may remain relatively unaltered for long periods of time.

SINGER: I would like to make a short comment. One simply has to stain for nerve fibers in order to observe that the decline and loss of taste buds are directly correlated with the presence or absence of nerve fibers. As for specificity, I think all information would point at the moment to a non-specific nature of the trophic influence. Trophic influence can be obtained in the presence of a pure motor supply, sensory supply or a pure central nervous system supply. So I think it is safest at the moment to assume that all fibers are trophic fibers though they may differ quantitatively from one another.

I wanted to ask you: in Sarah Tower's cases, did she use postnatal or prenatal animals, and did she get full degeneration or not?

ZELENÁ: Sarah Tower's experiments were made on adult cats. She did not get full degeneration; when muscle spindles were counted in the extensor digiti V muscle 1 year after denervation, there was no decrease in their number in comparison with the control side.

As for specificity, your experimental analysis proves beyond doubt that nervous influence on limb regeneration is non-specific in nature and that it can be exerted by all kinds of nerve fibers. I do not think, however, that this applies for receptor organs. Motor fibers *e.g.* were found to be without influence in mammalian tongue; they cannot induce regeneration of taste buds although they invade the epithelium. In your experiment with Poritsky (1963) on tongue-to-orbit transplants in *Urodeles* you clearly demonstrated induction of taste buds by non-gustatory fibers; it has not been studied, however, whether this effect is due to sensory or to motor reinnervation, or whether it can be attributed to a non-specific influence of both components. In muscle spindles motor and sensory fibers exert — as has been found by Sarah Tower (1932) and Boyd (1962) — trophic influence on different parts of intrafusal muscle fibers, and they obviously cannot substitute each other in this specific effect. The present evidence does not support the assumption that all fibers may have a non-specific trophic influence on receptors, and it is necessary to wait for further experiments on different kinds of receptors in different species, before some conclusions concerning specificity can be drawn.

SZENTÁGOTHAI: Could we not get closer to the question of specificity in case of the taste buds by taking into consideration the origin of the sensory epithelia and the innervating neurons involved? The sensory epithelia are of placodal origin and so are, at least in part, the ganglia that innervate them. The controversial results found in amphibia and mammals with the heterotopic reinnervation might be caused by their reinnervation from the lateral line organs also of placodal origin in the former animals. It might be worth while studying experimental reinnervation of mammalian taste buds by nerves with and without ganglion cells of placodal origin.

ZELENÁ: In *Urodeles* even heterotopic fibers of non-placodal origin can induce taste uud formation, as is the case with tongue transplants in *Triturus*. In mammals cross-bnion experiments are too scarce to allow any conclusions and further experiments with reinnervation of receptors by different nerves are most desirable.

Nerves as Morphogenetic Mediators in Regeneration

H. A. L. TRAMPUSCH

Division of Eperimental Morphology, Department of Anatomy and Embryology, University of Amsterdam, Amsterdam

Many experiments have shown that after a partial loss extremities of amphibian larvae regenerate from the stump, when the amputation wound is left uncovered until it closes spontaneously by epithelium deriving from its edge. When Godlewski (1928) sealed the site of amputation by flaps of skin, regeneration ceased instantly. This standstill was not due to mechanical impediment, because once the tip of the stumps were provided with wound epithelium, they developed into complete extremities in spite of the grafted skin, through which they pierced their way without difficulty.

Apart from epithelialization, the regenerate depends on intact innervation to allow the fibres sprouting from the severed nerve to penetrate unhampered into the wound epithelium. In cases where the nerve had been interrupted proximally near the plexus (Butler and Schotte 1941), no regeneration occurred till the incision was bridged by newly formed nerve fibres. Further experimental evidence of the relationship between nerve and epidermis for regeneration was recently reviewed by Rose (1962).

Stumps with nerves in working condition, preserved for histological examination at short intervals, showed the following initial events preceding regeneration.

Immediately after amputation of a hindlimb the severed skin as well as muscles retract without much loss of blood from the wound area (Fig. 1 A). Fluid leaking from the damaged tissues coagulates to a fibrinous clot, which covers the protruding femur with the attached sciatic nerve. It will serve as a guiding ground-mat during the coming cell migration. A distortion of the basal cells originally arranged in a parallel form precedes the movement in the epithelium of the skin. Its columnar elements, which bordered the basement membrane* with their small side only, change to a transverse position or even lie flat against the new interface, the fibrinous clot (Fig. 1 C). Increased adhesion to the substratum, combined with a diminished cell to cell contact, alters the shape of the epithelial cells, while the nuclei distend in volume. The contents of the Leydig cells in the skin liquefy or are expelled in a granular form. Sometimes these cells contain two or more nuclei, which — since only scanty mitoses appear in the skin during this period — may be attributed to amitotic

---

* Some authors designate the stratum under the epidermis of the urodelean skin, which consists of different fibrous layers connected by a ground substance, as 'basement membrane', others prefer to call it 'dermis'. Although both denominations seem hardly adequate to characterize the structure concerned, the former expression will be used in this paper.

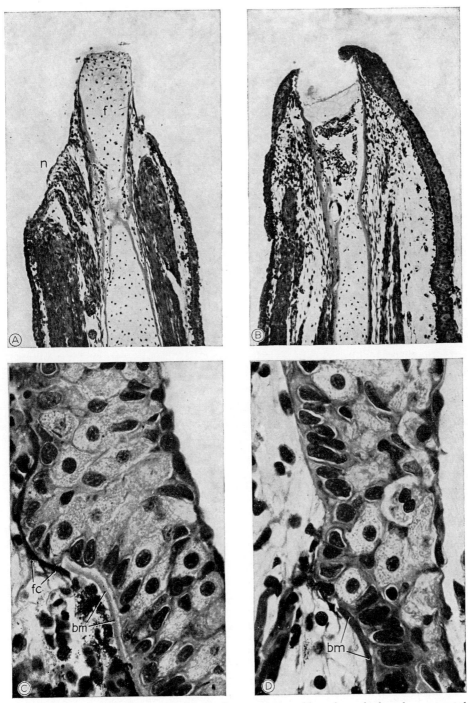

Fig. 1A. Section through limb stump shortly after amputation, skin and muscles have been retracted, leaving the femur (f) with the attached nerve (n) bare, × 50. B. Section through limb stump during wound closure, the covering wound epithelium advances over the tip of the protruding bone, × 50. C. Epithelium of the skin moving over different interfaces, the border between basement membrane (bm) and the fibrinous clot (fc) marks the plane of amputation, × 310. D. Epithelium of the skin at the same level, but at a later moment. The increase of nuclear volume in the basic layer of the epidermal cells is striking, when compared with the younger stage (C). Note a binucleated Leydig cell, × 310.

divisions, since dumb-bell shaped or lobated nuclei may be encountered in large numbers (Fig. 1 D). Cells deriving either from the original basal layer or polyedric Leydig cells, swollen through secretion, change into a uniform wound epithelium and move as large flat elements tangentially across the fibrin clot. They glide over the open wound area till they reach the protruding bone (Fig. 1 B), cover it gradually and due to their mutual approach, come to a standstill by forces which Abercrombie (1961) has called 'contact inhibition'. In this way a wound epithelium, which thickens progressively, is formed until it arranges itself into an apical epidermal cap (Thornton 1954), initiating the accumulation of mitotically active cells of a uniform appearance: the blastema of regeneration.

While the individual as well as the social behaviour of the epidermal cells changes during the migration, the dedifferentiated epithelium shifts across the transected nerve (Fig. 2 A). Here, covered by wound epithelium a kind of pustule is formed, containing oedema fluid rich in detritus. Although we do not possess silver-stained preparations among our histological series to prove it, the locally interrupted fibrinous clot over the pustule points clearly to a direct contact between sprouts of the nerve and the wound epithelium (Fig. 2 B). Only here can the bare nerve fibres penetrate between the epithelial cells, as neither basement membrane nor fibrin clot prevent their intimate contact, which according to Singer (1948) is indispensable for a successful regeneration.

During microscopical study of the preparations another coincidence concerning the behaviour of the nerve came to the light. Whereas hardly any mitoses could be found in the limb stump during wound closure, their number increased in the neurilemma and in the sheath of the nerve stump with striking frequency (Fig. 2 C). When the growing fibres of the axon reach the wound epithelium, mitoses appear there and later also apically in the mesenchymal tissues of the stump. Referring to the mitotic activity, which Overton (1950) provoked in larval Ambystoma opacum by implanting neural tissue into the dorsal fin, a relation between nerve growth in the regenerating limb stump and mitoses seems feasible. Chalkley's (1954) painstaking examination with cell counts and mitotic indices points in the same direction. To evaluate this relation in regard to the development of a blastema is beyond the scope of this paper.

Before entering upon our recent experiments, a few words about speed and duration of the different processes in the course of regeneration may be in place. The pace of development changed not only from one species to another, it depended also on the temperature applied. Young specimens regenerated much quicker than those which approached metamorphosis. When wound closure in animals of the same age, even from the same batch of eggs, was already completed after amputation through the ankle, it had not yet started in cases where the limb was severed across the thigh. Thus to avoid more controversial data, adding to those already existing in literature, temporal comparisons have been deliberately disregarded here.

In a denervated limb, amputated distally through its stylopodium, only migration of epithelium took place to cover the wound. Due to lack of innervation, however, no apical cap and therefore no regenerate arose, as long as the severed nerve had not recovered. A limb stump exposed to X-rays prior to amputation displayed an almost

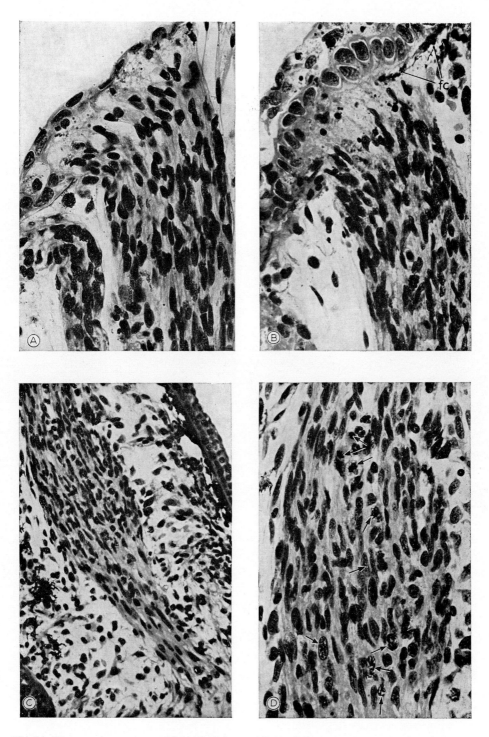

Fig. 2A. Transected nerve covered by a single layer of flat cells, forerunners of the wound-epithelium, with no basement membrane in between, × 250. B. Transected nerve end in immediate contact with wound epithelium, unimpeded by basement membrane or fibrinous clot (fc), × 250. C. Section through nerve sheath containing many mitoses, × 125. D. Same preparation at high power, mitoses indicated by arrows, × 250.

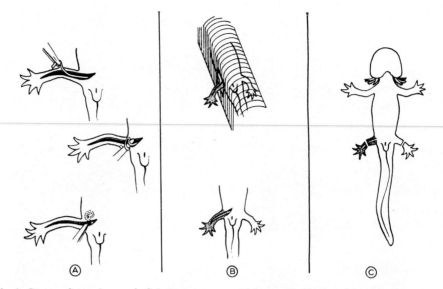

Fig. 3. Course of experiment: A. Sciatic nerve extracted from a hindlimb and hidden under the skin of the flank; B. The non-irradiated nerve is replaced after irradiation of the nerveless limb; C. Amputation of experimental and control limbs.

similar picture and failed to develop a regenerate (Trampusch 1959). This striking correspondence in behaviour as well as in histological aspect invited the question how those two manners of inhibiting the course of regeneration could be related to each other. Is it not feasible that the effect of radiation is reflected in the nerves, whereupon regeneration ceases due to lack of some nervous impulse?

To prove this assumption one of my former students, Vergroesen (1958) performed some introductory experiments, which since then have been pursued and extended in various directions. A sciatic nerve, extracted distally from a hindlimb of a young axolotl, was coiled up and slipped under the skin of the flank (Fig. 3). Then the nerveless extremity was exposed to X-rays, whereas the body of the animal with the hidden nerve was shielded under a leaden case. After irradiation the non-irradiated nerve was put back into its original bed and the wound closed. When the latter had healed, the limb was severed across the thigh. The same operation was performed on the opposite hindlimb, but as a control the nerve had been replaced already *before* irradiation. In other cases the irradiation of the controls was ommitted.

All of 27 irradiated limbs provided with non-irradiated nerves accomplished a more or less complete regenerate, whereas the stumps of the irradiated controls remained almost unchanged (Fig. 4). This result gave weight to the assumption, that an influence exerted from the non-irradiated nerve eliminated the effect of irradiation and revived regeneration.

From previous experiments with axolotls it was already known that the deleterious effect of irradiation on the regenerative capacity could be counteracted by implantation of various non-irradiated tissues: skin, bone or muscle restored regeneration in an irradiated limb stump (Trampusch 1951, 1957). Initially, therefore, it did not seem

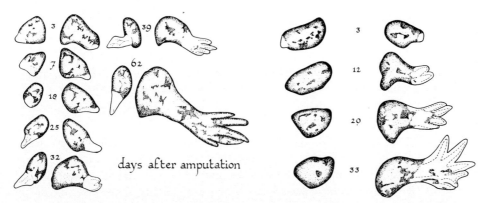

Fig. 4. Camera lucida drawings of successive stages of irradiated limb stumps provided with non-irradiated nerves and their respective controls.

worthwhile to us to report about the same ability of non-irradiated nerves, because this result may not so much be ascribed to the influence of the nervous tissue as such, as to its non-irradiated state. The situation changed, however, when loose pieces of non-irradiated nerves, transplanted into irradiated limbs, failed to stimulate regeneration. The different behaviour of intact nerves and loose pieces invited the possibility to search for the factor, antagonistic to irradiation, in the neurons of the spinal cord and to attribute to the axon a conductive function only.

To evaluate this assumption, both hindlimbs, including their axons, were exposed to X-rays, the median region around the spinal cord being protected. For this purpose, my co-worker Verwoerd (1963) designed a special lead 'parasol', which safeguarded

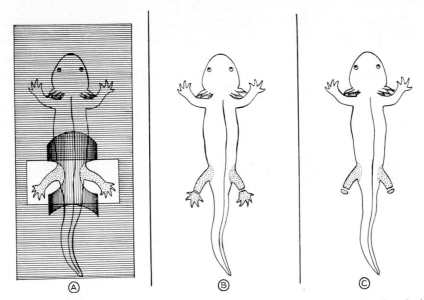

Fig. 5. Course of experiment: A. Irradiation through a window in a lead box, protecting the spinal cord with a 'parasol'; B. Amputation of the irradiated limbs through the basipodium; C. The apical scar-tissue is repeatedly removed from the stump.

the spinal region during irradiation, while the regenerative capacity in the extremities was destroyed. Wounds after amputation through the basipodium healed quickly, but the stumps produced apically only some growth, reminiscent of a blastema, which showed neither increase nor differentiation. Alternately they shrank and reappeared and finally became buried under a heavy scar. On the whole, they did not differ from stumps which were only irradiated for control purposes. Not a single case showed a spontaneous regeneration.

But if after some time the tips of the stumps were revulnerated and the scars carefully removed, the entire aspect began to change. Sometimes after the first, frequently after repeated incisions into the amputation site, a strong, almost unpigmented blastema arose, which developed slowly, but steadily. Thirty-six out of 38 irradiated stumps regenerated after reopening of the wound. Fifteen of them differentiated into thigh and shank and often formed an even more than complete foot (Fig. 6). Others started distally to the knee or consisted of a foot only. Twelve regenerates developed into a kind of spike when the experiment was terminated. All of them, however, showed the tough persistence of the nerve action, which neutralized the effect of irradiation irrespective of whether the axon had been irradiated or not.

Results were as expected: The nerve action originated indeed somewhere in the spinal cord and proceeded along the axon, but it came only into being, when its influence interacted with a susceptible skin, which allowed the nerve fibres to penetrate. Scars proved entirely unsuitable for this purpose.

On the occasion of a symposion arranged during the Developmental Biology Conference Series at Providence (1956) Brunst objected to the author's experiments, stating that according to his experience the amount of irradiation applied was insufficient to suppress regeneration completely. Although the irradiation in all the experiments presented at this meeting, as well as in the later experiments had been checked upon by irradiated and amputated control limbs, it now becomes possible to understand Brunst's objection in the light of the above interpretation, for Brunst irradiated his animals through a so-called 'localizer'. By this device he exposed only the extremity to the beam and not the spinal cord.

PXIX

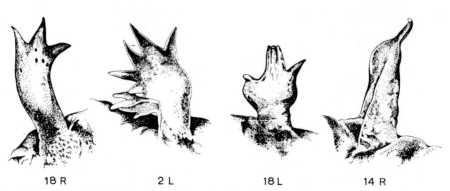

18 R   2 L   18 L   14 R

Fig. 6. Examples of limbs regenerated from irradiated stumps after protection of the spinal cord from irradiation.

Within the same category may be placed the results of Lazard's experiments (1959). Against all expectations, but also against the experience of other investigators, she obtained regenerates from 10 out of 27 irradiated hindlimbs, after covering the stump with skin from the trunk. As evidence had been provided that body skin contrary to skin from the appendices, was unable to evoke regeneration (Trampusch, 1958). Lazard's controversial outcome was rather puzzling. In a personal interview it became clear, however, that also Madame Lazard limited the irradiation to the extremities only, without exposing the pelvic region.

Verwoerd's experiments offered not only the key to a satisfactory explanation of the above divergence, they gave also rise to the following question: If a non-irradiated spinal cord *in situ* could eliminate the effect of irradiation, would an isolated piece of it, implanted into an irradiated limb, achieve the same performance?

To answer this query Verwoerd irradiated the pelvic region and both hindlimbs of axolotls of 80–90 mm length and inserted 7 days later, by mouth pipette a piece of spinal cord from a non-irradiated donor into the basis of an irradiated limb, parallel to the femur. After another week he amputated the limb through the thigh severing the opposite limb at the same level (Fig. 7).

Although in the beginning the stumps displayed but little activity, 34 out of 42 carried regenerates after 2 months. In contrast to the former experiment, however, the regenerates resembled anything but a limb. They were turgescent outgrowths, 3–4 times longer than broad, bilaterally flattened and without any articulation or fingers (Fig. 8). Some were apically bent by unequal growth, others protruded stiffly from the stump with a broad notched edge. The covering skin was only poorly pigmented, similar to that of a fin, of which it also possessed the rigidity.

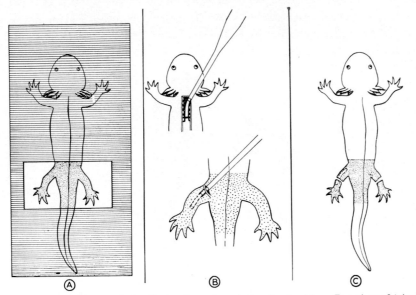

Fig. 7. Course of experiment: A. irradiation through a window in a lead box; B. a piece of spinal cord from a non-irradiated donor is inserted into the irradiated limb; C. the grafted and control limbs are amputated at the same level.

Histological sections lend support to this impression. The regenerate consists of 2 parallel sheets of skin with abundant loose connective tissue in between (Fig. 9 A). Muscle tissue is confined to the base, but in the core of the growth the implanted spinal cord, with its outgrowing nerves, is situated. In some cases, following the direction of the femur stump and parallel to the graft, a rod of cartilage develops, suggestive of a vertebral column, though smooth and unjointed (Fig. 9 C). An implant of spinal cord in an irradiated stump has in fact the capacity to revive regeneration, although the regenerate is a fin and gives a tail-like character to the limb.

Collateral evidence had been reached by other authors: Holtzer (1956) had shown that pieces of spinal cord brought into ectopic position against the myotome induced in the adjacent myotomic material the development of cartilage. She also pointed to the steering role of the spinal cord during regeneration of the tail. Holtzer *et al.* (1955) provoked additional tails by deflecting the spinal cord into the dorsal fin attributing to it a morphogenetic influence. Finally, our experiments disclosed an even twofold morphogenetic task: The implanted spinal cord not only opposed the effect of irradiation and re-initiated a regenerate, it gave to the new growth a tail-like appearance and altered thus its morphogenetic nature. As the latter is beyond the frame of this discussion, we will confine our attention to the former.

If a non-irradiated spinal cord, whether implanted or *in situ*, can recover the regenerative capacity of an irradiated stump, could irradiation of the median region alone, including the spinal cord, prevent an otherwise healthy animal from regenerating?

Although the respective experiments did not meet our expectations, they nevertheless opened up a new outlook: In fact, after some hesitation, the stumps produced regenerates, without taking much notice of the irradiation applied. Since, however, the spinal cord should have been condemned to morphogenetic inactivity by irradiation and inactive nerves prevent regeneration, as we have seen, the behaviour of the stumps allowed for the only conclusion, that the spinal cord must have *recovered from the damage of irradiation* in the meantime.

$CzP_{\underline{V}}$

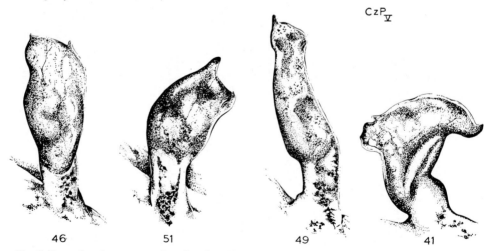

46   51   49   41

Fig. 8. Examples of regenerates from irradiated limb stumps in which non-irradiated spinal cord was inserted. Note the fin-like appearance of the regrown part.

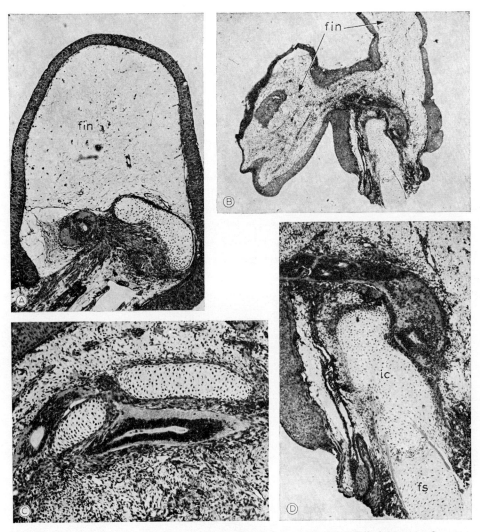

Fig. 9A. Section through a fin-like regenerate grown from an irradiated limb stump, after non-irradiated spinal cord was inserted. Note the graft and the cartilage rod it has induced in the connective tissue of the fin, × 25. B. Section through a similar regenerate, in which the graft induced new cartilage in continuation of the femur stump, × 12.5. C. The grafted spinal cord twisted around the induced cartilage at higher magnification, × 50. D. Same section at higher magnification. The borderline between the femur stump (fs) and the induced cartilage (ic) is clearly discernible, × 30.

Admittedly, such an argument may sound somewhat far-fetched at first sight and not entirely convincing. On further consideration, however, it is less strange than it seems. As already stated, irradiated limbs were re-endowed with regenerative ability after their skin had been replaced by non-irradiated skin. Following an amputation across the graft, the stump regenerated as if it had never been exposed to X-rays, whereas no control limb without a graft ever displayed any sign of regeneration. But as the re-grown extremities are not only made up of skin originating from the graft, but contain also bone and muscles, a complete reversibility of the regenerative capacity after irradiation must receive serious consideration. Where else can bone and muscle of the regenerate derive from, if not from the irradiated stump? If we accept, however, a recovery of bone and muscles to their original state under the influence of the transplanted non-irradiated skin, must not the same apply to the neurons in the spinal cord after an exposure to irradiation?

From this assumption follows inevitably that the epithelium of the skin, by closing the amputation wound of a non-irradiated stump, equals in function a non-irradiated graft. They both must produce an inciting agent, which is carried centripetally by the nerves to the spinal cord and has the ability to counteract the effect of irradiation. In this way the original interrelation between skin and nervous system becomes renewed and regeneration can take its usual course again.

The real existence of such an agent and its transport by the nerves has been proved with the following experiment, devised by my associate Mrs. Harrebomée: After irradiation of both hind-limbs and the pelvic region of 80–90 mm long axolotls, the main nerves (sciatic + peroneal) from the extremity were extracted between basis and autopodium and deviated to a window in the flank passing under the skin. The window with the nerve ends was covered with a well-fitting piece of limb skin or body skin from a non-irradiated donor. In the centre of the graft a small, round hole had been pierced with a trepan beforehand. The limb which had been operated on as well as the undamaged control were both amputated across the thigh.

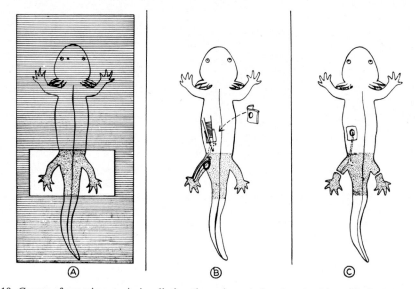

Fig. 10. Course of experiment: A. irradiation through a window in a lead box; B. deviation of the irradiated sciatic nerve to the flank, where it is covered with a flap of limb skin or body skin. C. amputation of the denervated and the control limb at the same level.

After the nerve frayed out into the limb skin, not only numerous cells accumulated under the window to constitute a blastema, which developed into a supernumerary extremity on the ectopic site, but also the irradiated stumps began to show signs of new activity. Shedding limp epithelial flanges, they originally behaved like irradiated stumps, incapable of regeneration, despite repeated re-epithelialization. When, however, the nerves had acted upon the tissue for some weeks, the covering epithelium began to fill up gradually from the stump and, notwithstanding irradiation, a pale blastema arose. The growth flattened apically into a toe plate and fashioned into a small but well-shaped extremity. Thus the irradiated stumps recuperated after some

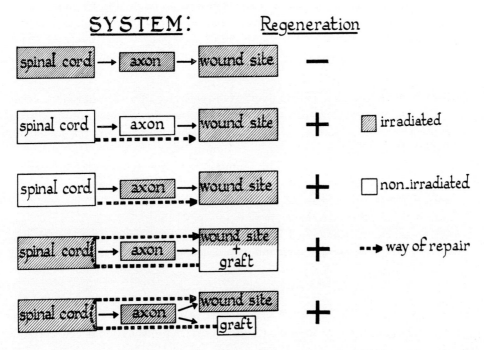

Fig. 11. Neuronal or axonal action interrelated to the regenerate, its inhibition and repair after irradiation.

delay and brought forth almost perfect limbs, although they reached non-irradiated tissue only *via* the deviated nerve.

These results lend substance to the thought, that, in fact, it is the nerve which transports the seemingly radiosensitive agent responsible for regeneration. This mediator does not admit of 'one-way traffic' only, it once carries the agent from the non-irradiated spinal cord to the peripheral wound site, then, according to the need, from the non-irradiated graft centripetally to the spinal cord. In this way a system: spinal cord/amputation-site is established, which comprises the following possibilities:

While an extremity after irradiation of the *whole* system is incapable of any regeneration, a local peripheral lesion can recover and allow for complete, if at times delayed, regenerates, irrespective of whether the X-rays, hit the wound site only or also the axon. The recuperating agent leaks from the non-irradiated spinal cord or axon to the periphery to cure it from the effect of the irradiation endured.

When the totally irradiated system is brought into contact with a non-irradiated graft — be it at the wound site itself or *via* a deviated nerve — the agent of the graft penetrates centripetally and back to the wound site again. After recovery of the damaged agent, regeneration proceeds undisturbed as if no irradiation had taken place.

The character of this morphogenetic agent can hardly be guessed, no more than the way in which it reaches the nerve and is transported by it. As it apparently originates from the cell nuclei of the neurons or from the highly activated cells of the migrating epithelium of the skin, the assumption seems justified to relate it to the nucleic acids and their metabolism. The way it promotes mitotic activity may be an argument in favour of this speculation.

SUMMARY

(*1*) Results of various experiments point to the existence of a morphogenetic agent, which initiates regeneration. This agent originates from the cell nuclei of the affected neurons or from the migrating epithelium of the skin, which covers the wound site caused by an amputation.

(*2*) The agent initiating regeneration promotes mitotic activity at successive stages in the nerve sheath, in other tissues of the stump and in the blastema.

(*3*) Experiments prove that the inciting agent is carried to and fro along the axon and can move in either direction from or to the spinal cord.

(*4*) The experiments described lend substance to the thought, that the effect of irradiation may have more in common with denervation than is generally assumed.

ACKNOWLEDGEMENT

Experiments carried out for the purpose of this paper were supported by the Netherlands Organization for Pure Scientific Research (ZWO), for which aid sincere gratitude is expressed.

REFERENCES

ABERCROMBIE, M., (1961); The bases of the locomotory behaviour of fibroblasts. *Exp. Cell Res.*, Suppl. **8**, 188–198.

BRUNST, V. V., (1959); *Regeneration in Vertebrates*. Ch. S. Thornton, Editor. University of Chicago Press (p. 95).

BUTLER, E. G. AND SCHOTTE, O. E., (1941); Histological alterations in denervated non-regenerating limbs of urodele larvae. *J. exp. Zool.*, **88**, 307–330.

CHALKLEY, D. T., (1954); A quantitative histological analysis of forelimb regeneration in *Triturus viridescens*. *J. Morphol.*, **94**, 21–70.

GODLEWSKI, E., (1928); Untersuchungen über Auslösung und Hemmung der Regeneration beim Axolotl. *Wilhelm Roux' Arch. Entwickl.-Mech. Org.*, **114**, 108–143.

HOLTZER, H., HOLTZER, S. W., AND AVERY, G., (1955); An experimental analysis of the development of the spinal column. IV. Morphogenesis of tail vertebrae during regeneration. *J. Morphol.*, **96**, 145–168.

HOLTZER, S. W., (1956); The inductive activity of the spinal cord in urodele tail regeneration. *J. Morphol.*, **99**, 1–34.

LAZARD, L., (1959); Influence de greffes de tissu 'neutre' sur la régénération des membres chez Amblystoma. *C. R. Acad. Sci.*, **249**, 1819–1820.

OVERTON, J., (1950); Mitotic stimulation of amphibian epidermis by underlying grafts of central nervous tissue. *J. exp. Zool.*, **115**, 521–559.

Rose, S. M., (1962); Regeneration. *Physiology of the Amphibia*. J. Moore, Editor. New York, Academic Press.

Schotte, O. E., and Butler, E. G., (1941); Morphological effects of denervation and amputation of limbs in urodele larvae. *J. exp. Zool.*, **87**, 279–322.

Singer, M., (1949); The invasion of the epidermis of the regenerating forelimb of the urodele, *Triturus*, by nerve fibers. *J. exp. Zool.*, **111**, 189–204.

Thornton, Ch. S., (1954); The relation of the epidermal innervation to limb regeneration in Amblystoma larvae. *J. exp. Zool.*, **127**, 577–597.

Trampusch, H. A. L., (1951); Regeneration inhibited by X-rays and its recovery. *Proc. Kon. Ned. Akad. Wet. Ser. C*, **54**, 373–385.

Trampusch, H. A. L., (1957); Het effect van Röntgenstralen op het regeneratie vermogen. *Ned. T. Geneesk.*, **101**, 605–606.

Trampusch, H. A. L., (1958); The action of X-rays on the morphogenetic field. I. Heterotopic grafts on irradiated limbs. *Proc. Kon. ned. Akad. Wet. Ser. C*, **61**, 417–430.

Trampusch, H. A. L., (1959); The effect of X-rays on regenerative capacity. Regeneration in *Vertebrates*. Ch. S. Thornton. Editor. University of Chicago Press.

Trampusch, H. A. L., and Harrebomée, A. E., (1961); 'Embryonic' induction in the adult organism. *Acta Morphol. neerl.-scand.*, **4**, 287–288.

Vergroesen, A. J., (1958); Het aandeel van de zenuwen tijdens de regeneratie van bestraalde ledematen bij Amphibia. *Ned. T. Geneesk.*, **102**, 1624.

Verwoerd, C. D. A., (1963); Regeneration dependent on nerves. *Arch. néerl. Zool.*, **15**, 364–365.

The Trophic Quality of the Neuron:
Some Theoretical Considerations

M. SINGER

Department of Anatomy, School of Medicine, and Developmental Biology Center, Western Reserve University, Cleveland, Ohio (U.S.A.)

It is commonly understood that when a bit of cytoplasm without the nucleus is separated from the cell it wastes and dies. The remainder of the cell may reconstitute itself and regenerate the missing part. The processes of the neuron, being living cytoplasm, also degenerate and die when separated from the cell body; and new processes may then regrow. The dependence of neuronal processes upon the cell body for their maintenance is, therefore, not a unique phenomenon but a dependence exhibited by the cytoplasm of all cells. What is unique about the dependence of the neuronal processes upon the perikaryon is the tremendous amount of cytoplasm involved, the great distances over which the influence of the perikaryon must be exerted because of the length of the processes, the dramatic functional consequences of denervation, and the dependence of structures associated with the processes upon the integrity of the neurite, such as the surrounding sheaths, and, indeed, the organ upon which the neuron ends.

In the evolution of the neuron the development of long processes for conducting information rapidly over long distances required at the same time some adjustment and elaboration of the cytoplasmic mechanism for the maintenance of parts of the cell removed by so great a distance from the cell body. The nature of this mechanism is not known but, presumably, it is both chemical and physical; chemical for the metabolism and synthesis of the cytoplasm of the neurites, and physical for the transport of substances along their entire length.

As for the metabolic and synthetic mechanisms, perhaps they are not unlike in kind those found in the cytoplasm of other cells because the structure of the axonal cytoplasm resembles that of other cells. Indeed, ultrastructural studies of axonal cytoplasm show that it contains a general protoplasmic ground substance plus mitochondria, vesicles, granules and in some neurites obvious secretory globules. In addition, neurofilaments are found as a regular constituent; yet, filaments, albeit of other sorts, have been reported in the cytoplasm of diverse cells. It is true that the axon lacks, according to our present information, elaborate reticulum, Golgi structures and Nissl substance, at least in identifiable concentrations. Yet, in cells in general there are large regions of the cell body, particularly near the protoplasmic membrane, which do not have these structures.

Although a close resemblance in the constitution of cytoplasm of the neurite can be drawn with other cells and therefore presumably essential metabolic needs of the two may be of the same kind, yet the neurite differs in a number of ways, one of the most salient differences being in the amount of cytoplasm and therefore in the quantitative demands upon the mechanisms of maintenance and synthesis of cytoplasm. The volume of the neuronal process is very great and may exceed the parent cell body by a thousand times. Such a mass of cytoplasm strung out over a long distance is obvious for the longer neurons, for example the sensory ones which extend from somewhere in the lower limb to the medulla, a distance of more than a meter in many animals. In the larger mammals, including man, there are many neurites which exceed this length. Moreover, each axon branches repeatedly and there may be many collaterals as well. The maintenance of such a volume of cytoplasm is a great burden on the metabolic machinery of the cell, a liability unlike that borne by other cells. The burden requires a quantitative control rather than a special qualitative need. Therefore, what cells do in general to maintain the integrity of their cytoplasm must be done all the more by the neuron for its extended and voluminous processes. Moreover, whatever the nature of the metabolic contribution to maintenance and structuring of the cytoplasm, the neuron has the added burden of moving the important chemical substances long distances to the very ends of the neurites. If the flow is impeded by transection of the axon or by a persistent pressure block, then the process dies.

The 'trophic' agent of the perikaryon is not known; but, it is generally implied to be chemical in nature. Perhaps, it is whole cytoplasm of the cell body; or, it may be only certain special substances. If the latter, then the agent must be the building blocks or axoplasmic messengers that structure substances available at the periphery. It is possible that not everything required for the maintenance, and indeed the regrowth of the fiber, traverses the entire length of the process to the very ends. Some substances may enter the processes directly. Indeed, in studies of neurosecretory droplets some workers have suggested that they are synthesized at least in part in the axon as well as in the perikaryon (see Green and Maxwell, 1959; De Robertis, 1962; Diepen, 1962). Yet, the very fact of dependence upon the perikaryon and the demonstrated centrifugal flow means that there must be essential substances that descend from the perikaryon the length of the processes.

The theory of axoplasmic flow from the perikaryon peripherally has been held for some time. When the axis cylinder is transected, there is an outflow of axoplasm from the cut end (see Young, 1942). It is only recently that strong evidence has been presented for such a movement. Weiss and Hiscoe (1948) showed that, when the nerve is squeezed by a narrow cuff, the cytoplasm proximal to the cuff becomes dammed and swells (see also Guttman and Medawar, 1942). Distal to the cuff the fibers narrow. Upon release of the cuff the damming subsides. Another evidence of flow emerged from attempts to trace radioactive substances from the perikaryon into the axon. The results of Shepherd (1951, reviewed by Weiss, 1961), Samuels *et al.* (1951), and Ochs and Burger (1958) with radioactive phosphorus suggested such a flow. Waelsch (1958) obtained some success in demonstrating a flow of ^{14}C lysine into the axon after incorporation in the perikaryon. Weiss (1959) used a mixture of ^{14}C labelled lysine, leucine, iso-leucine, valine and phenylalanine in the Mexican axolotl and observed a linear gradient in the lateral line nerves. Calculations suggested a rate of movement of the order of 1 mm/day which is the approximate regeneration rate of amphibian axons. Very recently labelled leucine has been followed in the mammal from its incorporation in the cell body and thence distally into the axis cylinder for varying distances, the rate of movement in the mammal being estimated at about 1.5 mm/day (Droz and Leblond, 1962). There is disagreement on whether ribonucleic acid moves into the axis cylinder, a problem as yet unresolved. Such a movement could provide a ready scheme for the distal construction of cytoplasmic proteins, although other mechanisms of synthesis may exist.

The movement of substances down the axis cylinder requires some sort of physical mechanism the elaboration of which during the course of evolution of the neuron was also prerequisite for the maintenance of the processes. Abrams and Gerard (1933) refer to films of Speidel (1932) of living nerve showing 'active constriction and distention of the axis cylinder, sometimes moving like a peristaltic wave and much exaggerated in a sectioned fiber' (see also Gerard, 1950, p. 200). Lewis (1950) speaks of contractions in the cell body as seen in tissue culture and that this contraction drives along the axoplasm. Weiss (1950, 1961) evaluated the possible theoretical mechanisms of axonal flow and speculated that the axis cylinders themselves must pulsate, perhaps in peristaltic fashion and in this way move along a stream of cytoplasm. Recently, Weiss et al. (1962) demonstrated such movements in lapsed-time cinephotomicrography. And Ochs (1963) showed that the axis cylinder is not a structure of uniform diameter, as commonly envisaged; instead, that it is beaded along its length suggesting active constriction which serves to move the cytoplasm. Much remains to be done to define the nature and significance of these movements. Yet, they do reflect the fact that the neuronal processes are no exception to the rule that cytoplasm is a restless substance in continuous movement.

These, then, the physical agitation of the neurite and the chemical contributions from the cell body, serve to maintain the processes and to keep the entire neuron a single functional unit. The axonal flow must also provide the needs for growth of the process and therefore for the formation of new protoplasm. Indeed, the processes may be logically envisioned as growing continuously. All the neuronal processes may best be considered in a dynamic state in which endings are retracted and reformed or in other ways refashioned to suit physiological demands. Moreover, collaterals may be fashioned, retracted or pinched off continuously. Apparently, the neuron commits its energy of growth to continuous modulation and reconstruction of its processes rather than to reproduction by mitosis as in the case of other cells. If we accept, then, the idea of continuous growth throughout the life of the neuron, then regeneration of the interrupted axon from the proximal stump is just a special condition of the events of growth already existing in the neuron. In other words, injury to the processes does not change qualitatively the metabolic activity important for growth. However, there may be a quantitative change in the metabolism and rate of movement from the perikaryon to satisfy heightened growth needs; and more of the same is now delivered at a greater rate.

The idea of continuous flow, heightened perhaps under conditions of injury, has other implications. The integrity of the neuron is also known to be necessary for the maintenance and regeneration of the myelin sheath; and, indeed, for the maintenance and growth of tissues upon which the neuron ends. For example, taste buds of vertebrates and lateral line organs of fish require the nerve for their morphological integrity; after denervation the organelles waste and disappear and only reappear when the nerve of supply has regrown to the epithelium. Striated muscle likewise depends upon the nerve for maintenance of structure. A more dramatic example is the influence of the nerve upon regeneration of a body structure in the lower vertebrates (see reviews, Singer, 1952, 1959). Fins, tails, limbs and other parts, ordinarily capable of regrowing after amputation, do not regenerate when the nerves of supply are cut. The action of the nerve, commonly called 'trophic', on these peripheral structures shows that the function of maintenance and growth of morphological structure is not confined to the nerve processes themselves but is exerted on the organs of innervation as well. Without invoking a separate mechanism it may well be that the agent of the neuron responsible for these peripheral effects is the same as that required for maintenance and growth of the neuronal process. Moreover, there is a possibility that the axoplasmic flow spills over onto the periphery in a continuous ooze from the end of the neurite or is pinched off in quantum packets as the end of the fiber is refashioned. In this way cytoplasmic substances so important for the axis cylinder itself come to play an important role in the maintenance and growth of associated structures.

SUMMARY

In regeneration of external body parts in lower vertebrates the nerves at the wound surface play an essential role. Without the nerves regrowth does not occur. The axonal processes themselves are dependent for their integrity and growth upon their cell bodies, as is well known. It is proposed here that both the extracellular and the intracellular growth influences are the same and that nerve fibers continuously leak 'trophic' substance into peripheral tissues. Moreover, it is also proposed that the trophic qualities of the neuron, demonstrated so well in maintenance and growth of its own processes and of tissues upon which it ends, are not unique for the neuron alone. They are shared by living cells in general, the difference being that the neuron, because of its tremendous volume of peripheral cytoplasm, has specialized quantitatively in their production. These theories are discussed against the background of some modern views of axoplasmic flow and neuronal metabolism.

REFERENCES

ABRAMS, J., AND GERARD, R. W., (1933); The influence of activity on the survival of isolated nerve. *Amer. J. Physiol.*, **104**, 590–593.

DE ROBERTIS, E., (1962); Ultrastructure and function in some neurosecretory systems. *Neurosecretion*. H. Heller and R. B. Clark, Editors. Proc. 3 int. Symp. Neurosecretion (1961). New York. Academic Press (pp. 3–20).

DIEPEN, R., (1962); The difference between the neurosecretory pictures in various mammals. *Neurosecretion*. H. Heller and R. B. Clark, Editors. Proc. 3 int. Symp. Neurosecretion (1961). New York Academic Press (pp. 111–124).

DROZ, B., AND LEBLOND, C. P., (1962); Migration of proteins along the axons of the sciatic nerve. *Science*, **137**, 1047–1048.

GERARD, R. W., (1950); Some aspects of neural growth, regeneration, and function. *Genetic Neurology*. P. Weiss, Editor. Chicago. Univ. of Chicago Press (pp. 199–207).

GREEN, J. D., AND MAXWELL, D. P., (1959); Comparative anatomy of the hypophysis and observations on the mechanism of neurosecretion. *Comparative Endocrinology*. A. Gorbman, Editor. New York. Wiley (pp. 368–392).

GUTTMAN, L., AND MEDAWAR, P. B., (1942); The chemical inhibition of fiber regeneration. *J. Neurol. Psychiat.*, **5**, 130.

LEWIS, W. H., (1950); Motion pictures of neurons and neuroglia in tissue culture. *Genetic Neurology*. P. Weiss, Editor. Chicago. Univ. Chicago Press (pp. 53–65).

OCHS, S., (1963); Beading phenomena of mammalian myelinated nerve fibers. *Science*, **139**, 599–600.

OCHS, S., AND BURGER, E., (1958); Movement of substance proximo-distally in nerve axons as studied with spinal cord injections of radioactive phosphorus. *Amer. J. Physiol.*, **194**, 499–506.

SAMUELS, A. J., BOYARSKI, L. L., GERARD, R. W., LIBEL, B., AND BRUST, M., (1951); Distribution, exchange and migration of phosphate compounds in the nervous system. *Amer. J. Physiol.*, **164**, 1–15.

SINGER, M., (1952); The influence of the nerve in regeneration of the amphibian extremity. *Quart. Rev. Biol.*, **27**, 169–200.

SINGER, M., (1959); The influence of nerves on regeneration. *Regeneration in Vertebrates*. C. S. Thornton, Editor. Chicago, Univ. of Chicago Press.

SPEIDEL, C. C., (1932); Studies of living nerves. I. The movements of individual sheath cells and nerve sprouts correlated with the process of myelin sheath formation in amphibian larvae. *J. exp. Zool.*, **61**, 279–332.

WAELSCH, H., (1958); Some aspects of amino acids and protein metabolism of the nervous system *J. nerv. ment. Dis.*, **126**, 33.

WEISS, P., (1950); An introduction to genetic neurology. *Genetic Neurology*. P. Weiss, Editor. Chicago. Univ. of Chicago Press (pp. 1–39; see p. 12).

WEISS, P., (1959); Evidence by isotope tracers of perpetual replacement of mature nerve fibers from their cell bodies. *Science*, **129**, 1290.

WEISS, P., (1961); The concept of perpetual neuronal growth and proximo-distal substance convection. *Regional Neurochemistry*. S. S. Kety, Editor. 4th int. Neurochem. Symp. New York, Pergamon Press (pp. 220–242).

WEISS, P., AND HISCOE, H. B., (1948); Experiments on the mechanism of nerve growth. *J. exp. Zool.*, **107**, 315–395.

WEISS, P., TAYLOR, A. C., AND PILLAI, P. A., (1962); The nerve fiber as a system in continuous flow: microcinematographic and electronmicroscopic demonstrations. *Science*, **136**, 330.

YOUNG, J. Z., (1942); Functional repair of nervous tissue. *Physiol. Rev.*, **22**, 318–374.

Author Index*

---

* Italics indicate the pages on which the paper of the author in these proceedings is printed.

Subject Index

PRINTED IN THE NETHERLANDS